KTTSV
Don Garlick
1917 SE 112
Portland, OR 9
503-261-

by
Wilfred N. Caron

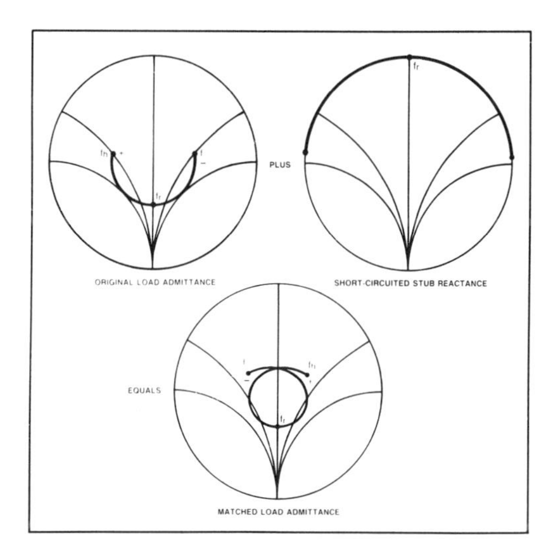

Published by the
AMERICAN RADIO RELAY LEAGUE
225 Main Street
Newington, CT 06111

Printed in USA

ISBN: 0-87259-220-0

$15.00 in USA and possessions

First Edition

FOREWORD

Proper impedance matching of an antenna to a transmission line is of concern to antenna engineers and to every radio amateur. A properly matched antenna as the termination for a line minimizes feed-line losses. Power can be fed to such a line without the need for a matching network at the line input.

Complex matching networks can be developed by using the Smith Chart. No special expertise is needed. In a typical situation, since both the antenna impedance and the transmission line impedance are known, the designer simply moves the antenna impedance points on the Smith Chart to find the most effective matching network. It is very much like a chess game; the chessmen are the impedance points and the chessboard is the Smith Chart.

Good chess players plan their moves or strategy far in advance of each play. Similarly, a good designer must plan and visualize the final results before making the first move. There may be several approaches to the matching problem, but only one really satisfactory solution. By visualizing the effect of each move, the designer may determine its outcome, thereby avoiding a trial-and-error method.

There is no mystique involved in designing even the most complex multielement networks for broadband coverage, such as those having 3, 4, and 5 or more elements. Instead, a logical step-by-step procedure is followed, as discussed within the pages of this book. With an understanding of this information, antenna engineers and dedicated amateurs alike will find it a relatively simple task to design networks that will yield optimum performance.

David Sumner, K1ZZ
Executive Vice President

Newington, Connecticut
April, 1989

PREFACE

The material for this text was originally collected over a period of many decades while I was working as an Electronic Countermeasures (ECM) Officer with the Air Force, and as an ECM Antenna Project Engineer with the aerospace industry. The challenges were great. ECM antennas must meet rigid electrical, mechanical and environmental military requirements. It was in this type of atmosphere where I became proficient with antenna matching. I was not an overnight success; I had to learn and struggle with the understanding of the antenna electrical parameters involved: impedance, admittance, susceptance, reactance, etc., not to mention radiation characteristics. Since my retirement from this occupation, to make it easier for the new aspirants, I decided to present this very important information in a simple instructive and understandable manner.

I am indeed very grateful to the many pioneers who gave us an understanding of antennas and of electromagnetic energy. I am also grateful to the Air Force for providing the challenges and to my friends in the aerospace industry for permitting me to continue this engrossing adventure in the antenna field.

Wilfred N. Caron
818 Sherri Street
Ridgecrest, CA 93555
April, 1989

ABOUT THE AUTHOR

Wilfred N. Caron was born in New Bedford, Mass. in 1920. He enlisted with the Army Air Force in 1941, and was assigned as a radio technician with the Airways and Air Communications Service. During his tour of duty he installed and maintained transmitting and receiving stations (AM, CW and RTTY) in Australia, New Guinea, Kwajalein and the USA. Caron advanced rapidly through the enlisted ranks and was awarded a direct commission as second lieutenant in recognition of work performance. After completion of training requirements, he was assigned to an electronic countermeasures reconnaissance squadron. He served in the Far East during the Korean War. After 20 years of active duty, he retired from the military in 1961.

In civilian life, Mr. Caron was employed as an antenna engineer with the Hallicrafters Co., Chicago, Ill. Later he went to TRW Systems, Redondo Beach, Cal., and became involved with spacecraft antenna system design. His career with the aerospace industry was concluded after he served as an ECM antenna integration and check-out engineer on the B-1B aircraft with AIL, Inc., Edwards AF Base, Cal. Since 1983, Mr. Caron has remained active restoring old cars and writing on a variety of subject matter from antennas to metaphysics.

CONTENTS

Contents

INTRODUCTION TO ANTENNA IMPEDANCE MATCHING

Introduction.

The central theme of this text is the impedance matching of antennas. Proper impedance matching of an antenna to a transmission line is vital to the design of radar, ECM, radio and communication equipment and systems. Unfortunately, impedance matching is the least understood phase of electronics and radio engineering. Relatively few engineers know how to develop narrowband matching networks and even fewer know how to develop broadband matching networks. The stumbling block in understanding matching techniques appears to be in the manner in which this information is presented. There is no general procedure to synthesize impedance matching from a set of antenna impedance points, even for simple narrowband antenna impedance curves. The information available, however extensive and technically accurate, gives the engineer little opportunity to visualize and therefore understand the influence each matching element has upon its adjacent and subsequent element.

It is a rare antenna that requires only one matching element. Most narrowband antennas require at least two elements. Broadband antennas may require three and even four elements. The matching process that takes place is that the initial antenna impedance curve is placed in a region by the first matching element that is most favorable for matching by the second, third or fourth element in a complex matching network.

The impedance matching techniques to be described are performed with the aid of the Smith chart. Once the Smith chart is understood the engineer needs no special expertise to use the Smith chart to solve impedance matching problems. In a typical situation, since both the antenna impedance and transmission line impedance are known, the engineer simply has to move the antenna impedance points on the Smith chart to find the most effective matching network. It is very much like a chess game; the impedance points are the chessmen and the Smith chart the chessboard.

Chess players must plan their moves or strategy far in advance of each play. Similarly, the engineer must plan and visualize the final results before he makes his first move. There may be several approaches to the matching problem but only one really satisfactory solution. This is what is lacking with prevailing antenna matching literature. Without being able to visualize the effects of each move the engineer has a great deal of difficulty in determining the outcome of each move. Often he resorts to a trial and error method.

The purpose of this book has become quite clear, to aid the engineer to visualize the significance of each matching step upon the overall matching solution.

General Considerations in Antenna Design.

An antenna may be defined as a transducer associated with the region of transition between a guided wave and a free-space wave, or vice versa. The characteristics which describe the properties of an antenna in accomplishing this transition are the input impedance, the antenna efficiency, the radiation pattern, and the polarization.

The input impedance is the parameter which describes the antenna as a circuit element. It is of primary importance in determining efficiency of transferring power from the source to the antenna and in determining the reaction of the antenna on the source. The antenna efficiency is the ratio of the power radiated into space to the power input at the antenna terminals. The radiation pattern and polarization describe the radiated electromagnetic field at large distances from the antenna. In this text we are primarily interested in the impedance characteristics of the antenna and in the methods of matching the antenna impedance to that of the transmission line.

Another important parameter which will be discussed is the bandwidth of the antenna. An antenna is equivalent to a series circuit consisting of a resistance, a capacitance and an inductance. At the resonant frequency the reactive components cancel each other, the impedance is a minimum, and the current is a maximum. Therefore the antenna operates best at its resonant frequency. How good the performance will be at other frequencies depends on the Q of the antenna. When bandwidth requirements become large provision must be made whereby the reactance introduced by the changing frequency is compensated by a reactance of opposite sign. In this way the impedance may be kept substantially resistive over a wide band. At low frequencies this is accomplished by the addition of inductors and capacitors. At higher frequencies reactive line sections can be employed or the reactive elements may be provided by the antenna configuration itself.

Since the actual impedance characteristics of a practical antenna have more than a slight resemblance to theoretical impedance data, it is always necessary to determine these characteristics by actual measurements if optimum antenna performance is desired. This is particularly true with VHF/UHF and lower frequency aircraft antennas, and for any antenna located on surfaces of curvature. In such cases the antenna impedance should be measured under conditions as nearly as possible with those under which the antenna is to be used in practice. The most satisfactory procedure, as far as results are concerned, is to conduct these measurements on the full-scale aircraft, removed as far as practicable from ground, with the antenna complete in every detail. Where this method is not practical, a poor second-best procedure is to measure the antenna impedance by means of models, a 1/n-scale model of the antenna being installed in the proper location of a 1/n-scale model of the aircraft and its impedance measured at n times the actual full-scale frequencies. This method is capable of good results only if great care is taken in scaling all details of the antenna, its mounting and feed system.

At high frequencies, if the aircraft surface constitutes a good approximate to a flat ground plane for at least one wavelength in all directions, satisfactory results may be obtained by means of impedance measurements made with the antenna working against a ground plane in a laboratory set-up. But in all cases an effort should be made to ensure that the antenna is studied under conditions which closely approximate actual conditions.

It is a rare antenna installation in which the transmitter or receiver can be located directly at the antenna terminals, the installation problem is usually complicated by the presence of a transmission line. In practice, the power transfer problem is solved by so designing the transmitter and the antenna that their respective input or output impedances are resistive and equal in value to the characteristic impedance of the line. Under these conditions the line is said to be "flat" or "matched", the energy delivered to the line reaches the antenna with a minimum of losses before being radiated into space.

Reasons for Impedance Matching.

A typical transmission system is composed of many components: cables, connectors, adapters and antennas. The impedance of all the components involved is made equal to the impedance of the transmission line which is usually connected between the components. When this is done, the components are said to be "matched" to the line. There are many reasons for matching antennas and other components to the impedance of the line:

- Maximum power is delivered to the antenna.
- Maximum power is delivered to free space.
- Transmission line losses are minimized.
- Voltage breakdown problems are reduced.
- Reduces the possibility of ghosts and aural echoes in a video/audio system.
- Reduces magnetron moding and frequency pulling in a radar system.

Antenna Reciprocity.

For the most part, this text will be concerned with transmitting antennas, not because a transmitting antenna is more important than a receiving antenna, but because the characteristics of a given antenna are the same whether the antenna is used for transmitting or receiving. This equivalence follows from the reciprocity law, which applies in antenna work and which is an extension of the well-known reciprocity theorem found in electric circuits. This theorem as applied to antennas may be stated as follows:

> If an electromotive force (emf) is applied to the terminals of an antenna A and the current measured at the terminals of a distant antenna B, then an equal current (in both amplitude and phase) will be obtained at the terminals of antenna A if the same emf is applied to the terminals of antenna B.

Figure A illustrates this concept.

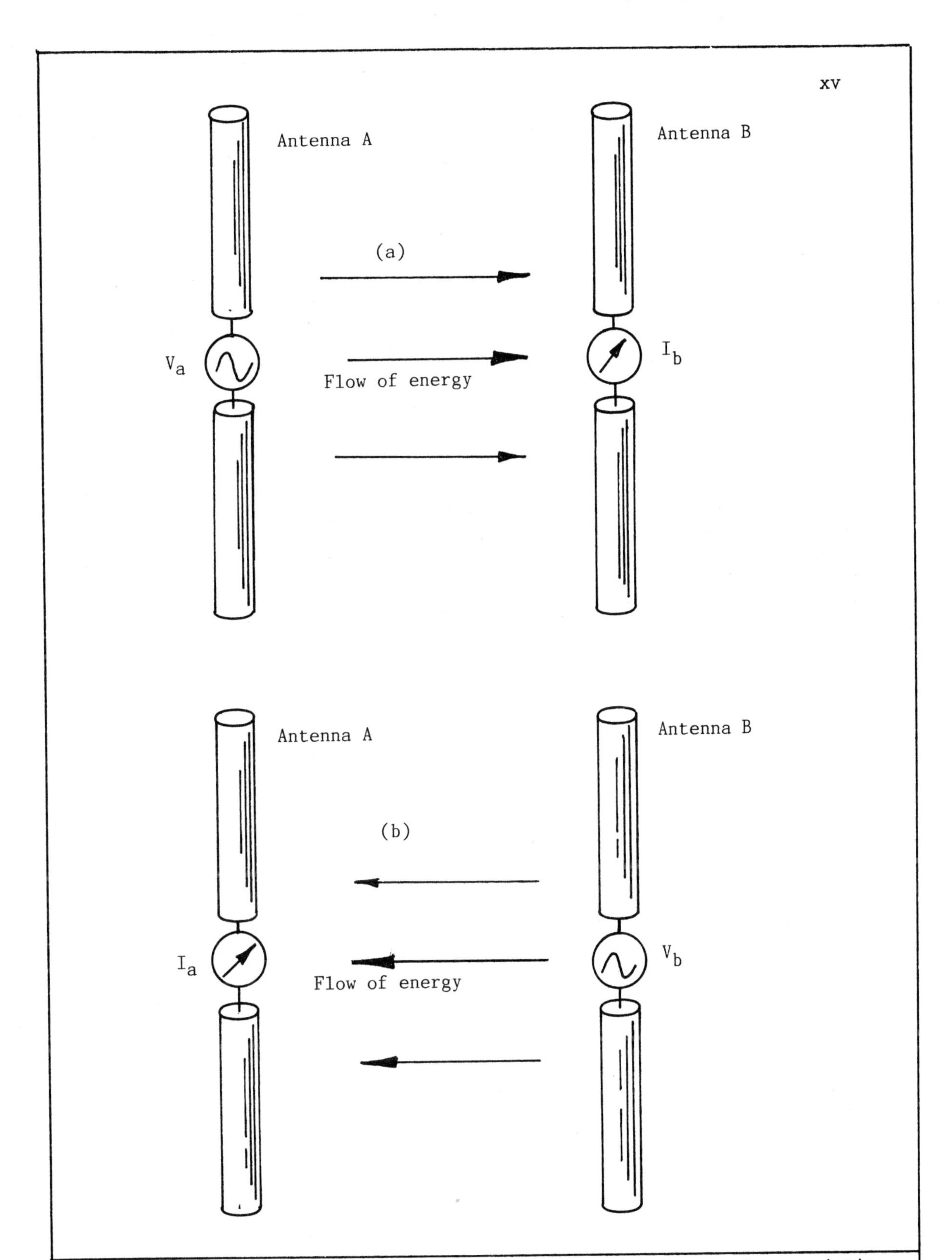

Figure A. Illustrations for reciprocity theorem. (a) Antenna A transmitting, (b) Antenna B transmitting.

CHAPTER I

THE TRANSMISSION LINE

General.

In radio-frequency work the transfer of electromagnetic energy from one point to another is accomplished by some form of transmission system consisting of two or more conductors. Generally, transmission systems take the form of two-wire lines and coaxial lines. Transmission system behavior differs at low and high frequencies, and the different behaviors are usually described in terms of lumped-constant and distributed-constant systems.

The Lumped-Constant System.

Lumped-constant circuits involve components (transistors, coils, resistors, capacitors, etc.) whose physical dimensions are much less than the wavelength of the propagating electromagnetic wave (i.e., less than one-eight of a wavelength). The impedance of low-frequency systems such as the 60-hertz electrical power system and the land-line telephone system is evaluated in terms of these components "lumped" or located at discrete points. A lumped-constant circuit, with physical dimensions of wire and components small with respect to wavelength, is illustrated in Figure 1-1.

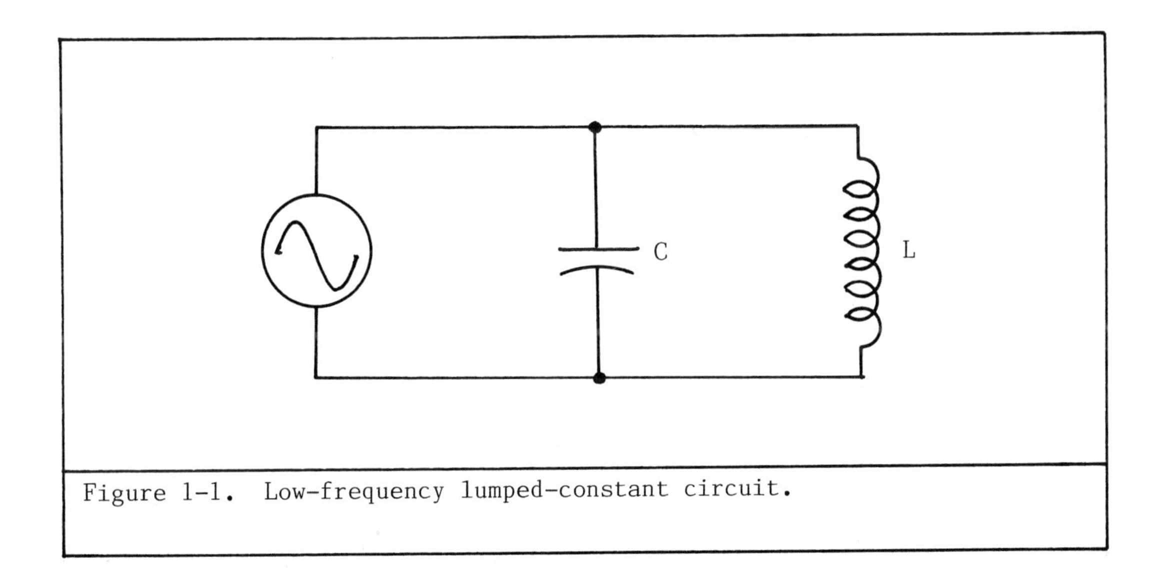

Figure 1-1. Low-frequency lumped-constant circuit.

The Distributed-Constant System.

When circuit components and connecting wires are of dimensions comparable to a wavelength of the propagating electromagnetic wave, then the circuit components and the wires effectively become distributed constants. This effect becomes increasingly noticeable at higher frequencies, since inductances of short lengths of conductors and capacitances between conductors and their surroundings are no longer negligible. A distributed constant circuit, representitive of a two-wire transmission line is shown in Figure 1-2.

It follows from this brief description that whereas some engineers may deal with one particular type of transmission line and some with another, they have many problems in common: to transfer the maximum amount of power from one point to another with a minimum of losses. While transmission lines are used for a variety of purposes, the basic theory, equations, problems and solutions that can be applied to one can also be applied to any other regardless of application or frequency.

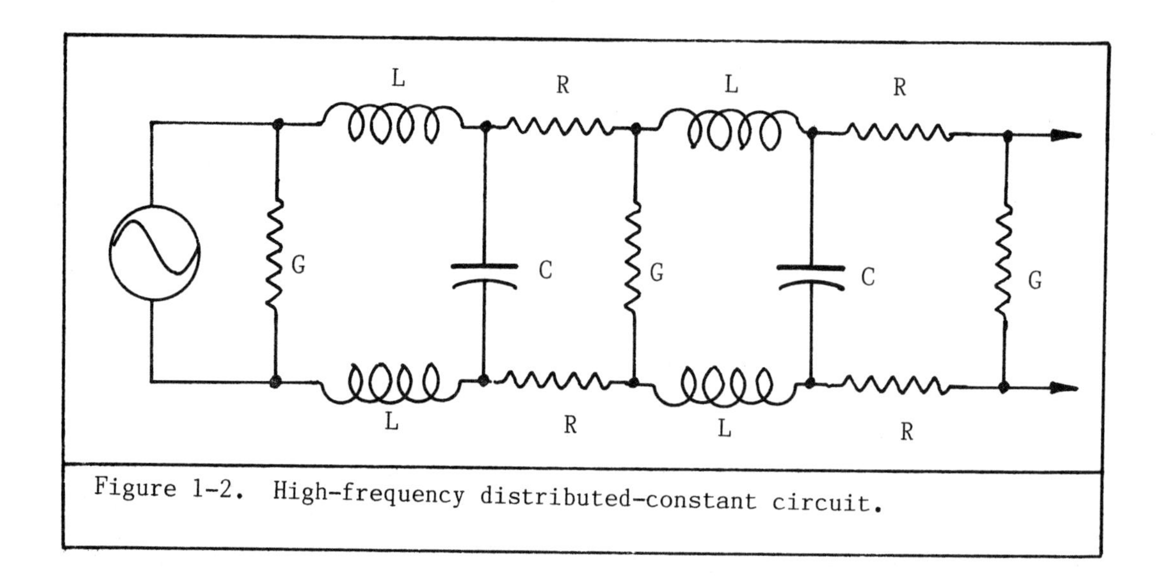

Figure 1-2. High-frequency distributed-constant circuit.

Impedance and Admittance Relationship.

The simplest transmission line is one which carries direct current. The parameters of interest for such a line is the resistance of the line which enters into measurements of voltage drop and I^2/R power loss in the line. At high frequencies, it was shown that the constants of the line are distributed. The parameters of importance in high-frequency transmission lines with distributed constants are inductance L per unit length, capacitance C per unit length, resistance R per unit length, and conductance G per unit length. The latter parameter, G, represents either leakage currents between the conductors or a power loss in the dielectric, i.e., in a coaxial cable. From these parameters the impedance and admittance relationship can be determined. If a signal with an angular frequency $2\pi f$ is applied to the line, the impedance per unit length is determined as

$$Z_o = R + j2\pi fL \tag{1-1}$$

and the admittance per unit length is

$$Y_o = G + j2\pi fC \tag{1-2}$$

Inherent Characteristics of a Transmission Line.

The discussion presented and most of the equations associated with line behavior will be developed for a two-wire transmission line because it lends itself to visualization much more easily as compared to a coaxial line. The same equations of electromagnetic wave behavior apply to any line, however, each kind of line has certain variations in parameter as a result of line geometry.

A two-wire line made up of wires having a diameter d and a distance D between their centers has a distributed capacity of

$$C = \frac{27.8 \times 10^{-12}}{\cosh^{-1} D/d} \quad \text{farads/meter of length} \tag{1-3}$$

where d and D are each in the same units. When the distance between the centers of the wires is greater than ten times their diameter, the equation can be simplified to

$$C = \frac{12.06 \times 10^{-12}}{\log_{10} 2D/d} \quad \text{farads/meter of length} \tag{1-4}$$

The distributed inductance of a parallel wire line is

$$L = \left[10 + 92 \log_{10} 2D/d\right] \times 10^{-8} \quad \text{henries/meter of length} \tag{1-5}$$

At radio frequencies, the ohmic resistance and shunt conductance of a line are very small and are usually neglected for purposes of calculations. Consequently, the characteristic impedance which is usually defined as

$$Z_o = \sqrt{\frac{R + j2\pi fL}{G + j2\pi fC}} \quad \text{ohms} \tag{1-6}$$

where
C = distributed shunt capacitance
L = distributed series inductance
R = distributed series resistance
G = distributed shunt conductance

becomes a pure resistance

$$Z_o = \sqrt{L/C} \qquad (1\text{-}7)$$

at radio frequencies.

If the constant portion of the inductance equation (1-5) is neglected, the substitution of equation (1-4) and (1-5) into (1-7) for characteristic impedance gives

$$Z_o = \sqrt{\frac{92 \times 10^{-8} \log_{10}^2 2D/d}{12.06 \times 10^{-12}}} \quad \text{ohms}$$

$$Z_o = 276 \log_{10} 2D/d \quad \text{ohms} \qquad (1\text{-}8)$$

For comparison purposes, the capacity of a coaxial line is equal to

$$C = \frac{10^{-9}}{41.4 \log_{10} b/a} \quad \text{farads/meter of length} \qquad (1\text{-}9)$$

where
b = inside radius of outer conductor
a = outside radius of inner conductor

The distributed inductance is

$$L = 4.6 \times 10^{-7} \log_{10} b/a \quad \text{henries/meter of length} \qquad (1\text{-}10)$$

Neglecting negligible shunt and series losses, the characteristic impedance becomes

$$Z_o = \frac{138.1 \log_{10} b/a}{\sqrt{\varepsilon}} \qquad (1\text{-}11)$$

where
ε = dielectric constant of insulation between conductors

Characteristic Impedance.

Consider a uniform two-wire transmission line of infinite length as shown in Figure 1-3(a). A signal travels down the line toward infinity, and because there is no end to the line, it is obvious that the signal is never reflected. In other words, the infinite line absorbs all the energy fed to it. If we now measure the line with an rf bridge we would see that the line looks like a pure resistance. This particular value of resistance is called the characteristic impedance of the line (frequently called surge impedance) and is expressed as

$$R = Z_o = \sqrt{L/C} \tag{1-12}$$

If we now cut the line at some reference A-A', as shown in Figure 1-3(b), and terminate the line with a resistor $R = Z_o$ as shown in Figure 1-3(c), this resistor will absorb all the energy fed into the line. Such a line is said to be matched into its characteristic impedance.

The characteristic impedance may also be expressed in terms of power flow W and either voltage V or current I. For a line terminated into its characteristic impedance both V and I are in phase and Z_o can be expressed as

$$Z_o = \frac{V}{I} = \frac{V^2}{W} = \frac{W}{I^2} = \sqrt{Z/Y} = \sqrt{\frac{R + j2\pi fL}{G + j2\pi fC}} \tag{1-13}$$

Since the quantity on the right of (1-13) has the dimension of impedance, and since it is "characteristic" of the line itself except for the frequency, it is assigned the symbol

$$Z_o = R_o + jX_o \tag{1-14}$$

The factor j is an operator to indicate that the current is leading or lagging depending on whether $2\pi fL$ is larger or smaller than $1/2\pi fC$. This quantity is known as the circuit reactance and is designated by the letter X. The impedance, therefore, is the vector sum of the ac resistance R and the reactance X. Figure 1-4 illustrates how the vector sum is derived from R and X. Figure 1-5 illustrates a circuit containing R, L and C in series.

Sometimes it is convenient to use the reciprocal quantity, the "characteristic admittance" of a line

$$1/Z_o = Y_o = \sqrt{\frac{G + j2\pi fC}{R + j2\pi fL}} = G_o + jB_o \tag{1-15}$$

This is the most convenient form for combining shunt elements.

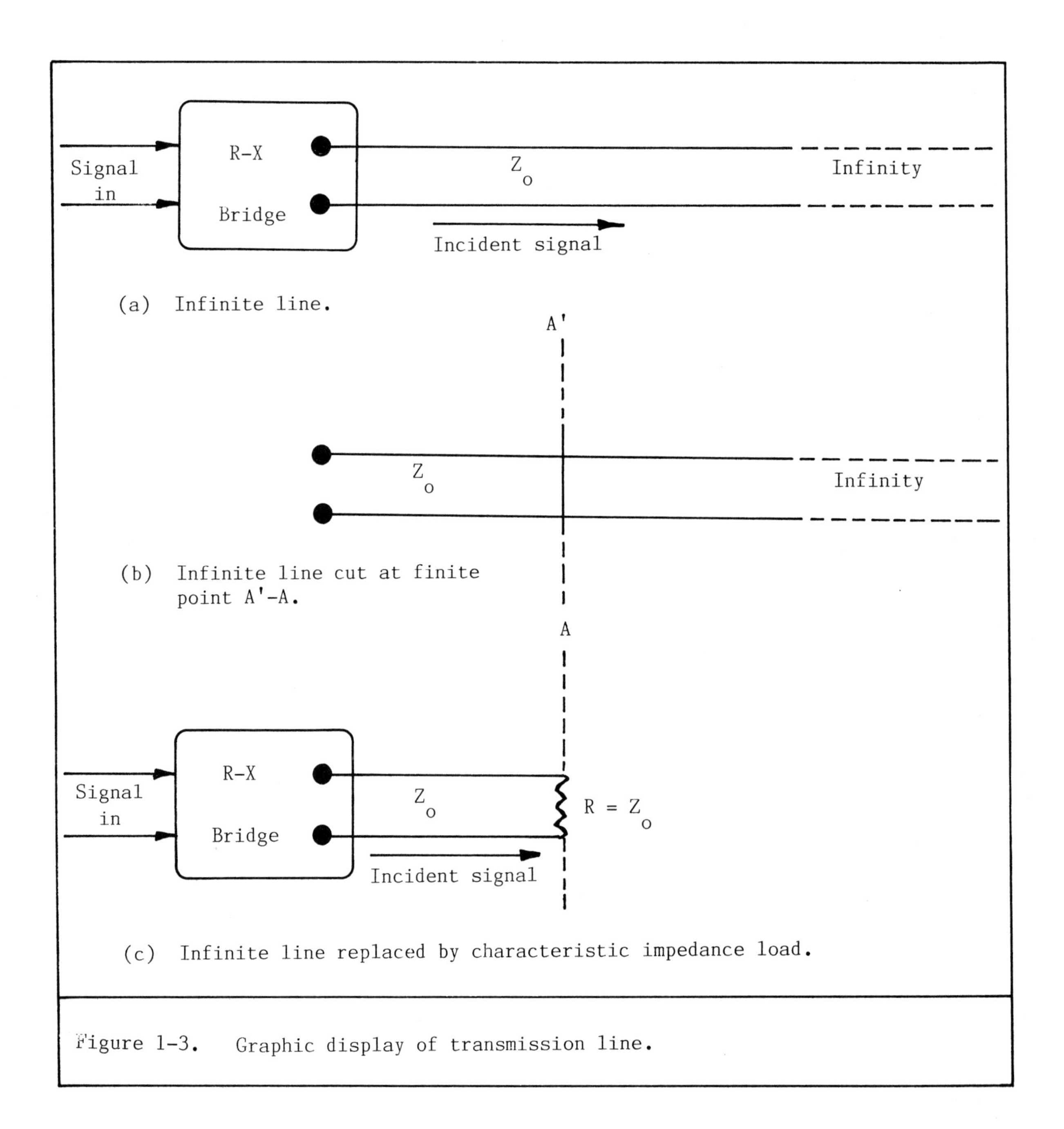

Figure 1-3. Graphic display of transmission line.

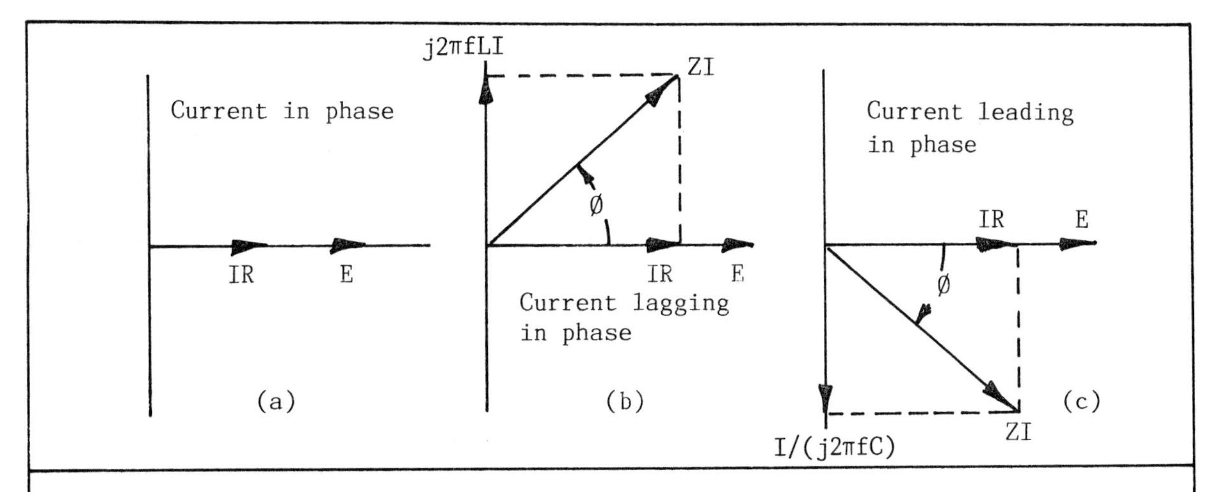

Figure 1-4. Vector representation of AC circuits.

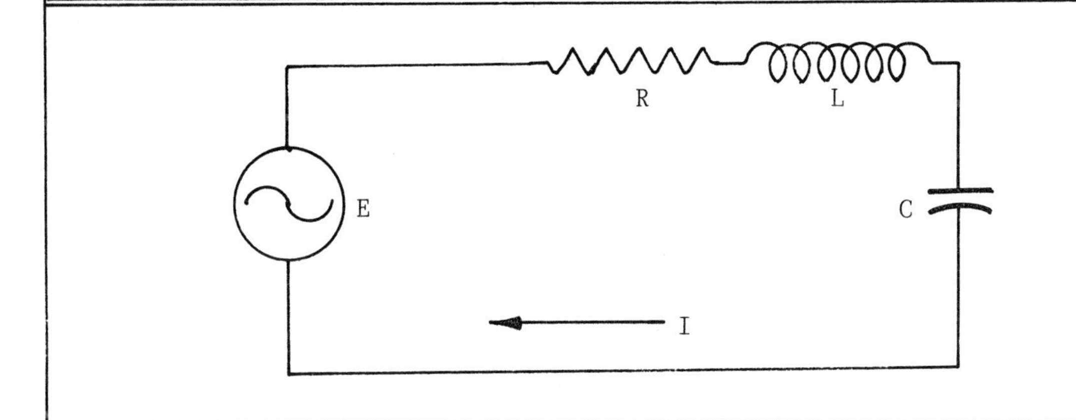

Figure 1-5. Series connected RLC circuit.

Phase Velocity, Free Space, and Line Wavelength.

The line wavelength λ_ℓ or the wavelength on a transmission line is the distance traversed by the electromagnetic wave in order for its phase to be retarded by 2π radians. Hence

$$\beta\lambda_\ell = 2\pi$$

or

$$\lambda_\ell = \frac{2\pi}{\beta} \tag{1-16}$$

Thus the phase constant β determines the wavelength, and for this reason it is sometimes called the wavelength constant. The phase velocity v_p is given by

$$v_p = \lambda_\ell f \tag{1-17}$$

which may be explained by the fact that the wave moves at a speed of one wavelength per hertz, or λ_ℓ meter per hertz, and since there are f hertz per second, the wave moves λ_ℓ f meters per second. The phase velocity may be expressed as

$$v_p = \frac{2\pi f}{\beta} \tag{1-18}$$

A wave traveling on a line may be shown graphically in a number of different ways. In Figure 1-6 the voltage wave is shown both vectorially and sinusoidally. Vector E^+ represents the phase and magnitude of the wave travelling towards the antenna or load end. E_R^+ is taken as the reference axis. At a point on the line distant d from the load, the phase is advanced by an angle βd; since the line is lossless the magnitude E^+ is unchanged. As d increases, vector E^+ turns counterclockwise, and the vector traverses a circular locus. One trip around the locus corresponds to one wavelength along the line.

When the losses on a transmission line are small, the velocity becomes

$$v_p = \frac{c}{\sqrt{\mu\varepsilon}} \tag{1-19}$$

where

c = velocity of light = 3×10^8 meters/second

μ = permeability of the medium separating the conductors (air = 1.257×10^{-6} henry per meter)

ε = permittivity of the medium separating the conductors (air = 8.85×10^{-12} farad per meter)

Of interest, $\sqrt{\mu/\varepsilon}$ gives us the characteristic impedance of free space

$$\sqrt{\frac{1.257 \times 10^{-6}}{8.85 \times 10^{-12}}} = \sqrt{14.2 \times 10^4} = 376.7 \text{ ohms}$$

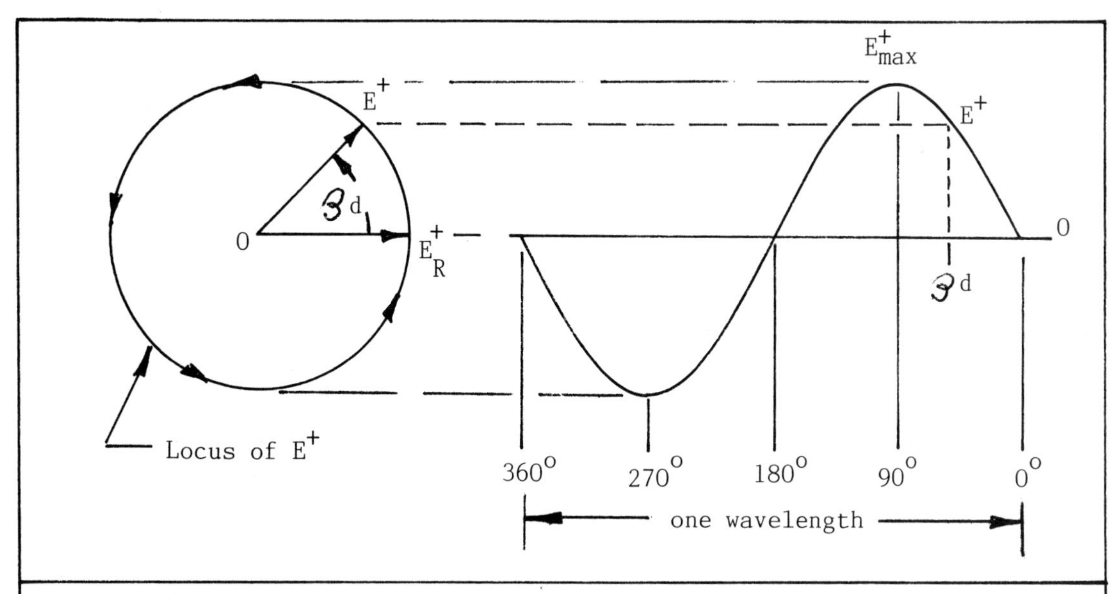

Figure 1-6. Vectorial and sinusoidal representation of a travelling wave.

Reflection Coefficient.

In practical transmission line systems, it is most desirable to have a matched system in order to reduce the detrimental effects of reflections. Such a transmission line is an efficient means of transmitting energy from a source to a distant load. A 300-ohm transmission line connected to a 600-ohm antenna is a mismatch. Maximum power cannot be transmitted to the antenna.

When the transmission line does not match the antenna impedance, reflections take place at the antenna, and some of the incident power is reflected to the source by the antenna. When mismatched conditions exist, then two current and two voltage waves are present on the line. One each of the two voltage and two current waves E^+ and I^+ travels towards the antenna and one each of the other voltage and current waves, E^- and I^-, travels away from the antenna. The ratio of the reflected wave (E^- or I^-) to the incident wave (E^+ or I^+) is called the reflection coefficient or

$$\Gamma_L = \frac{E_L^-}{E_L^+} \qquad (1\text{-}20)$$

Knowing the reflection coefficient of an antenna is useful in determining its impedance

$$Z_L = Z_o \frac{(1 + \Gamma_L)}{(1 - \Gamma_L)} \qquad (1\text{-}21)$$

where

Z_L = load impedance

Z_o = characteristic impedance of the line

Γ_L = reflection coefficient of the load

The relationship of reflection coefficient and VSWR is

$$\Gamma = \frac{E_{reflected}}{E_{incident}} = \frac{VSWR - 1}{VSWR + 1} \qquad (1\text{-}22)$$

This relationship is illustrated in Figure 1-7.

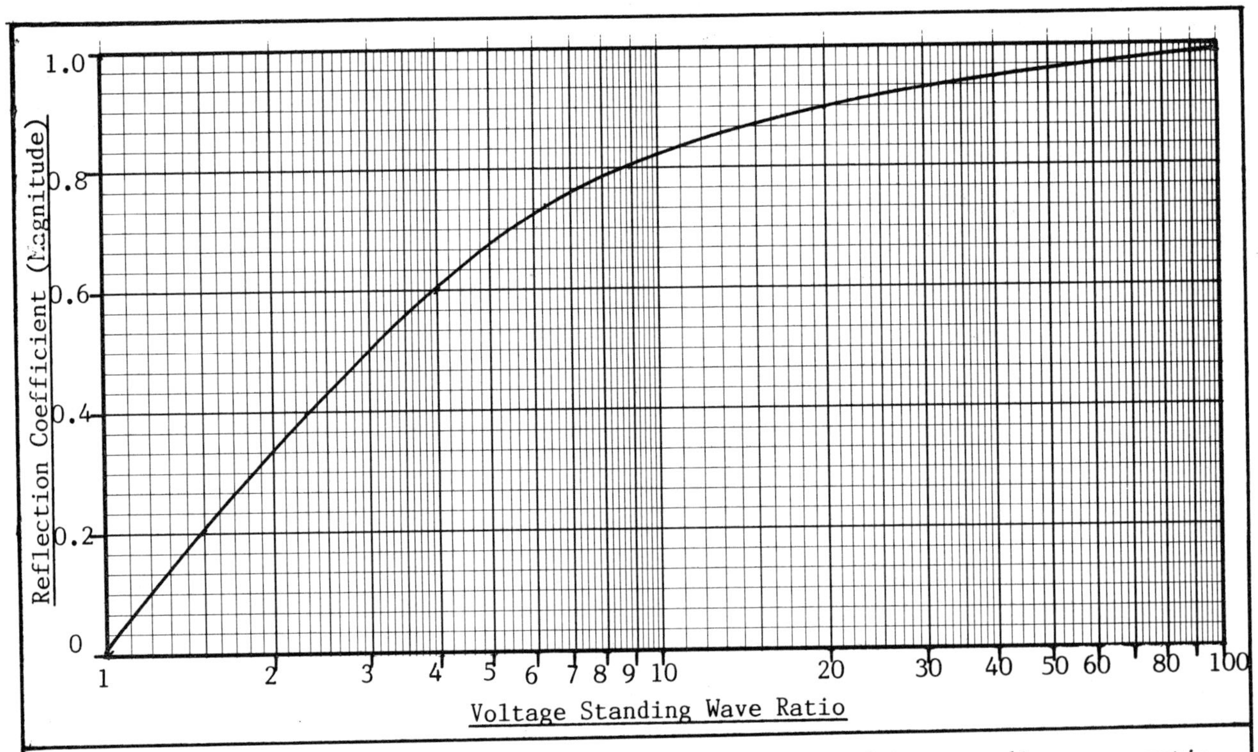

Figure 1-7. Magnitude of reflection coefficient versus voltage standing wave ratio.

Voltage Standing Wave Ratio (VSWR).

VSWR is the ratio of voltage standing wave maxima to minima caused by the reflected energy on the incident energy and is related directly to the impedance mismatch of the load to the transmission line impedance. VSWR in itself offers a means of determining impedance, and thus mismatch.

A standing-wave may be visualized as an interference pattern when a signal E^+ at a given frequency, travelling in a forward direction, interacts with a signal E^- at the same frequency travelling in the reverse direction. At the load, the ratio E^+ and E^- and the phase angle between them are uniquely determined by the load impedance. Anywhere along a lossless line the magnitude of this ratio remains the same. The phase angle between E^+ and E^-, however, will vary along the line as a function of the distance from the load. Figure 1-8 illustrates how a reflected signal combines with the incident signal. A wave is created that oscillates in amplitude but never moves laterally. That is why it is called "standing wave." A voltage standing wave is determined as follows

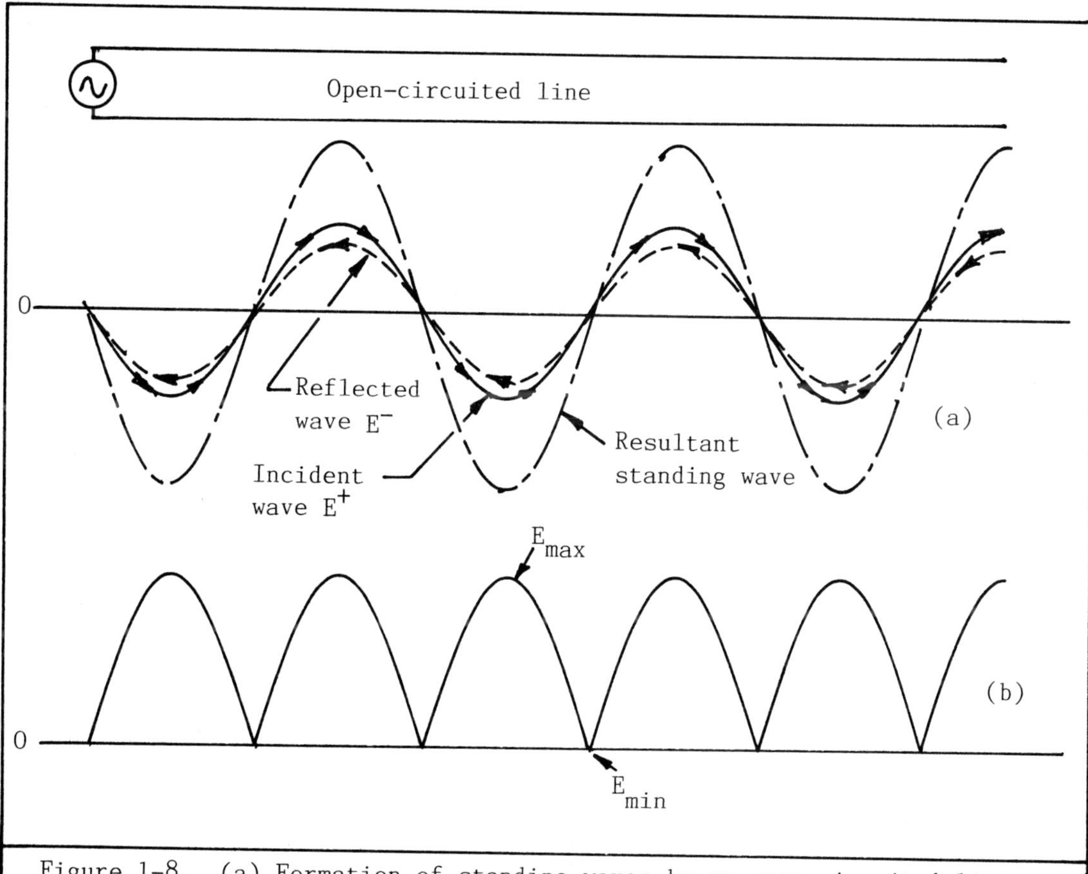

Figure 1-8. (a) Formation of standing waves by an open-circuited line. (b) Conventional representation of standing waves.

$$VSWR = \frac{E_{max}}{E_{min}} = \frac{|E^+| + |E^-|}{|E^+| - |E^-|} \tag{1-23}$$

where

E_{max} = maximum field intensity on the line

E_{min} = minimum field intensity on the line

E^+ = incident field or voltage wave

E^- = reflected field or voltage wave

The mismatch loss of an antenna with a low standing wave ratio is quite small, however, as the standing wave ratio increases, the mismatch losses rapidly increase. Figure 1-9 shows the effect of SWR on power transfer at the antenna terminals for a mythical case of a lossless line.

Standing-wave ratios can also be expressed in power, current and decibels. To express SWR in decibels

$$SWR_{dB} = 20 \log_{10} VSWR \tag{1-24}$$

To express SWR in power

$$SWR = \sqrt{PSWR} \tag{1-25}$$

Losses in Transmission Lines Not Properly Terminated.

As mentioned earlier, when an antenna is not properly matched into its characteristic impedance there will be two travelling waves on the line, the forward wave which carries power to the antenna and the reflected wave which carries power from the antenna. The net power delivered to the antenna is the difference in the power carried in the two waves. Since the transmission line absorbs power from both waves the effective attenuation of the line will be increased. The increase in line attenuation for a given minimum attenuation is shown in Figure 1-10. As shown, for a SWR of 3 to 1, line losses increase from a minimum of 0.5 dB to about 0.75 dB.

Power Lost in The Reflected Wave.

The power present in the reflected wave is really a portion of the power present in the incident wave, power that is not absorbed by the antenna. Since the power associated with each travelling wave varies as the square of their voltage E, the per cent of power reflected from a mismatched load is determined by

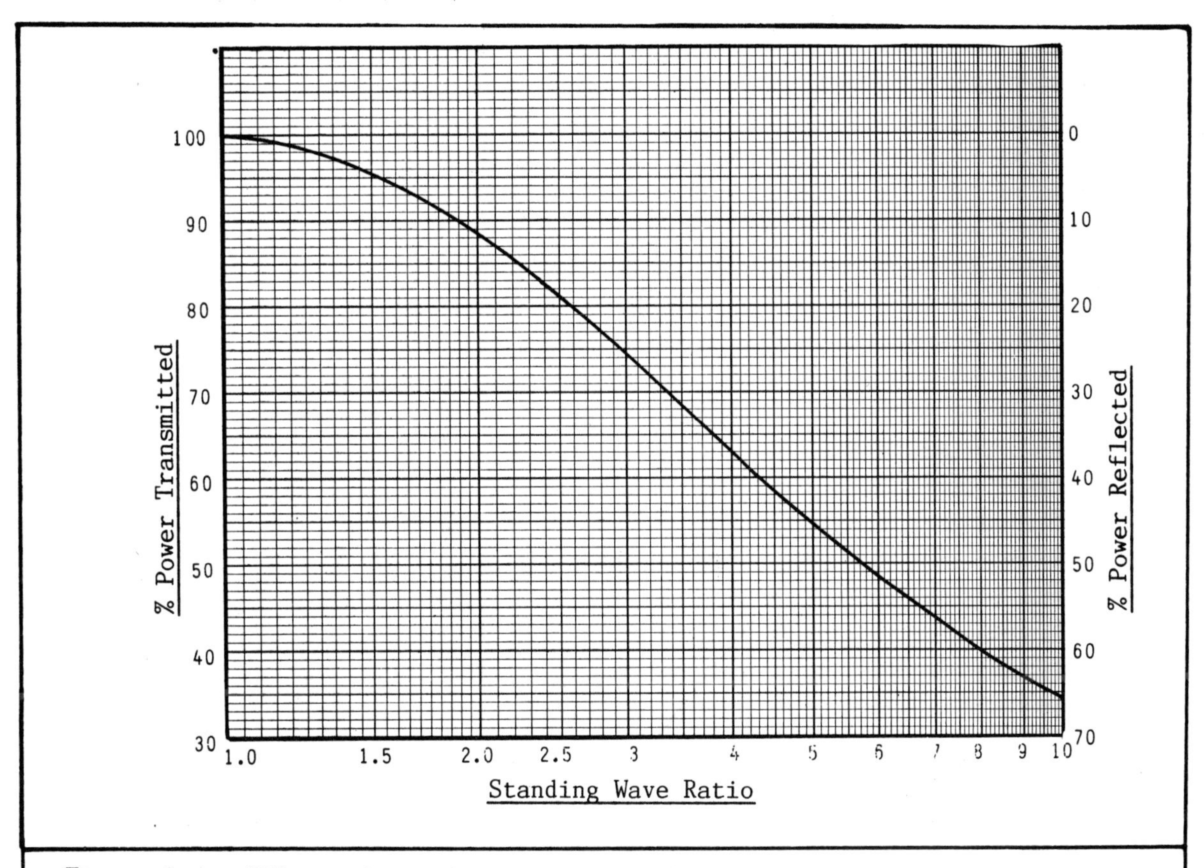

Figure 1-9. Effect of standing wave ratio (SWR) on power transfer into a lossless line.

$$\%\ \text{power reflected} = \frac{(E^+)^2}{(E^-)^2} \times 100 \qquad (1\text{-}26)$$

Since the magnitude of mismatch is usually presented in terms of SWR, the relationship between the percentage of power reflected to the SWR is given by

$$\%\ \text{power reflected} = \left(\frac{\text{SWR} - 1}{\text{SWR} + 1}\right)^2 \times 100 \qquad (1\text{-}27)$$

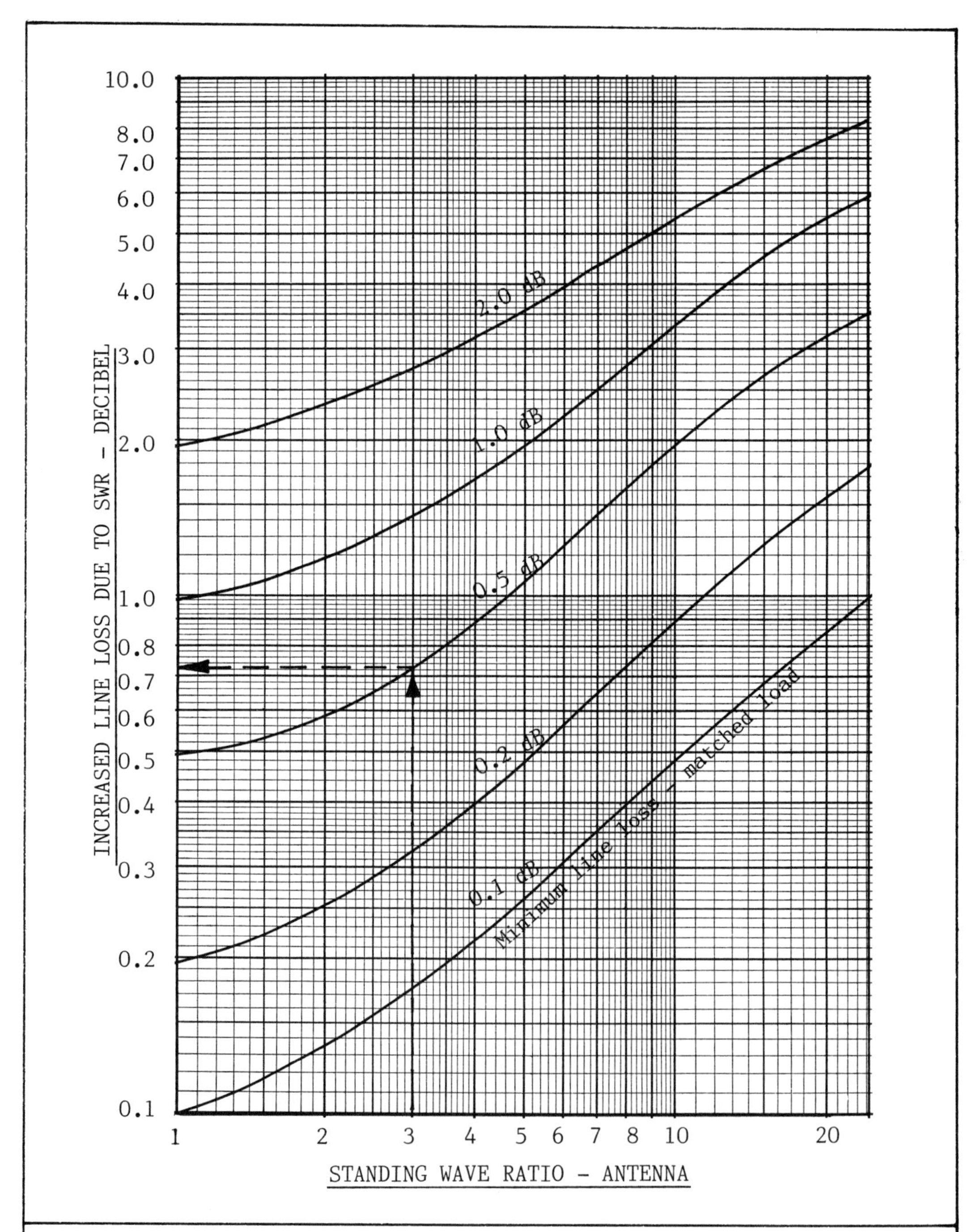

Figure 1-10. Increase in line losses caused by the presence of SWR on a transmission line.

Power Handling.

The size of a transmission line is the determinant factor that establishes the power handling capacity of the line. If, for example, a coaxial cable is used, the insulation between the conductors must be able to withstand the maximum voltage developed between the two conductors. Where standing waves are present, the voltage across the line will be considerably greater than the incident peak voltage E^+ thus increasing the possibility of a breakdown of the insulation. When such a breakdown occurs, it will be found to have taken place at a voltage maximum where the two travelling waves add in phase, that is,

$$E_{max} = E^+ + E^- \qquad (1\text{-}28)$$

CHAPTER II

THE TRANSMISSION LINE AS A CIRCUIT ELEMENT

General.

In the preceding chapter the characteristics of a transmission line were presented from the standpoint of transmitting electromagnetic energy from one point to another with maximum efficiency. Another useful quality of the transmission line is its ability to introduce into a transmission system impedance compensation by means of reactive networks, the magnitude and placement of which tend to cancel the reactance of the antenna.

Antenna Impedance Bandwidth.

Impedance matching consists of the transformation of the antenna impedance which has a greater mismatch than a specified limit to an input impedance value that has a mismatch equal to or less than the specified limit. When an antenna impedance is to be corrected at a single frequency it is always possible to obtain a perfect match with an appropriate matching network. However, as the bandwidth requirement increases from this critical frequency, the variation in reactance increases thus preventing complete compensation throughout the frequency band of interest; the greater the bandwidth the greater the compromise.

Bandwidth is a relative term that can be made definite only by specifying the maximum value of mismatch to be tolerated, i.e., a SWR not to exceed a specified limit which depends upon the purpose of the antenna or system requirements. SWR limits of 1.5 to 1 and 2.0 to 1 are common for transmitting systems whereas 5.0 to 1 and even greater are common for receiving systems.

The input impedance of an antenna at a given frequency may be expressed as a complex number $R + jX$ or $Z\underline{/\theta}$ and may be plotted as a point on a rectangular impedance chart, having abscissa R and ordinate X, see Figure 2-1. The chart is plotted on a base of a Cartesian coordinate system. The resistance part of an antenna impedance is always positive whereas the reactance part can be either positive or negative; that is why only the first and fourth quadrants of a rectangular coordinate system are used. We are thus able to plot any pair of numbers that represent the impedance of an antenna at a single frequency. If a band of frequencies is involved, the process is repeated for each frequency and the plotted points are then connected with a curve, see Figure 2-2.

Since this text deals mainly with the use of the Smith chart, the impedance points plotted in Figure 2-2 are transferred to a Smith chart as shown in Figure 2-3. Also shown is a definition circle representing a standing wave ratio of 2.0 to 1 which represents the design objective for the particular antenna being measured. Similar to the R-X diagram, the resistance axis of the Smith chart is horizontal, and the reactance axis is vertical; the inductive reactance +X above the horizontal resistance line and the capacitive reactance -X below the line. Unlike the R-X diagram, the limits of resistance and reactances are brought to a point to the right of the Smith chart. Figure 2-3 merely illustrates the type of problems with which we are concerned. In this example, the characteristic impedance of the transmission line is 50 ohms and the maximum acceptable SWR is 2.0 to 1. Figure 2-4 shows the compensated antenna impedance presented to the transmission line when the proper compensating network is used. The network employed is described in Chapter IV.

Types of Matching Networks.

There are many possible matching networks. At VHF/UHF frequencies and below it is possible to use lumped-constant matching networks, such as inductors and capacitors. At frequencies above 100 MHz, lengths of transmission line are more commonly used to perform the function that ordinary inductors and capacitors serve at lower frequencies. This is possible because at VHF and above the lengths of line are short enough to be practical, and their efficiency quite high. There are three types of matching networks that can be fabricated from transmission lines: (1) the line transformer, (2) the series network, open-circuited or short-circuited, and (3) the parallel network, open-circuited or short-circuited. The line transformer is simply a length of transmission line of a characteristic impedance different from that of the main transmission line and which is interposed between the antenna and the main transmission line, see Figure 2-5(a). The series network is a short section of line placed in series with the inner or outer conductor of a coaxial line or in series with both conductors of a two-wire transmission line, see Figure 2-5(b). The parallel network consists of a short length of transmission line placed in parallel with the antenna, see Figure 2-5(c).

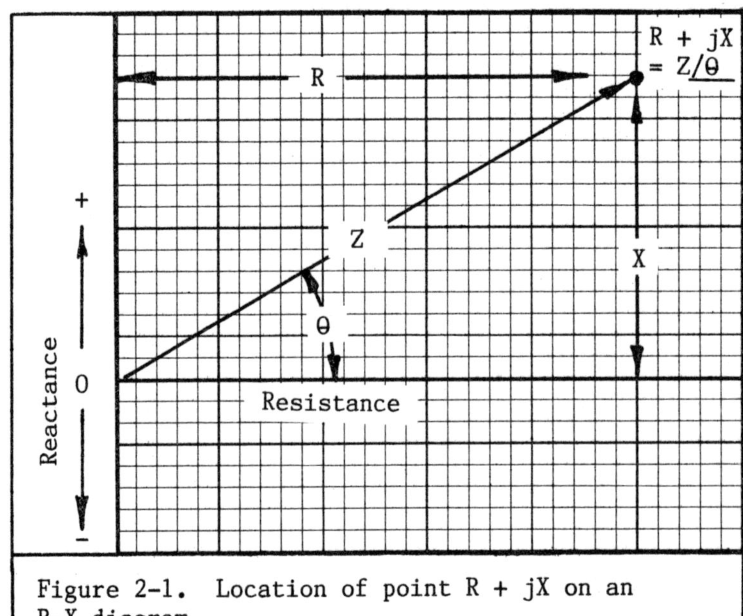

Figure 2-1. Location of point R + jX on an R-X diagram.

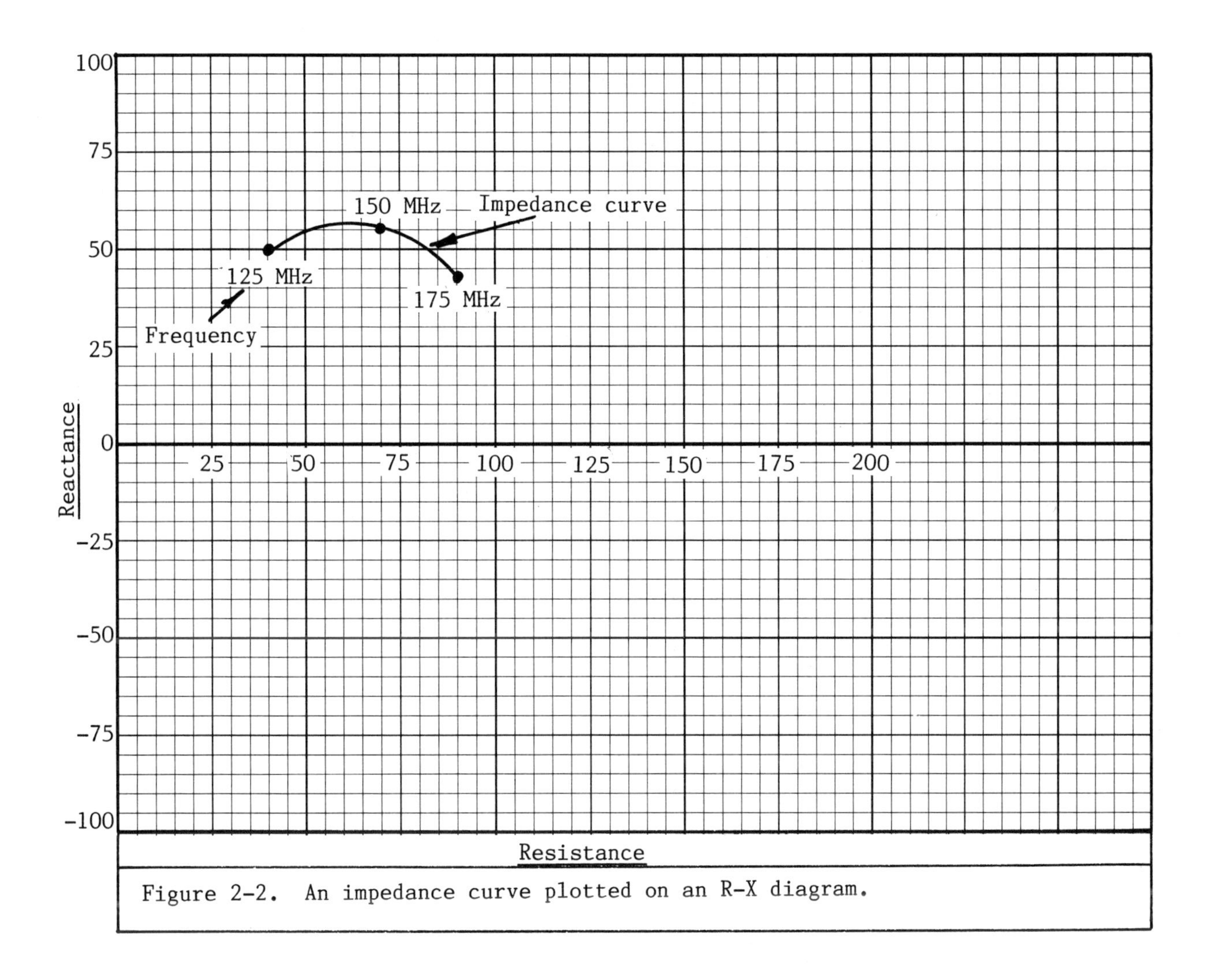

Figure 2-2. An impedance curve plotted on an R-X diagram.

The Transmission Line as a Reactive Element.

A transmission line terminated into its characteristic impedance is resistive. More importantly, from an antenna matching application, are its reactive properties. Short lengths of short-circuited lines, less than one-quarter wavelength long, have pure inductive reactance and open-circuited lines, less than one-quarter wavelength long, have pure capacitive reactance. Longer lengths of line, longer than one-quarter wavelength and less than one-half wavelength, have the opposite kind of reactance. Antenna impedance compensation or correction is accomplished by introducing into the transmission line, at the proper place, a reactive network of appropriate magnitude so that the reactive component of the antenna impedance is cancelled out. Examples of these line sections are shown schematically in Figure 2-6.

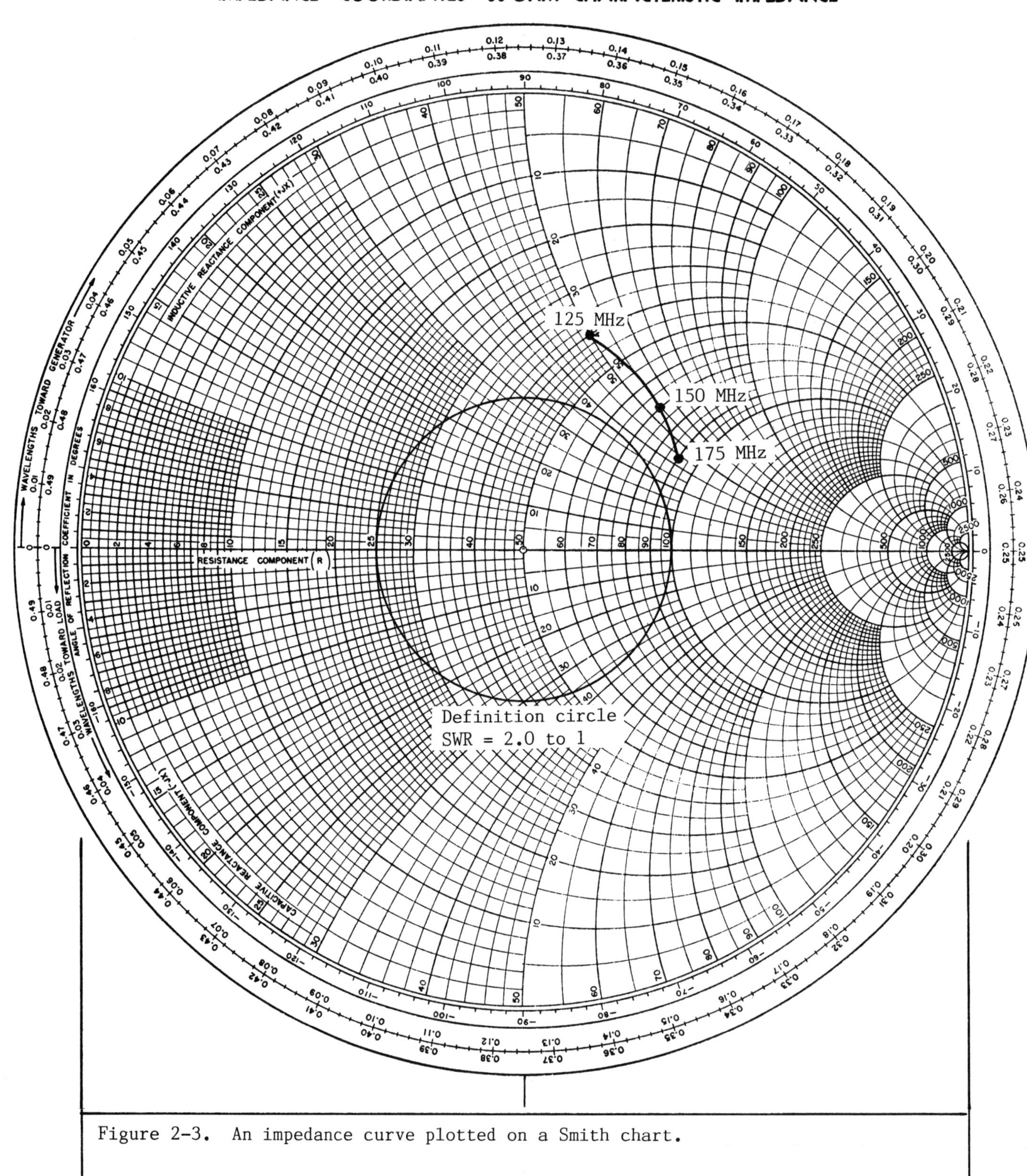

Figure 2-3. An impedance curve plotted on a Smith chart.

IMPEDANCE COORDINATES—50-OHM CHARACTERISTIC IMPEDANCE

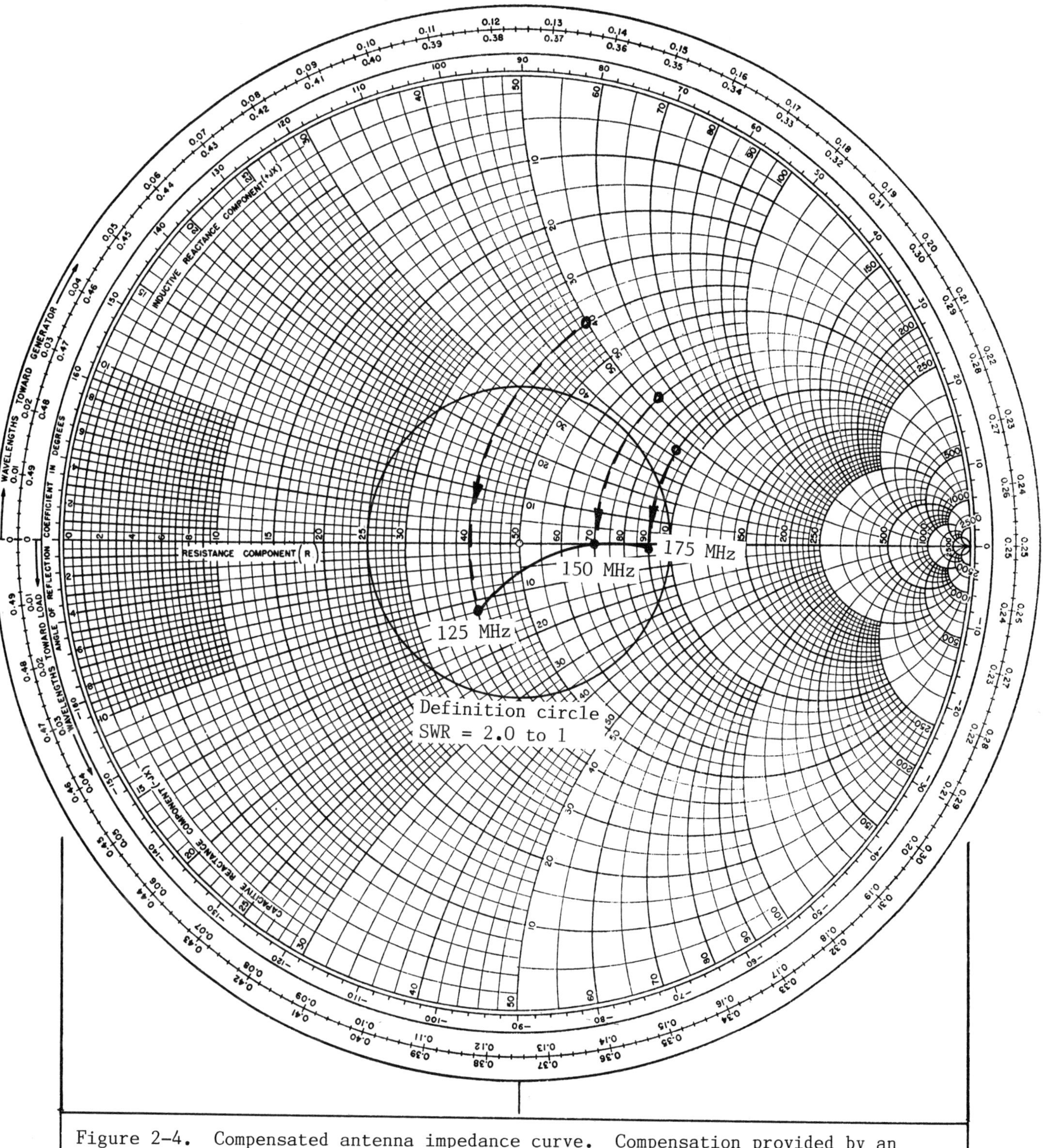

Figure 2-4. Compensated antenna impedance curve. Compensation provided by an open-circuited 25-ohm series stub 24.5 degrees long at 150 MHz.

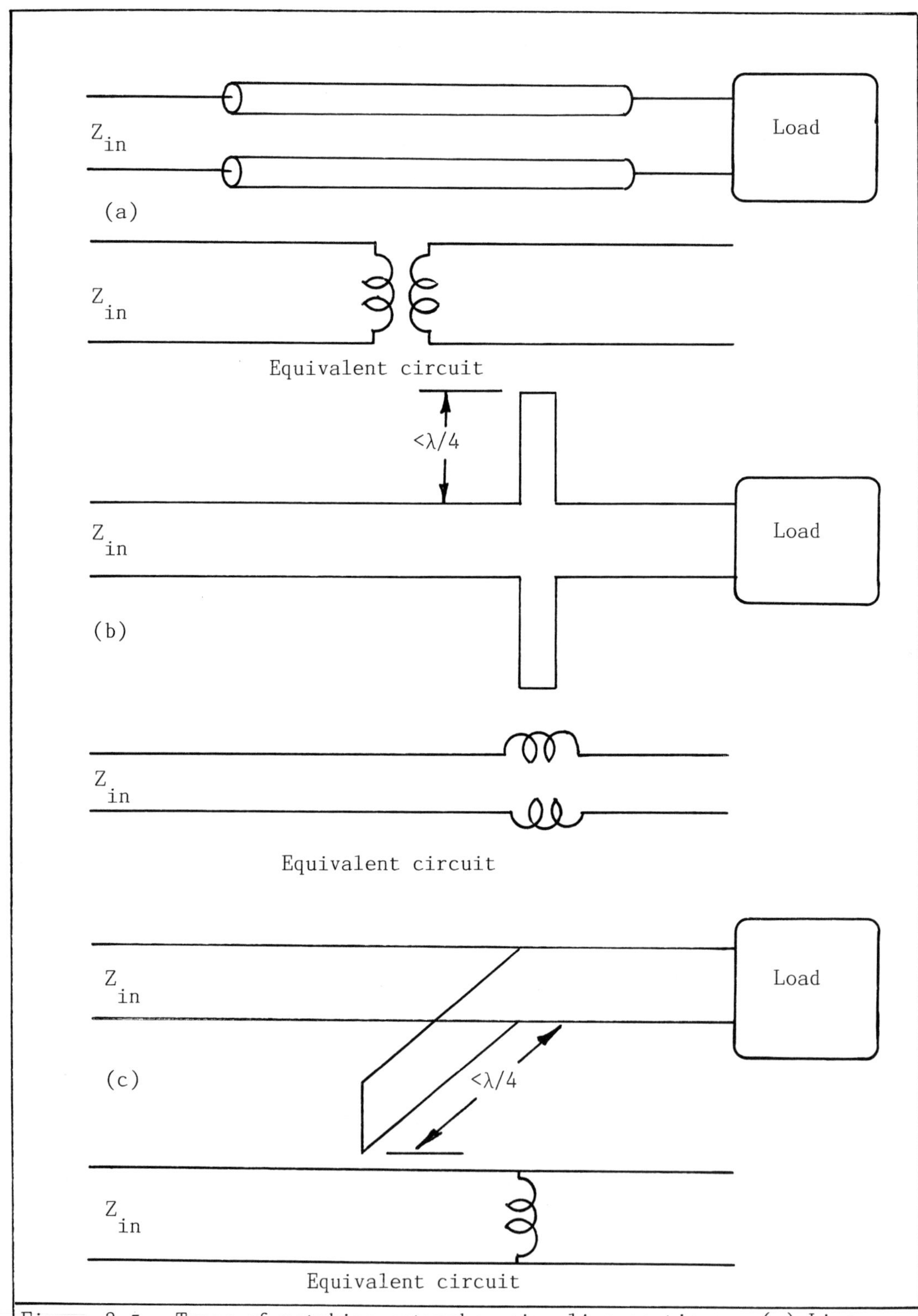

Figure 2-5. Types of matching networks using line sections. (a) Line transformer, (b) Short-circuited series network, (c) Short-circuited shunt stub.

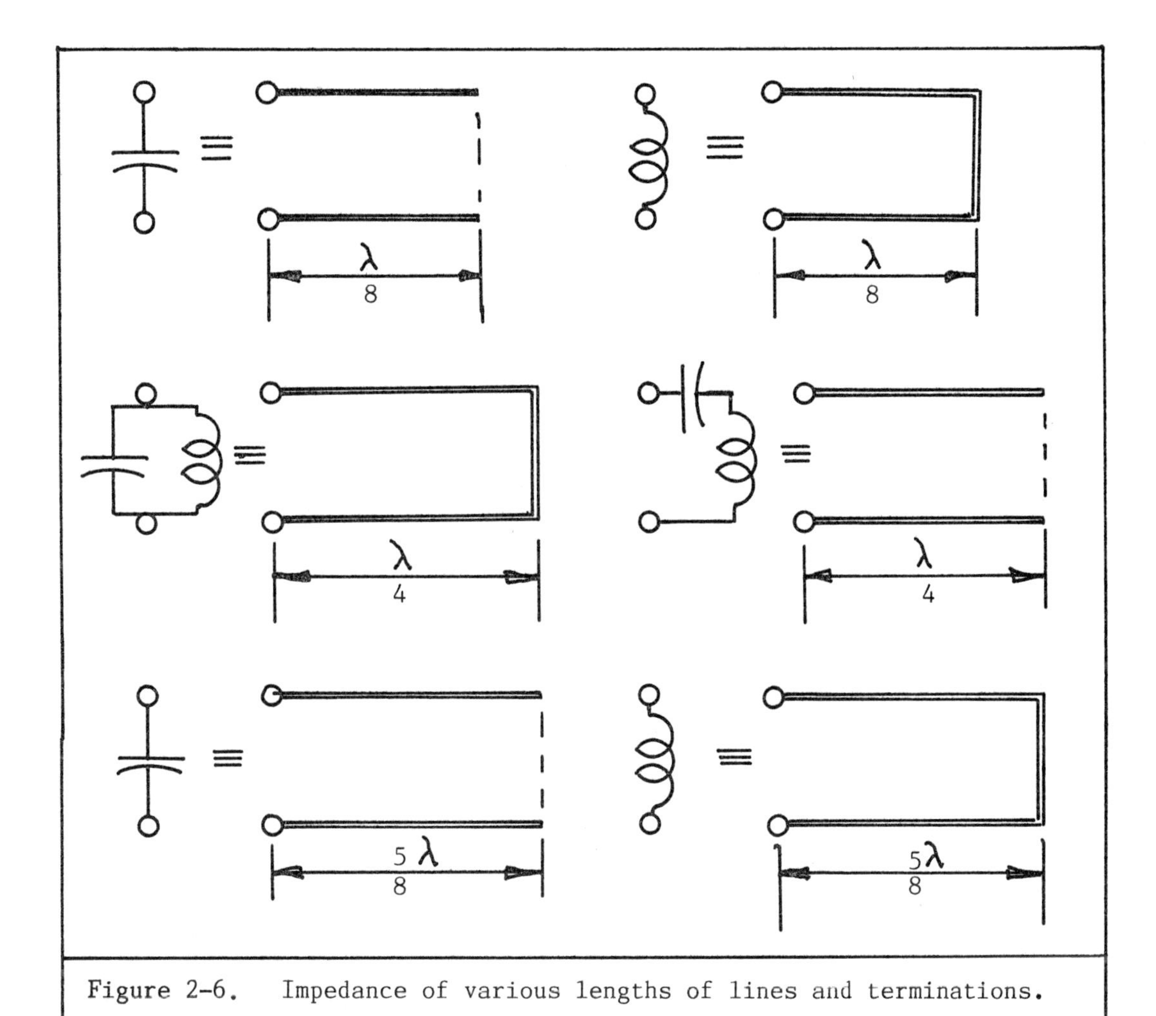

Figure 2-6. Impedance of various lengths of lines and terminations.

Consider the transmission line shown in Figure 2-7. The characteristic impedance of the line is Z_o, the load impedance is Z_a, and the electrical distance $\beta\ell$ is measured from the load end. The impedance at any point A-A', ℓ-distance from Z_a will be

$$Z_{A-A'} = Z_o \frac{Z_a + jZ_o \tan \beta\ell}{Z_o + jZ_a \tan \beta\ell} \tag{2-1}$$

If Z_a is a short circuit, then $R_a = X_a = 0$ and this equation becomes:

$$Z_{A-A'(sc)} = jZ_o \tan \beta \ell \qquad (2\text{-}2)$$

or, expressed in electrical degrees

$$Z_{A-A'(sc)} = jZ_o \tan \theta \qquad (2\text{-}3)$$

If Z_a is an open circuit, then $R_a = X_a = \infty$, and

$$Z_{A-A'(oc)} = -jZ_o \cot \beta \ell \qquad (2\text{-}4)$$

or, expressed in electrical degrees

$$Z_{A-A'(oc)} = -jZ_o \cot \theta \qquad (2\text{-}5)$$

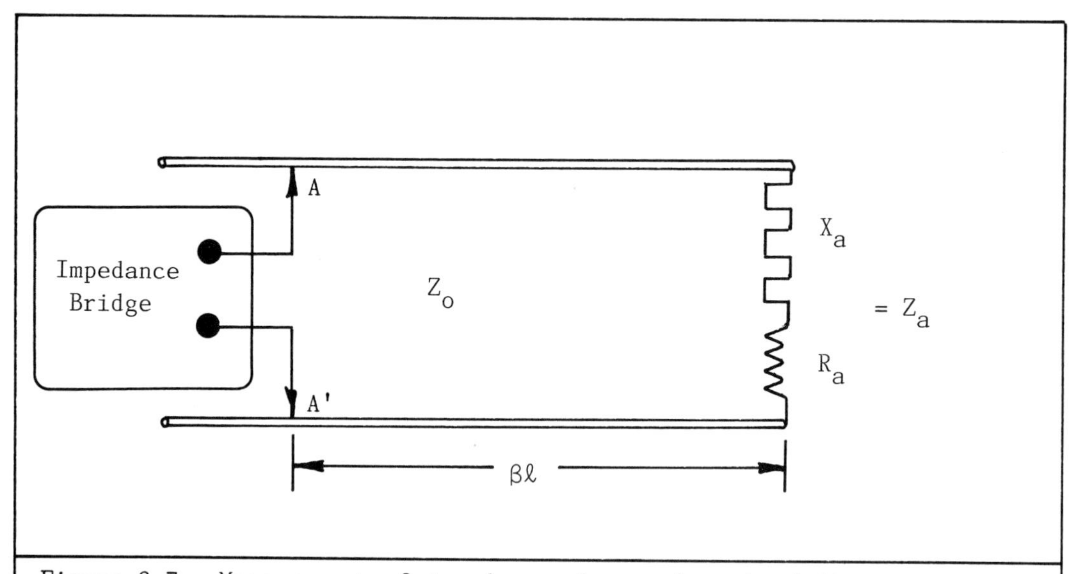

Figure 2-7. Measurement of impedance along a length of line.

On the Smith chart, $Z_{a(sc)}$ is located at $R_a = X_a = 0$ which is at the extreme left (zero impedance) while $Z_{a(oc)}$ is located at $R_a = X_a = \infty$, at the extreme right (infinite impedance). Both of these points are shown in **Figure 2-9.** Also shown is point A-A' (shown as $\beta\ell = 0.15$ wavelength from the load). The distance $\beta\ell$ is measured clockwise from the load.

Examination of Eq. (2-2) thru (2-5) show that only a pure reactance exists on the line at any point. Figure 2-8 shows the variations in reactance for a short-circuited line as its length is varied from $\theta = 0$ degrees to $\theta = 540$ degrees (three half-wavelengths). In this representation of reactances the familiar tangent curve should be apparent. Since the length of the line, measured in electrical degrees, is a function of frequency, for a line of given physical length, the reactance varies with frequency.

Further examination of Eq. (2-2) thru (2-5) show that the reactance is also a function of the characteristic impedance of the stub line. The curves presented in **Figure 2-10** are plots of Eq. (2-2) for five values of stub line impedance. **Figure 2-11** are plots of Eq. (2-4) for five values of stub line impedance.

The brief examples of the characteristics of short-circuited and open-circuited stub lines suggest their use as pure reactances in low loss impedance matching networks. The following discussion will deal with these uses as series and shunt matching networks.

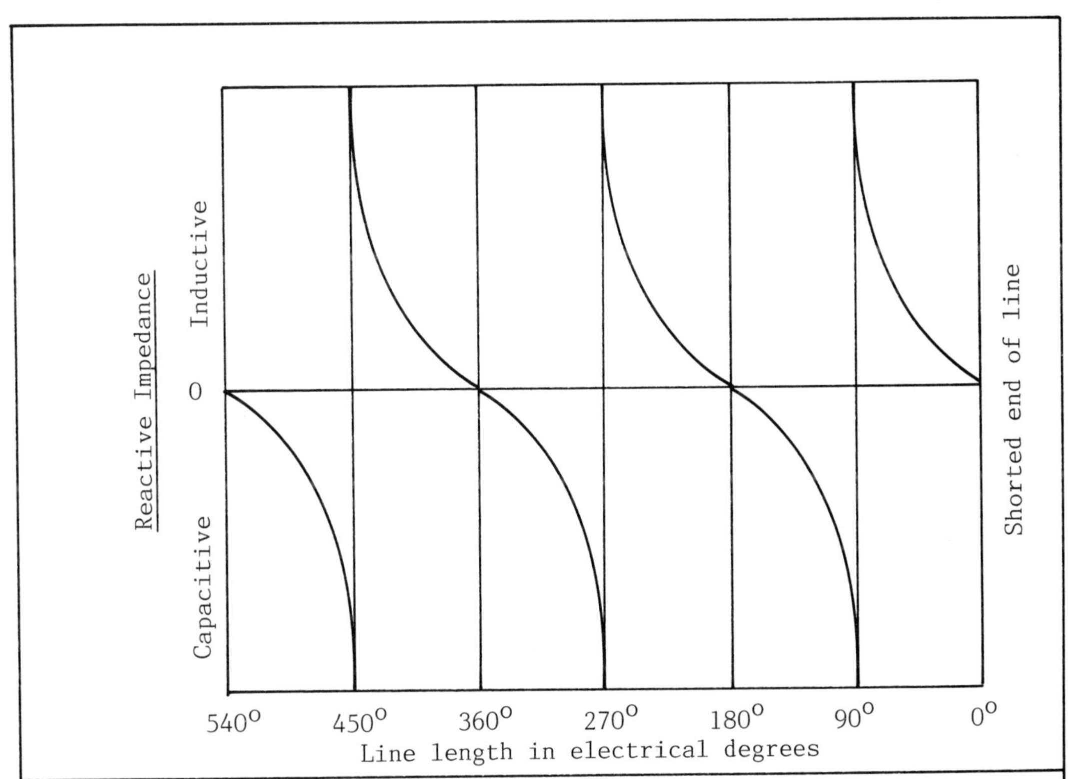

Figure 2-8. Input impedance of a short-circuited lossless line as a function of its electrical length.

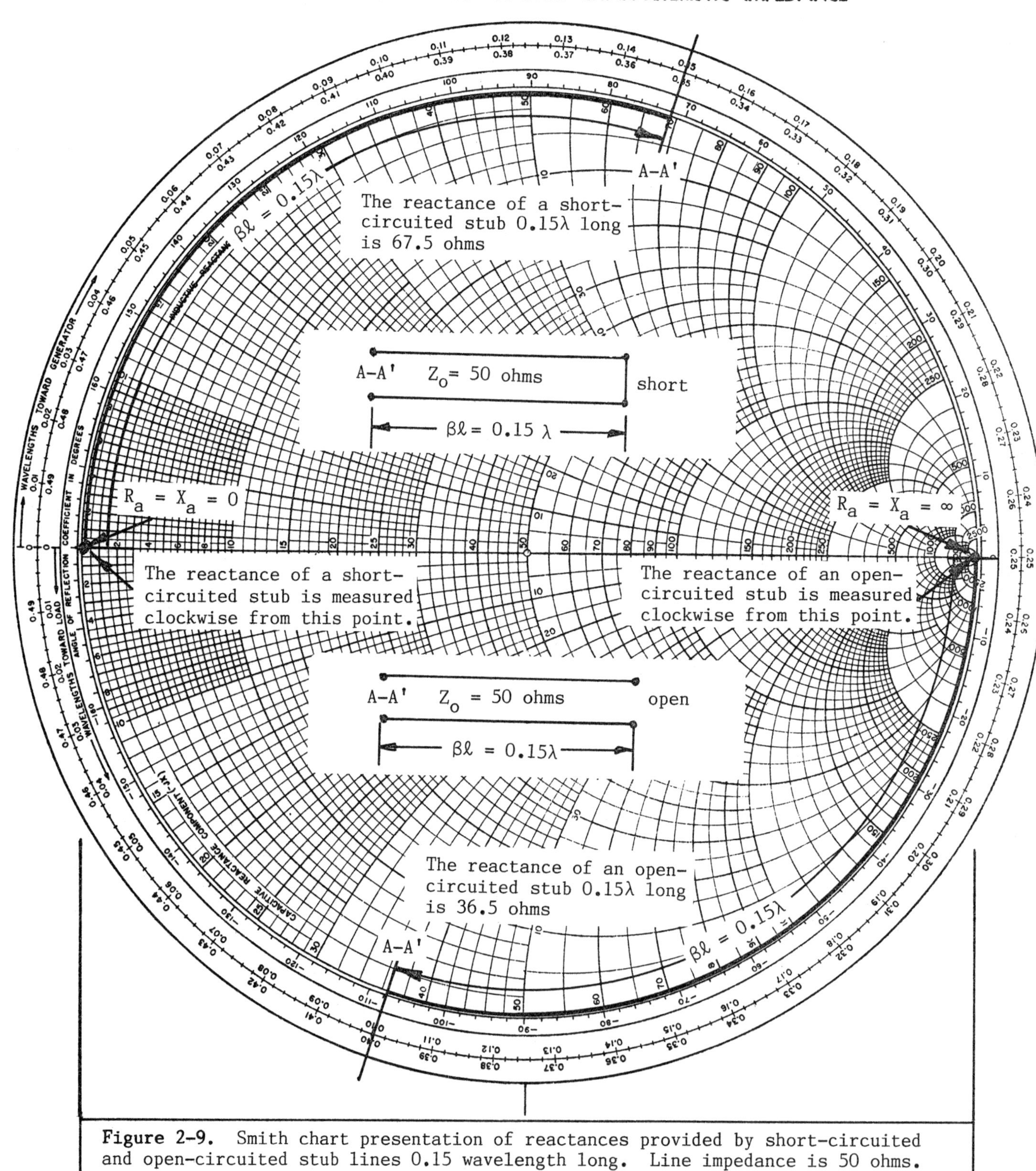

Figure 2-9. Smith chart presentation of reactances provided by short-circuited and open-circuited stub lines 0.15 wavelength long. Line impedance is 50 ohms.

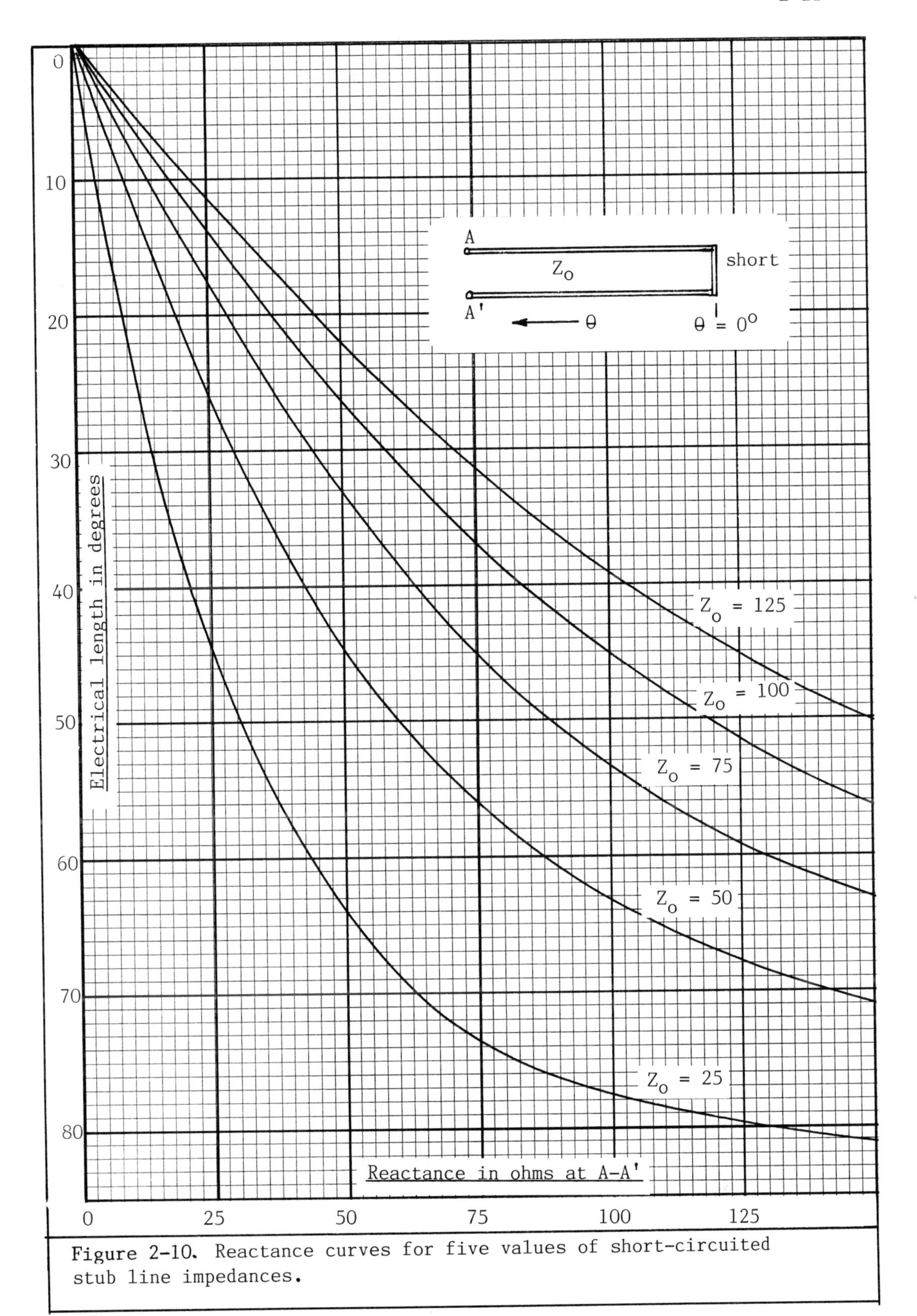

Figure 2-10. Reactance curves for five values of short-circuited stub line impedances.

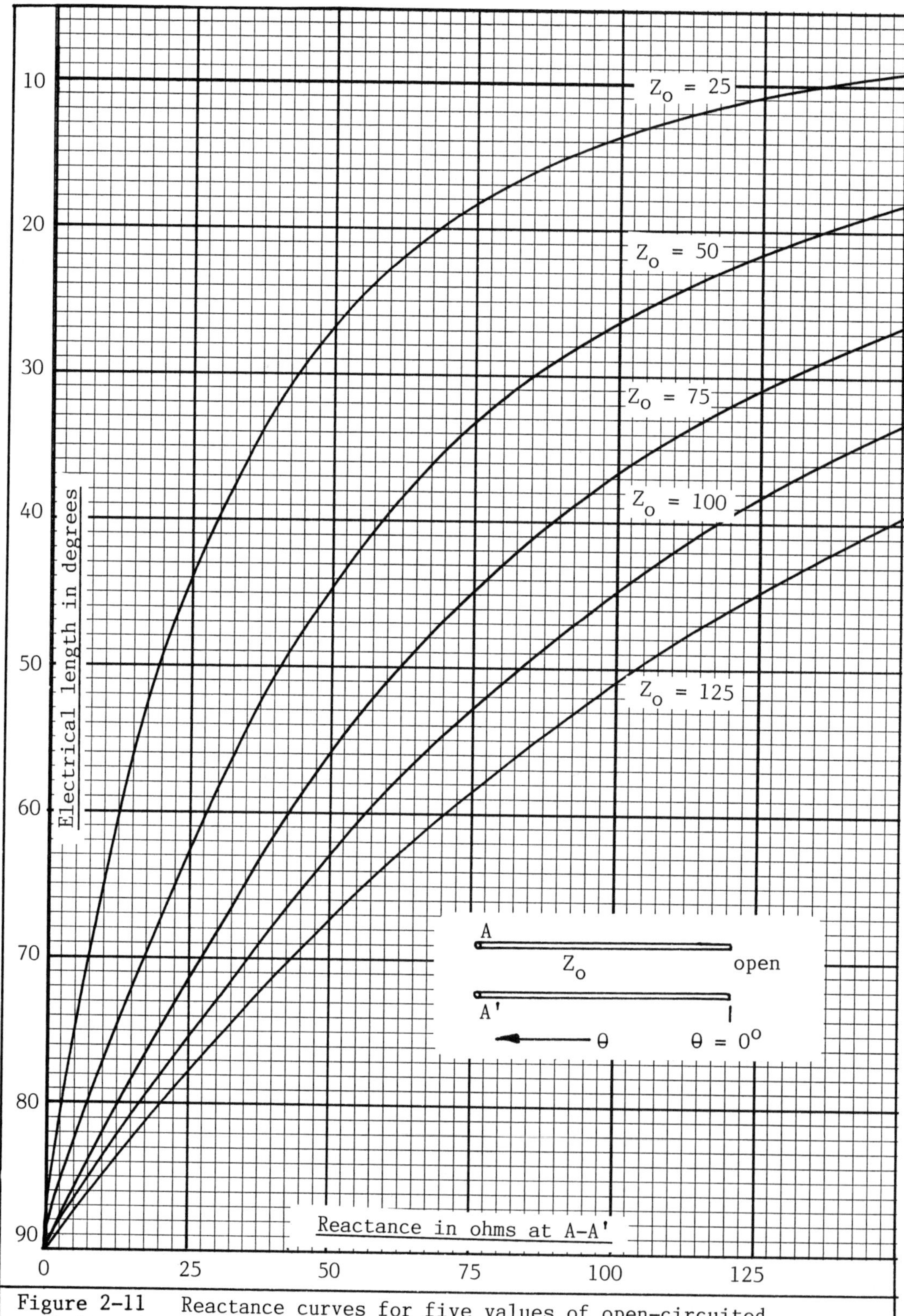

Figure 2-11 Reactance curves for five values of open-circuited stub line impedances.

Sometimes it is more convenient to compute stub line reactances in terms of electrical degrees as indicated by Eq. (2-3) and (2-5) instead of using $\beta\ell$. For this purpose the Smith chart shown in **Figure 2-12** has been prepared. As shown, the impedance of a short-circuited stub line is measured clockwise from the left terminus and the impedance of an open-circuited stub line is measured clockwise from the right terminus. The calibration shown is in terms of electrical degrees.

The Stub Line as a Series Matching Element.

In Figure 2-4 it was shown that if an equal and opposite reactance is added in series with that of a load, the performance of the transmission system is greatly improved. A similar problem is presented in **Figure 2-13** which shows an open-circuited stub line in series with the load. The required reactance of the stub is -j85 ohms if it is to cancel the +j85 ohms reactance of the load.

A study of **Figure 2-11** shows that a negative (capacitive) reactance of 85 ohms can be obtained from an open-circuited stub having a characteristic impedance of 25 ohms if the length of the stub is 16 electrical degrees long, from a 50-ohm stub line 30 electrical degrees long, or from a 75-ohm stub line 41 electrical degrees long. Any of the stub lines presented in **Figure 2-11** can be used to provide the required reactance. It should be noted that the 30-ohm resistance of the load is not altered in any way.

One important aspect of stub lines of various characteristic impedances is that they no not behave the same if a band of frequencies to be matched is involved. Some lines may be satisfactory, others not. This can be demonstrated by an example.

Example: With reference to **Figure 2-14**, a transmission line having a characteristic impedance of 50 ohms is terminated into a frequency sensitive antenna $Z_a = R_a + jX_a$ having the impedance values shown in the figure. Determine the best open-circuited stub impedance added in series to the antenna. The stub line impedances are those shown in **Figure 2-11**. Cut the length of the stub for optimum performance at the center frequency $f_c = 200$ MHz.

Solution: The best match (lowest SWR) is to be obtained at 200 MHz, therefore, the reactance of +65 ohms at 200 MHz must be cancelled out by the stub. This means that the stub must be open-circuited and of such a length so as to supply 65 ohms of reactance.

Let us first consider a 25-ohm stub line. With reference to **Figure 2-11** a 25-ohm open-circuited stub line 21 electrical degrees long will provide a negative reactance of 65 ohms. At 175 MHz its length will be shorter and at 225 MHz longer. The electrical length of the stub line will have the same ratio as the frequency, that is,

$$f/f_c \quad (2\text{-}6)$$

where

f = frequency of interest

f_c = center or design frequency = 200 MHz

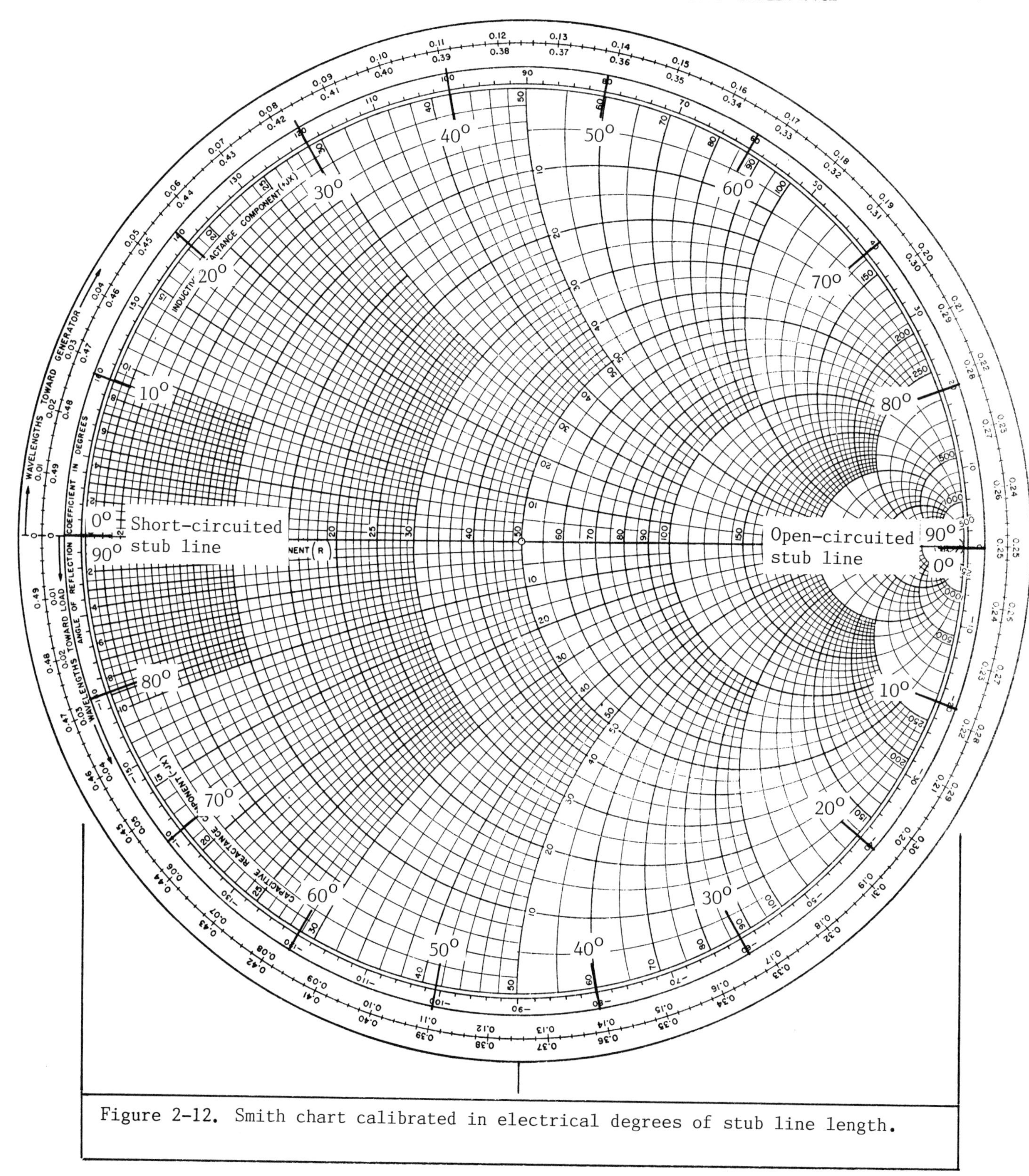

Figure 2-12. Smith chart calibrated in electrical degrees of stub line length.

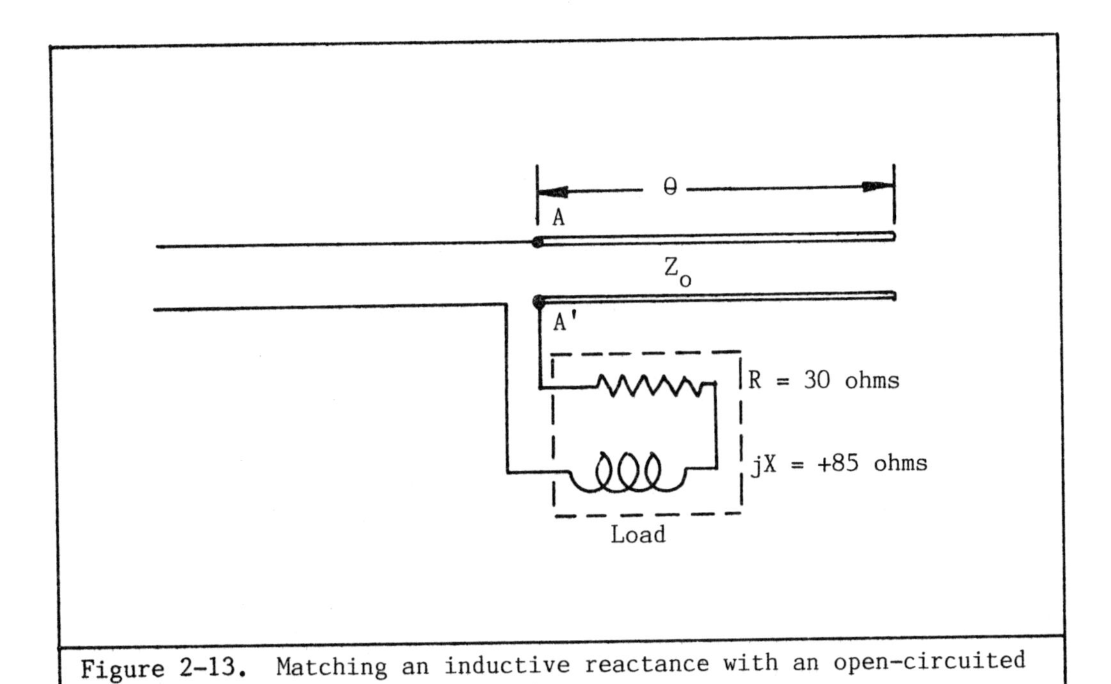

Figure 2-13. Matching an inductive reactance with an open-circuited stub line.

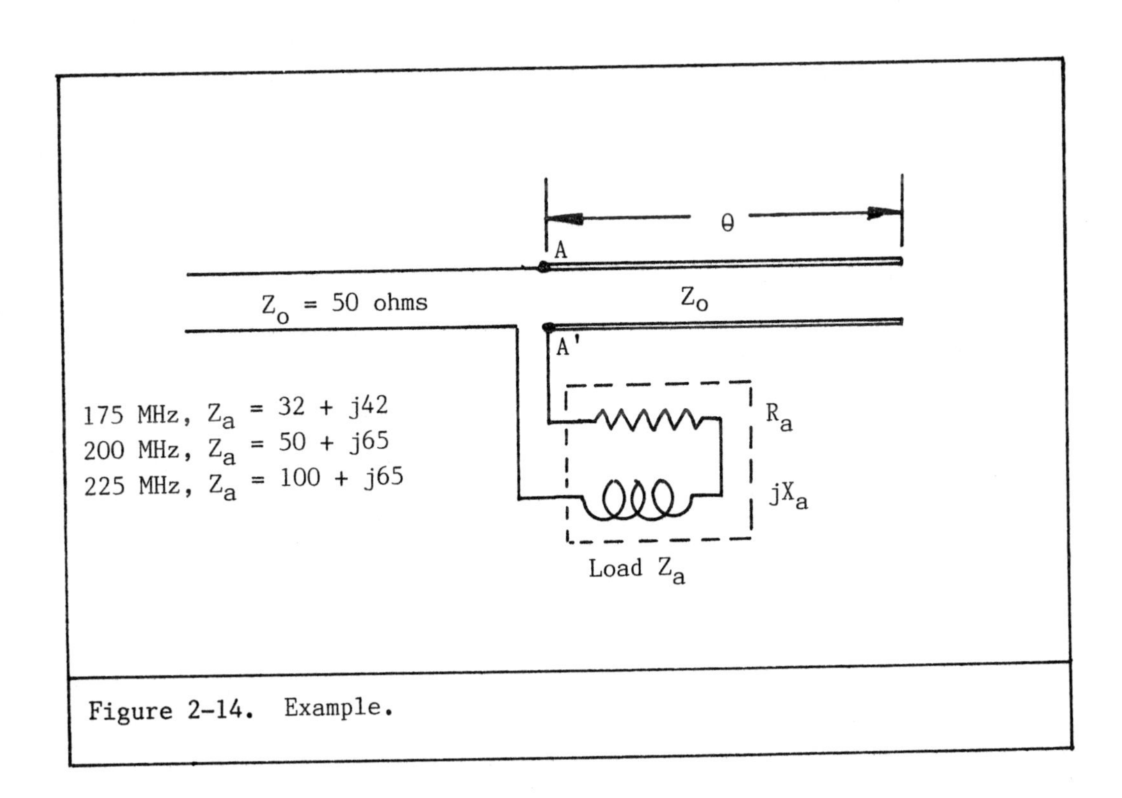

Figure 2-14. Example.

Table 2-1 shows the results of adding in series stubs of various impedances to the load. The results are then plotted on a Smith chart. Figure 2-15 is a Smith chart plot of this example. The effectiveness of each stub line can easily be evaluated by observation.

TABLE 2-1

			Z_o = 25 ohms			Z_o = 50 ohms		
Freq.	f/f_c	Z_a	θ	X_{stub}	$Z_{a(new)}$	θ	X_{stub}	$Z_{a(new)}$
175	0.875	32 + j42	18.4°	-75	32 - j33	32.4°	-77.5	32 - j35.7
200	1.000	50 + j65	21.0°	-65	50 + j0	37.0°	-65	50 + j0
225	1.125	100 + j65	23.6°	-57.5	100 + j7.5	41.6°	-57	100 + j8

			Z_o = 75 ohms			Z_o = 100 ohms		
Freq.	f/f_c	Z_a	θ	X_{stub}	$Z_{a(new)}$	θ	X_{stub}	$Z_{a(new)}$
175	0.875	32 + j42	42.9°	-80	32 - j38	49.4°	-85	32- j43
200	1.000	50 + j65	49.0°	-65	50 + j0	56.5	-65	50 + j0
225	1.125	100 + j65	55.1°	-52	100 + j13	63.6°	-47	100 + j18

For comparison purposes let us investigate the effects of a capacitor in series with the load impedance. To provide a negative reactance of 65 ohms at 200 MHz the size of the capacitor must be

$$C = \frac{1}{2\pi f X_c} \qquad 2\text{-}7$$

where

f = frequency = 200×10^6 Hz
X_c = reactance = 65 ohms
C = capacitance in farads

then

$$C = \frac{1}{6.28 \times 200 \times 10^6 \times 65} = \frac{10^{-12}}{0.08164}$$

$$= 12.25 \times 10^{-12} \text{ farad or } 12.25 \text{ pF}$$

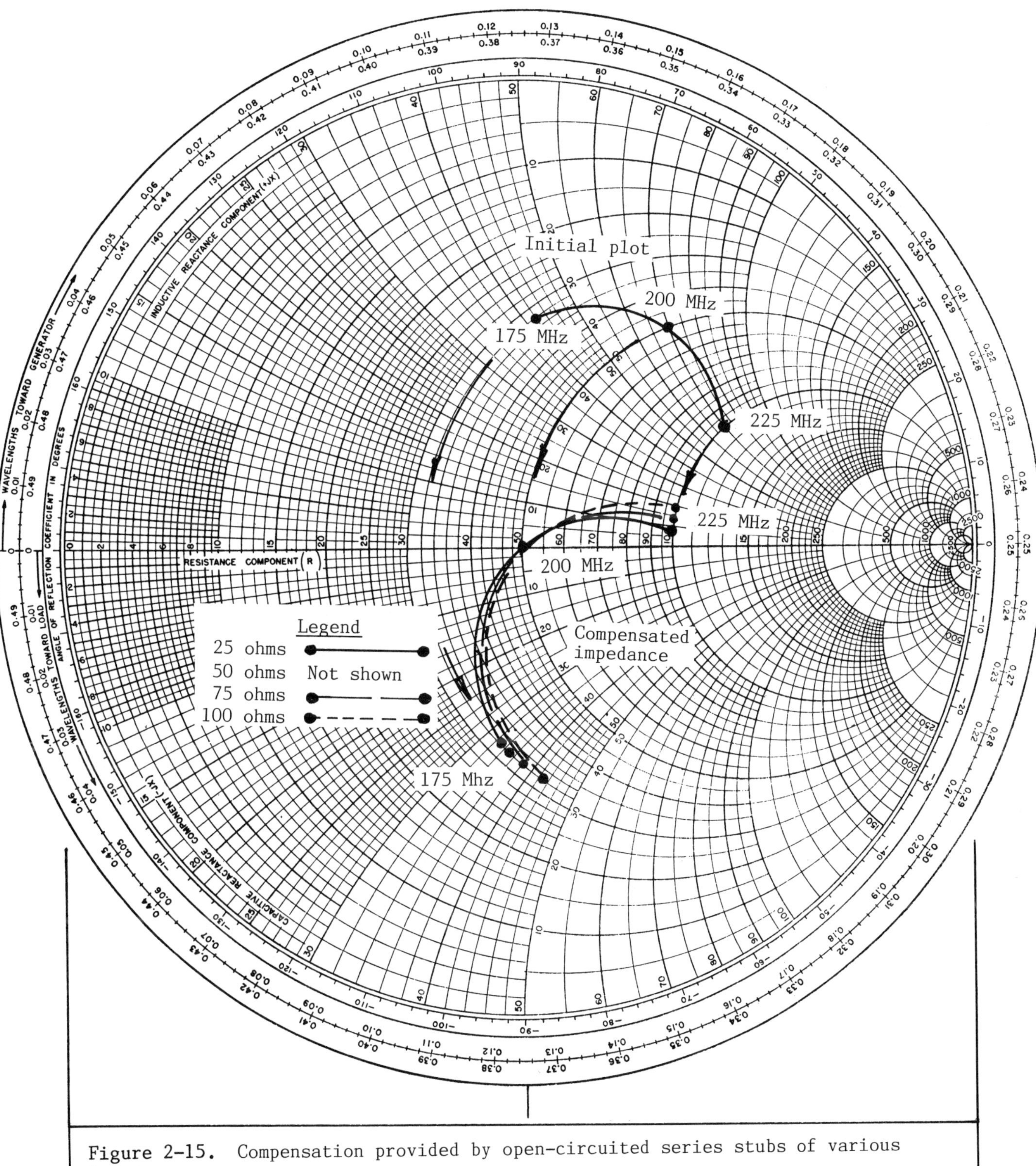

Figure 2-15. Compensation provided by open-circuited series stubs of various impedances.

To determine the reactance at other frequencies and the new impedance $Z_{a(new)}$ Table 2-2 has been prepared.

TABLE 2-2

			C = 12.25 pF	
Freq.	f/f_c	Z_a	X_c	$Z_{a(new)}$
175	0.875	32 + j42	56.9	32 - j14.9
200	1.000	50 + j65	65.0	50 + j0
225	1.125	100 + j65	73.1	100 - j8.1

It appears that an open-circuited series stub has a greater influence at the low frequency end whereas a series capacitor, providing the same reactance at the center frequency, has a greater influence at the high frequency end.

It can be see that by adding a series open-circuited stub having 65 ohms of negative reactance at 200 MHz the positive reactance at 200 MHz is cancelled out and the 200 MHz frequency point moves counterclockwise along a line of constant resistance, 50 ohms, to the center of the Smith chart where the SWR = 1.0 to 1, a perfect match. It appears that the 25-ohm series stub provides the best overall match. Also, under the conditions stated, a series capacitor would provide an even better overall match, being less frequency sensitive. These facts will be used to solve matching problems in the final chapter.

The Stub Line as a Parallel Matching Element.

The use of the open-circuited and short-circuited stub lines as matching devices in series with the load has been presented. There is one undesirable feature associated with the stub and that is it is difficult to incorporate into a system unless it is built into the antenna. Because of this limitation, stub lines connected across the load are more common. An example of the parallel connected stub line is shown in Figure 2-16. As shown, the transmission line is connected directly to the antenna and a suitable shunt reactance, commonly in the form of a short length of transmission line, is used to reduce or eliminate high standing waves between the shunt point and the transmitter. The reactance and resistance of the antenna are shown in a parallel arrangement because we are now dealing with admittance instead of impedance. For example, suppose the impedance of the antenna at a single frequency is $Z_a = 65 - j125$ ohms. The input admittance is

$$Y_a = 1/Z_a = \frac{65}{65^2 + 125^2} + j\frac{125}{65^2 + 125^2} = 0.00327 + j0.0063 \text{ mho}$$

The parallel equivalent circuit is then a resistance of 1/0.00327 = 306 ohms in parallel with a capacitive reactance of 1/0.0063 = 159 ohms. If a stub having an inductive reactance of 159 ohms is placed in parallel with the antenna the input impedance of the combination will be a resistance of 306 ohms.

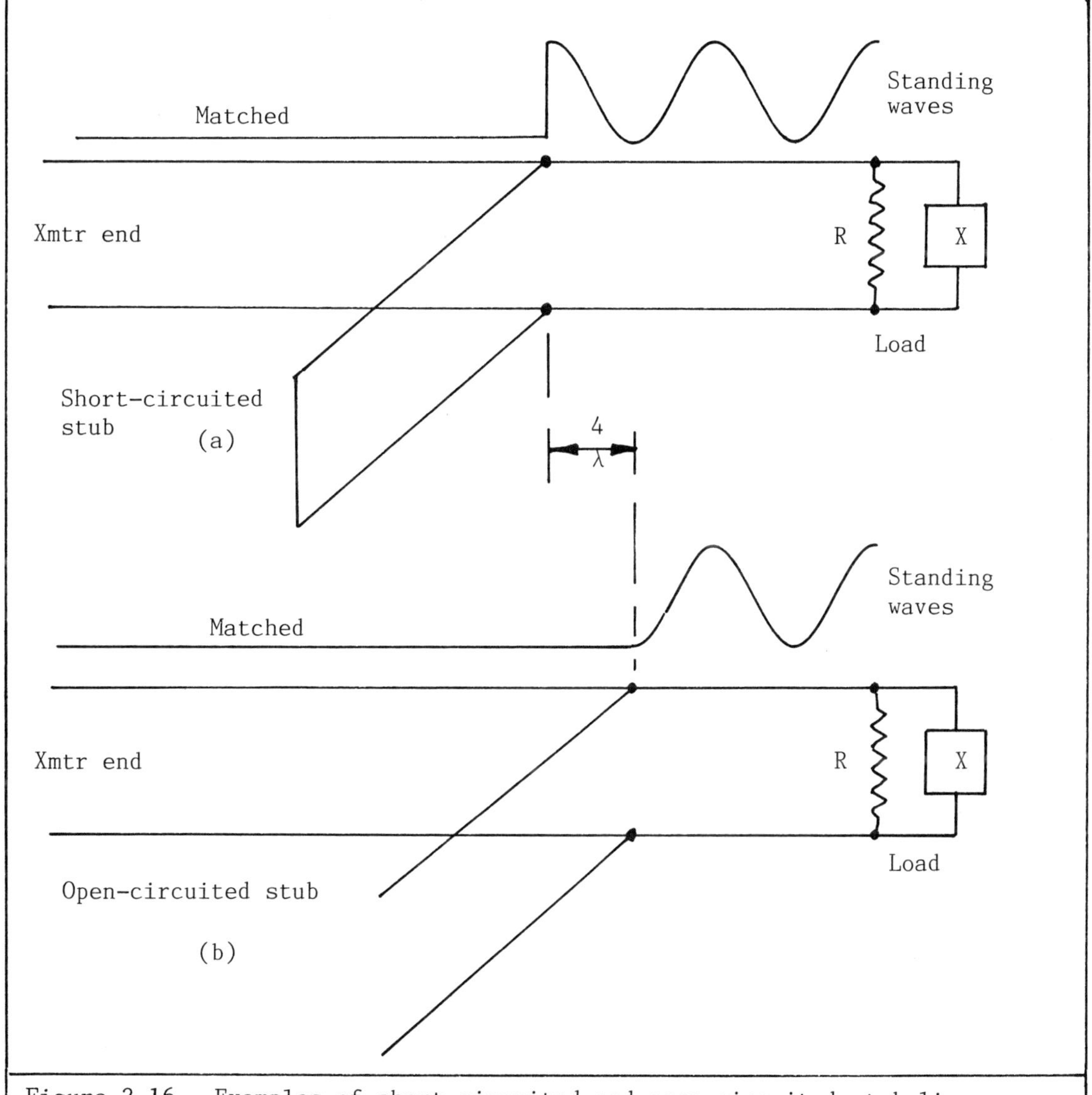

Figure 2-16. Examples of short-circuited and open-circuited stub lines across a load.

The shunting reactance must be placed at a point such that, when the impedance looking toward the load is paralleled by the shunt reactance, the impedance of the combination is a resistance equal in magnitude to the characteristic impedance of the line. The exact length and location of the stub may be obtained graphically from Figure 2-17. It should be noted that impedance measurements are not required; instead only the current or voltage standing wave ratio is required.

To illustrate, suppose $E_{min}/E_{max} = I_{min}/I_{max}$ is found to be

$$E_{min}/E_{max} = I_{min}/I_{max} = \frac{130}{650} = 0.20$$

by sliding an rf meter along the two-wire line, and it is desired to use a short-circuited stub line in parallel with the load. From Figure 2-17, $a = 0.183\lambda$ and $b = 0.08\lambda$.

When the stub line is adjusted to the correct length and properly located, standing waves appear on the transmission line only between the stub and antenna; the remainder of the transmission line is now working into its proper characteristic impedance. This procedure is illustrated in Figure 2-18.

It is not necessary to locate the stub line directly across the load. Very often it is a considerable distance from the load. Because of the change in impedance with distance along the line a better match can perhaps be realized by placing the stub where the impedance is more favorable to matching.

At VHF/UHF frequencies the stub can be incorporated into the antenna. This makes for a much more compact antenna design as shown in Figure 2-19. Within the hollow antenna elements the electrical fields present are only associated with the operation of the internal stub arrangement whereas on the outside of the antenna elements the electrical fields are only associated with the operation of the antenna. The two functions are completely independent of each other and do not interact.

The Short-circuited Shunt Stub as a Resonant Circuit.

Transmission lines that are not terminated into their characteristic impedances will act much like resonant circuits over certain narrow bands of frequencies. When the impedance goes through a maximum, its variation with changing frequency is similar to that occurring in a parallel resonant circuit, see Figure 2-8. The circuit of Figure 2-20 is the simplest representation of a parallel resonant circuit. It is evident that for this circuit the resonant frequency f_r at which the input impedance is real is identical with the frequency at which the input impedance magnitude is a maximum, and that the reactance of the inductor and capacitor are also equal in magnitude at this same frequency. Thus

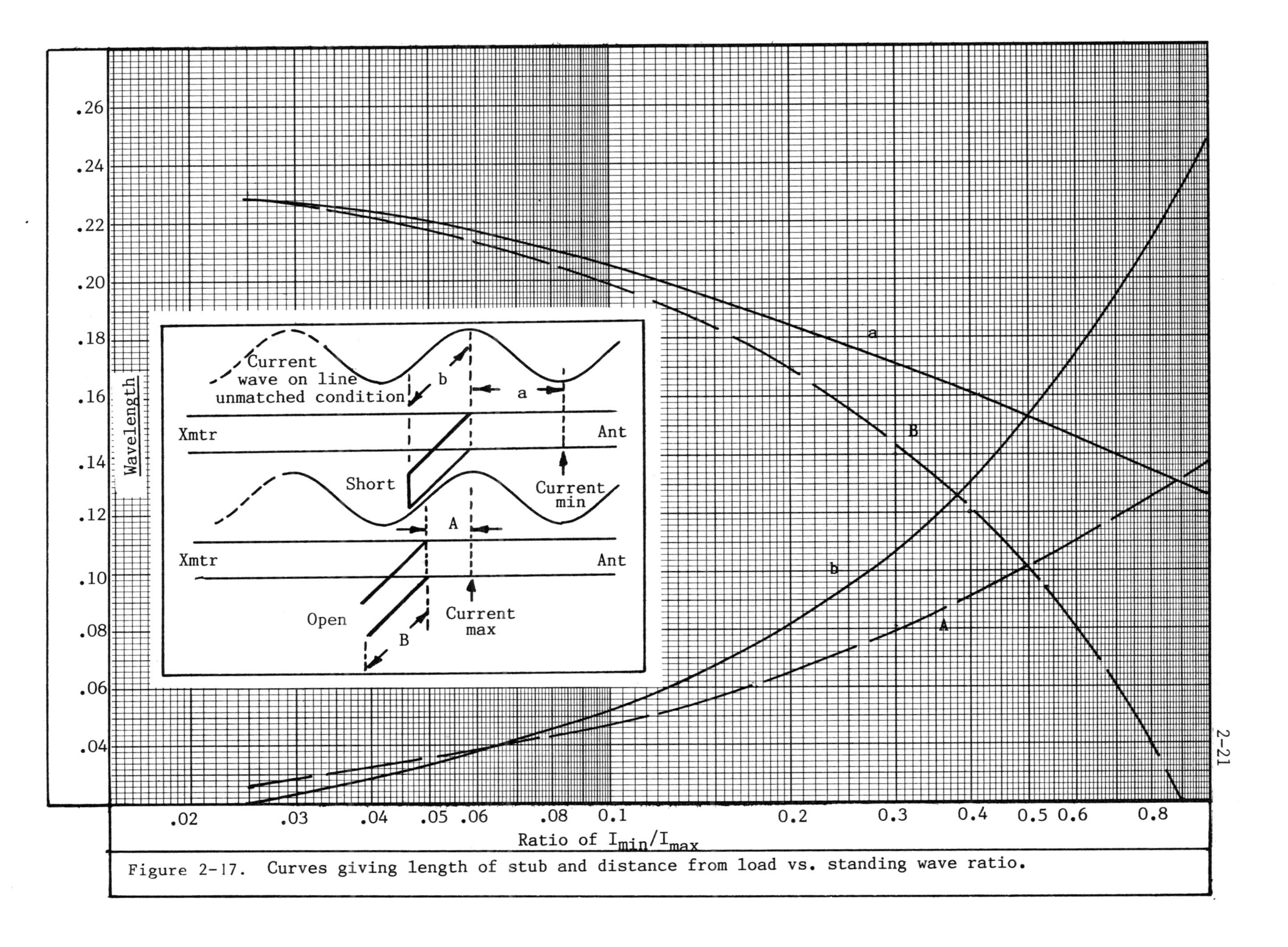

Figure 2-17. Curves giving length of stub and distance from load vs. standing wave ratio.

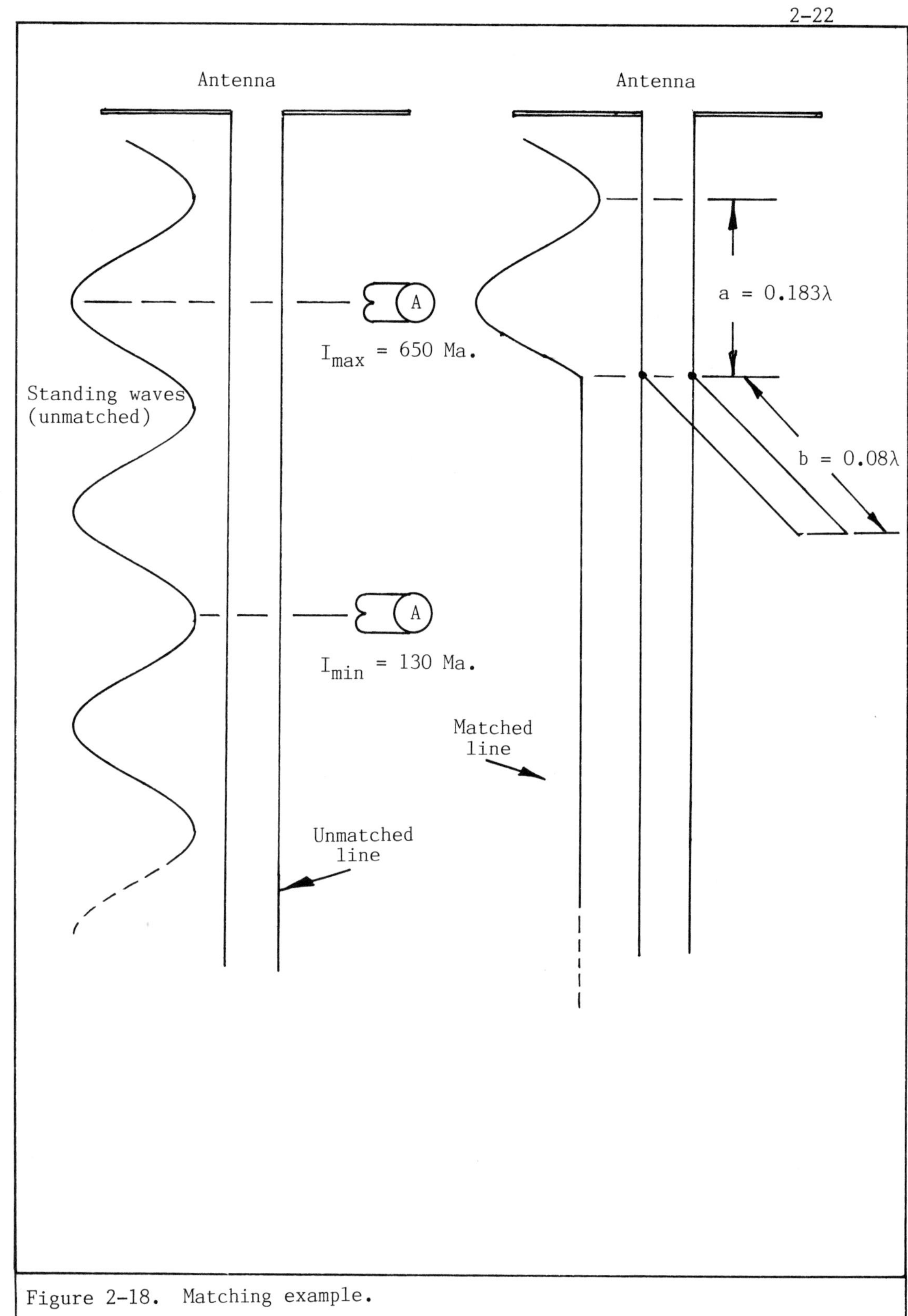

Figure 2-18. Matching example.

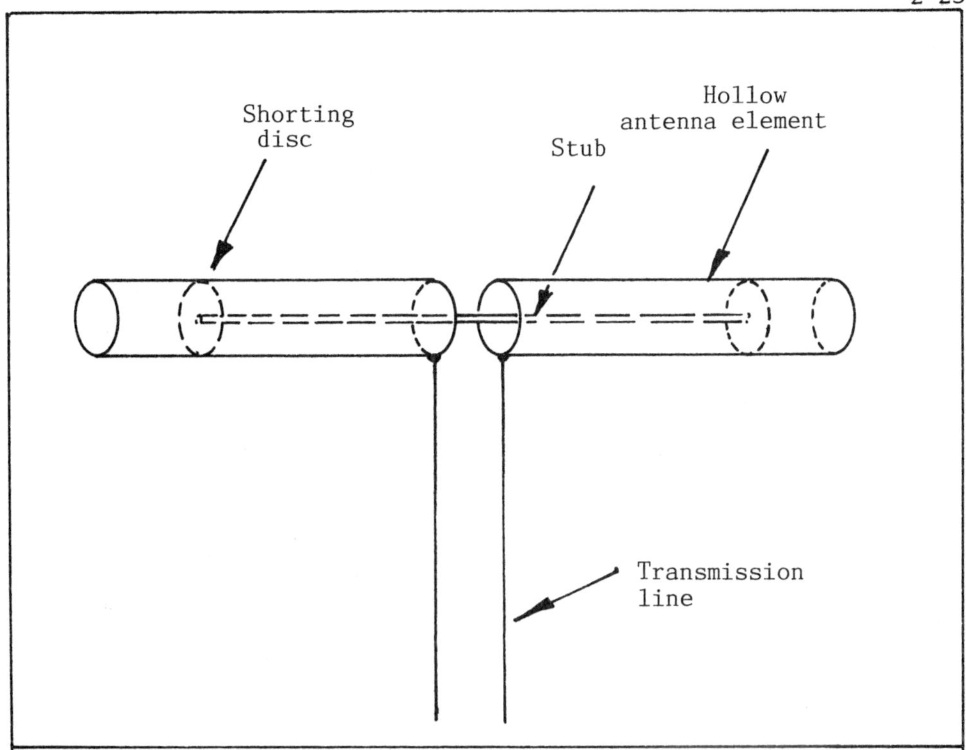

Figure 2-19. Arrangement of a half-wave dipole antenna with an internally constructed stub line.

$$f_r = \frac{1}{2\pi\sqrt{L_p\ C_p}} \qquad (2\text{-}8)$$

and

$$Z_r = R_p + j0 \qquad (2\text{-}9)$$

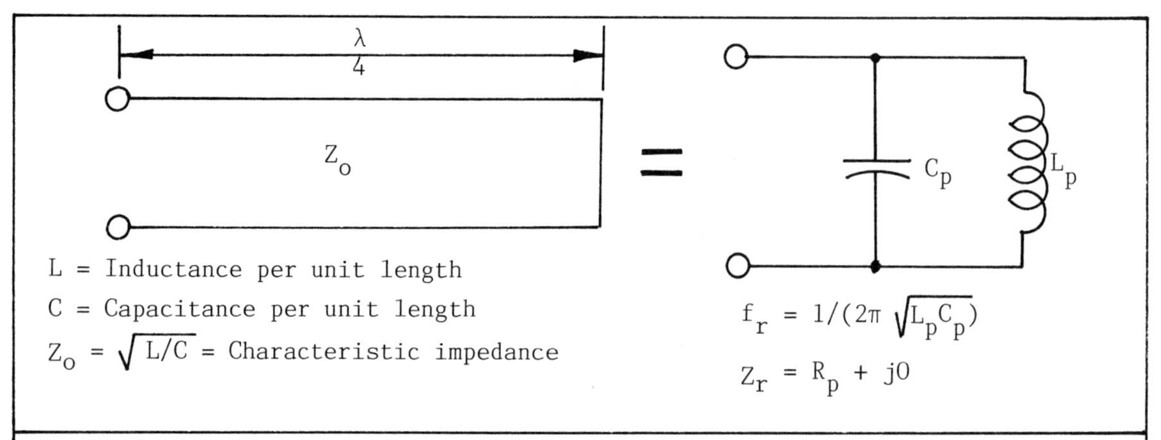

Figure 2-20. A one-quarter wavelength short-circuited transmission line, and the parallel resonant circuit to which it is equivalent.

Practical lumped element circuits deviate from the ideal representation of Figure 2-20 in many ways. Inductors have internal distributed capacitance between windings. The plates and leads of capacitors have distributed inductance. The stated deficiencies of lumped constants limit their general use to below the VHF/UHF range.

Let us now apply the principle of the short-circuited stub line to a matching problem. As shown in Figure 2-21, the LC product or the length of line is selected for resonance at f_r, the mid frequency of an impedance curve to be improved. By adding in parallel the reactances of a resonant short-circuited stub line the low-frequency and high-frequency ends of the load impedance curve are tucked towards the center while the mid frequency remains unchanged thus yielding a tightly knotted locus as shown.

In order for this matching technique to work it is first necessary to establish a definition circle into which all the points of the load impedance curve must fall. This is merely a circle enclosing all points which have a standing wave ratio not to exceed a specified value. Illustrated in the figure is a Smith chart with a SWR definition circle of 2.0 to 1. Such a circle crosses the resistance axis at 25 ohms and at 100 ohms. These two values of resistance establish the grids between which the real part of the load impedance must lie if it is to be matched into the circle. These grids form the upper and lower boundaries for the definition circle and obviously only those impedances lying between these two boundaries can be matched. Figure 2-22 illustrates why an impedance point which lays outside the boundary circles cannot be matched into the definition circle.

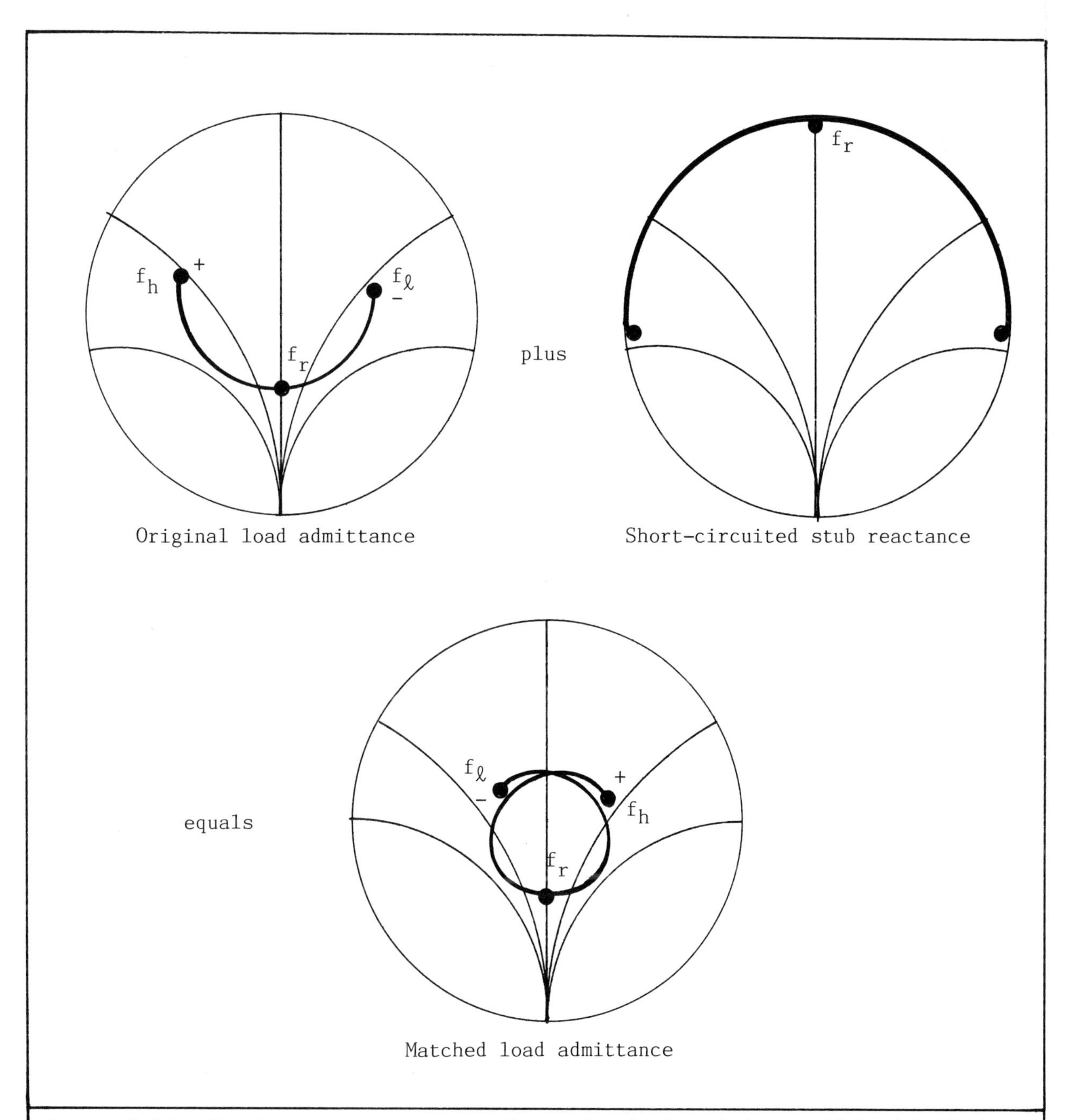

Figure 2-21. Matching with a resonant short-circuited stub in parallel with the load admittance.

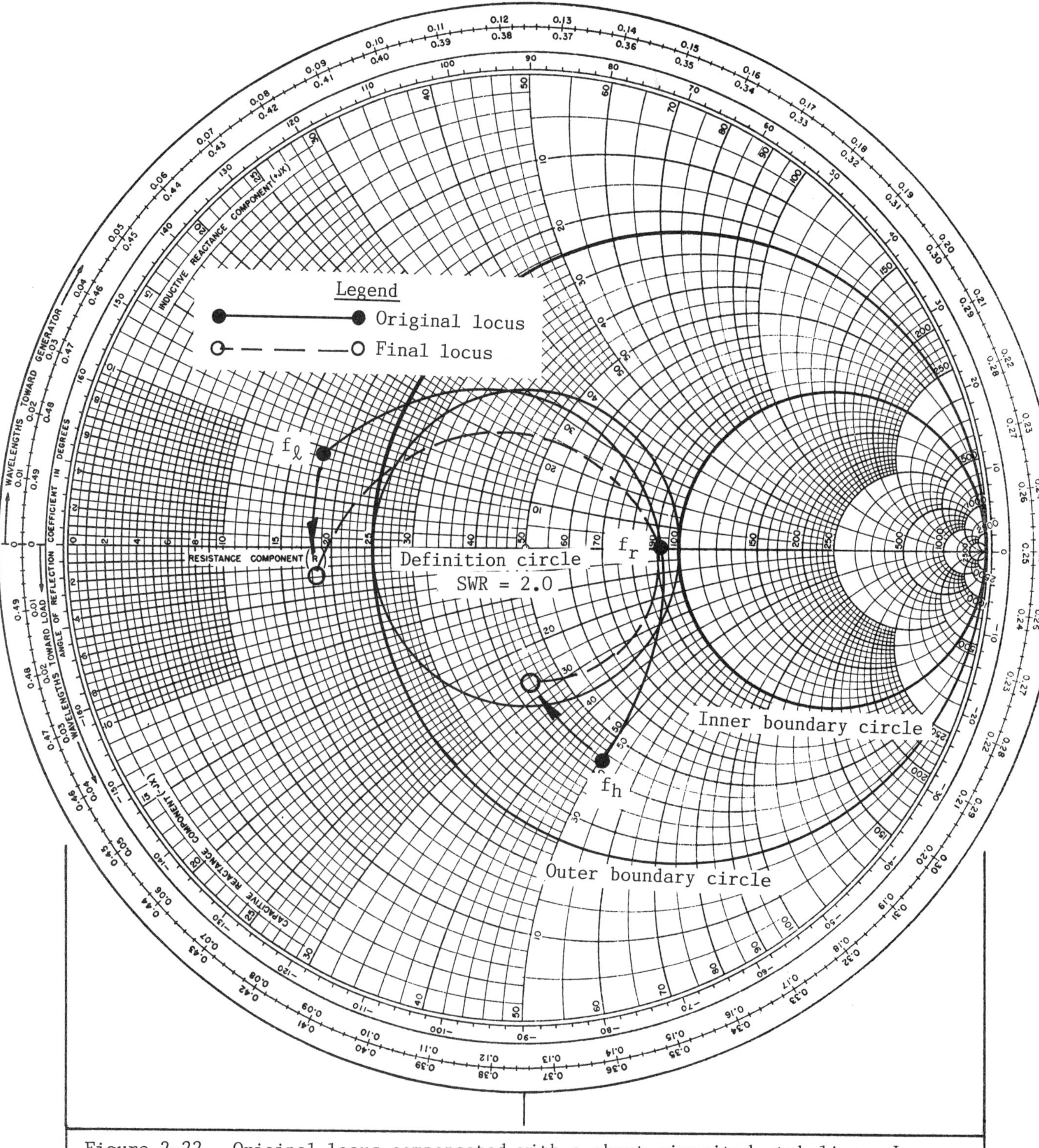

Figure 2-22. Original locus compensated with a short-circuited stub line. Low frequency point f_ℓ cannot be matched into the definition circle because it is outside the boundary circles.

The Transmission Line as an Impedance Transformer.

As its name implies, the line transformer is a short section of transmission line inserted between the antenna and the feed line. The impedance at the input to the line transformer is dependent upon a number of factors: (1) line length, (2) characteristic impedance of the line Z_o', and (3) the impedance connected at the load end Z_a. For any set of values for these factors the input impedance is found by the general equation

$$Z_{A-A'} = Z_o' \frac{Z_a + Z_o' \tan \beta \ell}{Z_o' + Z_a \tan \beta \ell} \qquad (2\text{-}1)$$

where

$Z_{A-A'}$ = impedance at the input to the line transformer
Z_a = impedance of the antenna
Z_o' = characteristic impedance of the line transformer
$\beta \ell$ = electrical length of the line

For any length an even number of quarter-wavelengths long this becomes

$$Z_{A-A'} = Z_a \qquad (2\text{-}10)$$

For any line an odd number of quarter-wavelengths long this becomes

$$Z_{A-A'} = \frac{(Z_o')^2}{Z_a} \quad \text{or} \quad Z_o' = \sqrt{Z_a Z_{A-A'}} \qquad (2\text{-}11)$$

It can be seen from Eqs. (2-10) and (2-11) that any line an even number of quarter-wavelengths long, no matter what impedance Z_a is terminating the line, the same impedance will be measured at the input terminals A-A'. On the other hand, if the line is an odd number of quarter-wavelengths long the impedance at A-A' will always vary inversely with Z_a.

For the condition where the line is properly terminated ($Z_o' = Z_a$) the input impedance $Z_{A-A'}$ will be equal to the characteristic impedance of the line Z_o', no matter what line length is being used. This can be seen by substituting $Z_a = Z_o'$ in either of Eqs. (2-10) and (2-11).

These very important principles are used in transmission lines operated as impedance transformers. For example, consider the problem of coupling a 600-ohm line to a 50-ohm coaxial line. A quarter-wavelength line will be used as an impedance matching section as shown in Figure 2-23. It is desired to terminate the 50-ohm line with its characteristic impedance of 50 ohms in order to prevent standing waves on the line and to obtain maximum power transfer. Obviously the coaxial line cannot be connected directly to the 600-ohm 2-wire line. Therefore a device is needed which, with 50 ohms at one end, will present an impedance of 600 ohms at the other end. A quarter-wavelength line section will do this very nicely. All that is necessary is that the line section have a characteristic impedance equal to

$$Z'_o = \sqrt{Z_a Z_{A-A'}} = \sqrt{600 \times 50} = 173 \text{ ohms}$$

The action of the quarter-wavelength transformer is illustrated in Figure 2-24.

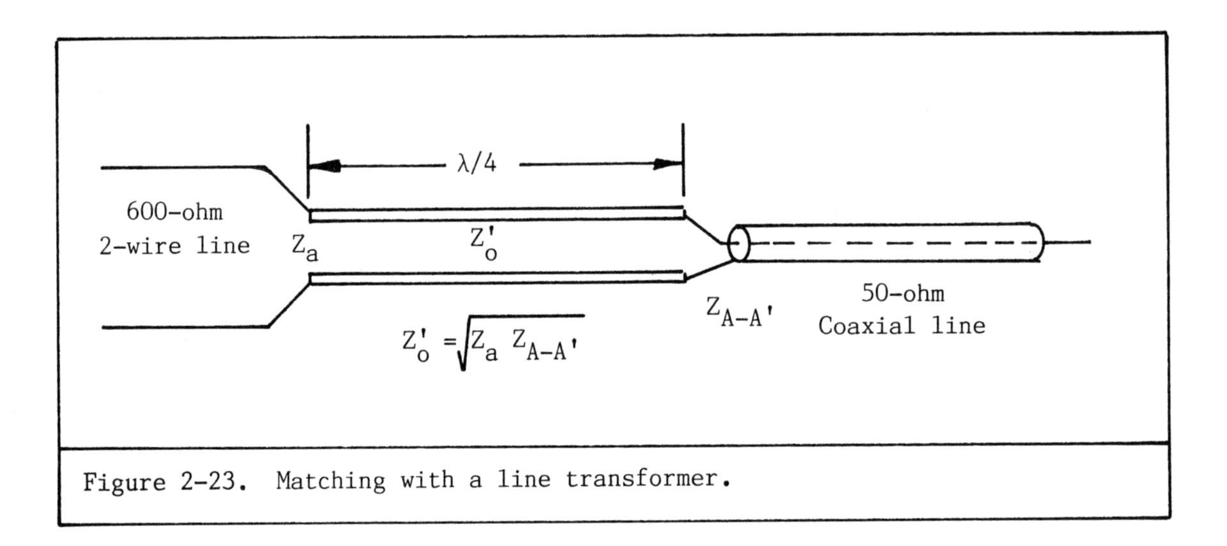

Figure 2-23. Matching with a line transformer.

Transmission Line Sections as Balancing Devices.

Frequently it is desired to couple energy from an unbalanced system to a balanced system, or vice versa. If a balanced system is fed directly with a coaxial line as shown in Figure 2-23, it would not be a strictly balanced system and the coaxial line would not operate normally. Currents would be present on the outer surface of the outer conductor of the coaxial line, causing it to radiate. In the interest of system performance, this condition must be avoided. A device commonly employed to maintain balance when going from a balanced system to an unbalanced one is called a "balun," an abbreviation for "balanced to unbalanced." One balun which performs the desired conversion without affecting the impedance characteristics of the system is shown in Figure 2-25. Because of its physical appearance, it is sometimes referred to as a "bazooka." When the length, $L = \lambda/4$, the outer sleeve acts with the outer conductor of the enclosed section of line to

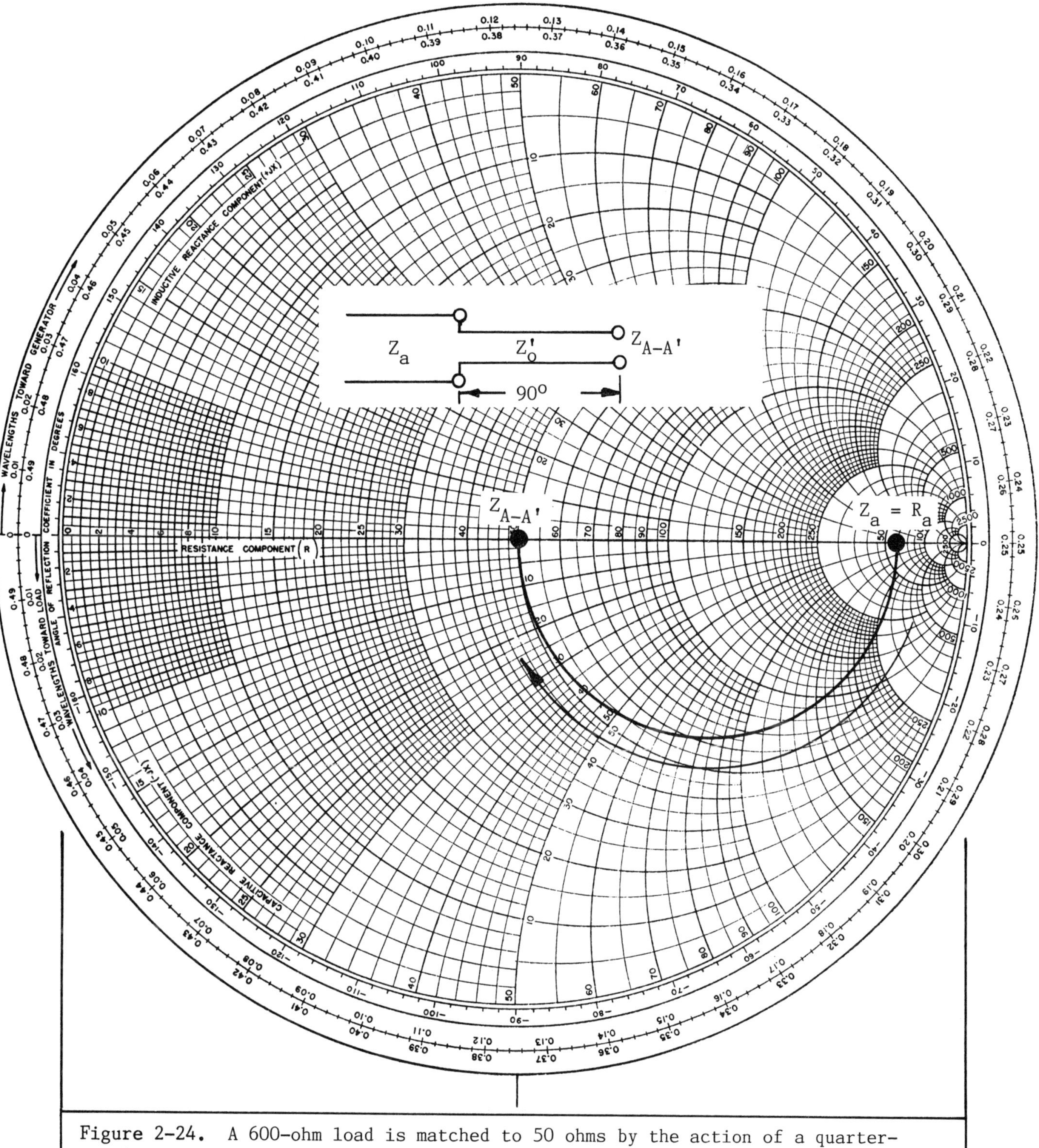

Figure 2-24. A 600-ohm load is matched to 50 ohms by the action of a quarter-wavelength line transformer.

form a quarter-wavelength coaxial section, causing a high impedance to exist between points 1 and 2. The result is little or no shunt path to ground from 2 to 1, no division of current at junction 2 and, consequently, equal currents in each conductor of the twin line 2 and 3. Since the currents in the twin line are equal and 180 degrees out of phase, the voltages to ground are also equal and 180 degrees out of phase, which then results in a balanced operation.

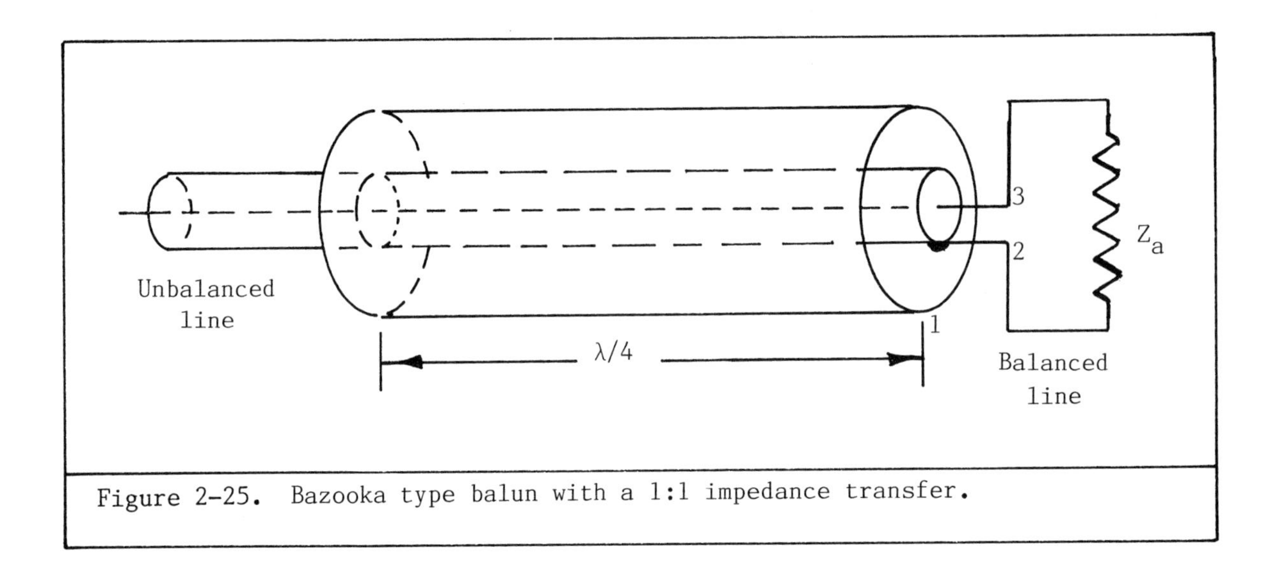

Figure 2-25. Bazooka type balun with a 1:1 impedance transfer.

The impedance between points 1 and 2 remains high only when the length L is near one-quarter wavelength long. Consequently, this type of balun provides good performance over a relatively narrow band of frequencies of about 10 percent. Where wide band operation is required, the "double bazooka" type balun, shown in Figure 2-26, may be used.

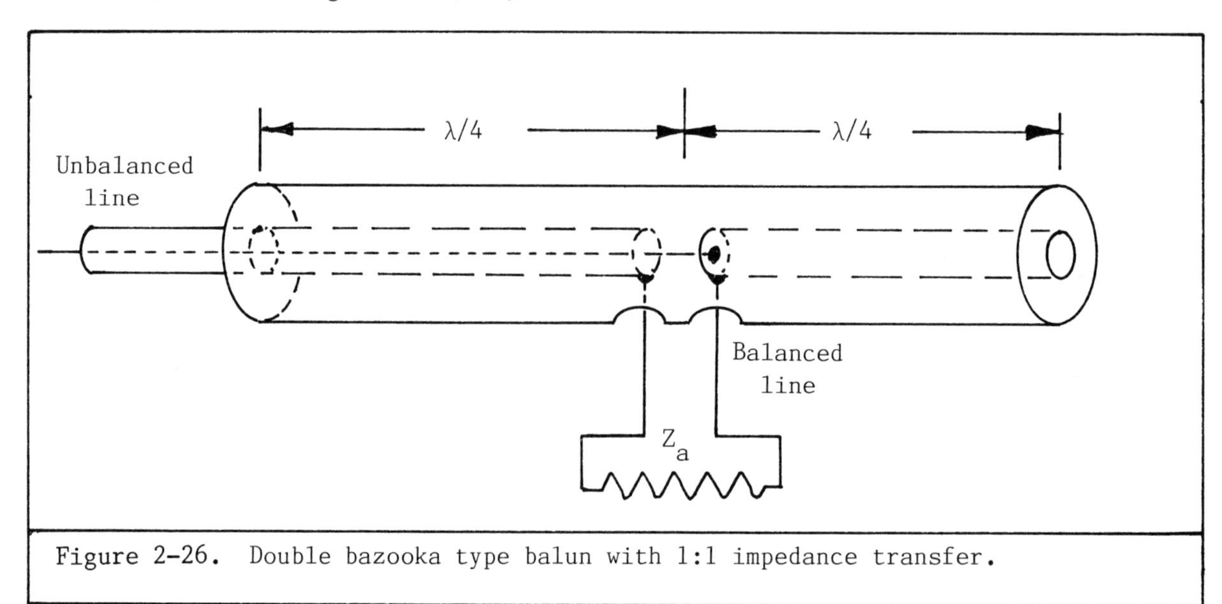

Figure 2-26. Double bazooka type balun with 1:1 impedance transfer.

A balun, the performance of which is superior to those just described, is shown in **Figure 2-27.** This type of balun functions similarly by preventing undesirable currents from flowing along the outside of the coaxial line. Here, however, this is accomplished by a cancelling effect rather than choking off the current as with the one-quarter wavelength sleeve section.

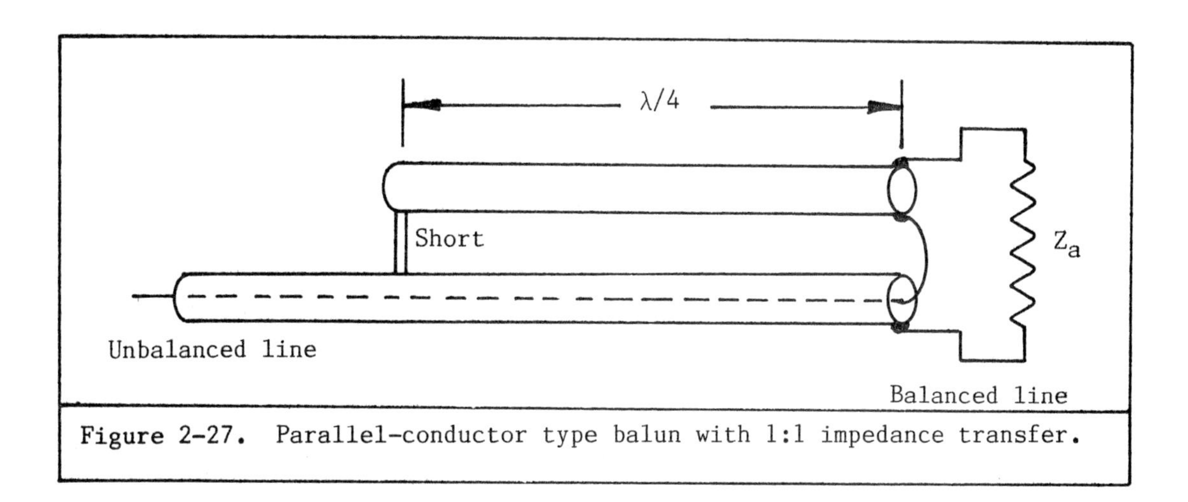

Figure 2-27. Parallel-conductor type balun with 1:1 impedance transfer.

It is frequently desirable to operate the balun at other than a quarter-wavelength in order to take advantage of the shunt reactance it presents to the load for impedance matching purposes. From the discussion on the transmission line section as a parallel-resonant circuit, it becomes apparent that the impedance characteristics of the shorted line section can be utilized here. Since the impedance of a center-fed half-wave dipole antenna resembles those of a series resonant circuit, the combined effect of the balun and the dipole result in a wider frequency range of operation where the reactance is negligible.

A balun which provides a fixed impedance transformation of 4:1 is shown in **Figure 2-28.** Advantage is taken of the fact that a half-wavelength section of line repeats its load but with a 180-degree phase reversal in voltage. Thus the voltages to ground from each side of the load impedance Z_a will be equal and 180 degrees out of phase, resulting in a balanced operation.

The half-wavelength balun can be used with the line transformer arrangement of **Figure 2-23.** Since $Z_{A-A'}$ is now 200 ohms instead of 50 ohms, the impedance Z_o' of the line transformer must be

$$Z_o' = \sqrt{Z_a Z_{A-A'}} = \sqrt{200 \times 600} = 346 \text{ ohms}$$

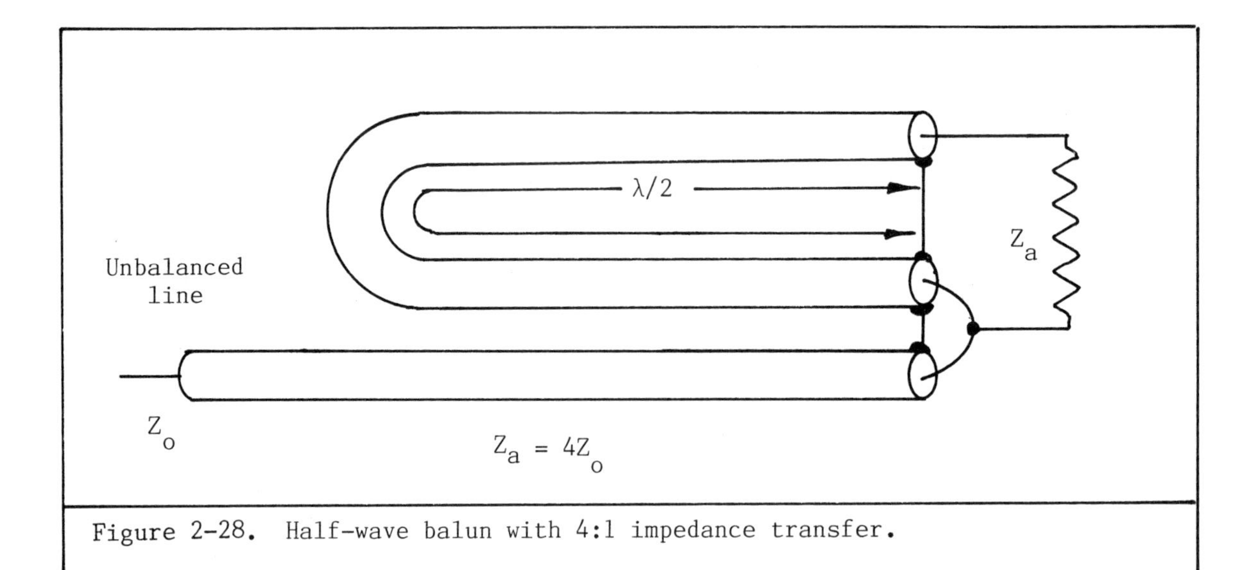

Figure 2-28. Half-wave balun with 4:1 impedance transfer.

It is not the purpose of this discussion to describe all possible balancing devices which may be employed in antenna systems. Those described here, however, are the more basic types and are representative of those commonly employed.

Lines With Attenuation.

If we were able to sample the energy propagating along a lossless line we would find that the SWR radius is constant. For instance, if we measured a SWR magnitude of 2.8 at the antenna terminals we would still have a magnitude of 2.8 at the generator terminals regardless of the line length. However, in real life, all lines have attenuation. This attenuation causes the incident wave to be attenuated as it travels toward the antenna and again as it returns as a reflected wave after reflection. It is evident that the SWR resulting from these two components varies in amplitude along the line. If the line is very long and the attenuation constant high, the reflected wave will be very small and the line will appear to be terminated in its characteristic impedance. This attenuation will be manifested as a spiraling inward towards the center of the Smith chart of the impedance point.

For this particular example, the length of line is 0.200 wavelength long with an attenuation of 1.4 dB. The load impedance is R = 1.65 and jX = 2.2. This value is plotted as Z_a in Figure 2-29. From the scale of attenuation at the bottom of the Smith chart, it is found that Z_a lies on a circle of constant attenuation corresponding to a value of about 1.8 dB. Travelling clockwise along this constant attenuation circle 0.200 wavelength we arrive at a second impedance point Z_b which corresponds to R = 0.28 and jX = -0.67.

Since the line attenuation is 1.4 dB, we now know that the input impedance Z_c when found will correspond to a point on another attenuation circle of constant attenuation of 1.4 dB higher than 1.8 dB at a distance 0.200 wavelength from the antenna. This 1.4 + 1.8 = 3.2 dB level is represented by another constant attenuation circle on the Smith chart of Figure 2-29. Point Z_c specifies the input impedance for this particular example. Its coordinates are R = 0.52 and jX = -0.57. Unfortunately the "in 1 dB steps" scale is not numbered. (See Figure 2-29). Assigning the number "0" to the first mark just under the scale designation, the subsequent marks can be numbered out to 15 dB.

It should be emphasized that point Z_b corresponds to an impedance point that would have prevailed had the line been without attenuation and with attenuation point Z_c as moved along the dashed spiral from Z_a to Z_c. If the lossy line were infinitely long the dashed line in Figure 2-29 would spiral to the center of the Smith chart and point Z_c would be R = 1.0 and jX = 0.

The use of attenuators or resistive pads to reduce the high SWR encountered with small low frequency receiving antennas is a common and accepted practice. Figure 2-30 illustrates the effect of attenuation on SWR.

If the length L of the transmission line and its attenuation A are known, then its effect upon the load SWR can be determined from

$$SWR_L = \frac{1}{\tanh\,[\tanh^{-1}\,(1/SWR_M) - AL]} \qquad \text{2-12}$$

where

SWR_L = SWR at the load end

SWR_M = measured SWR at input end

AL = Attenuation loss

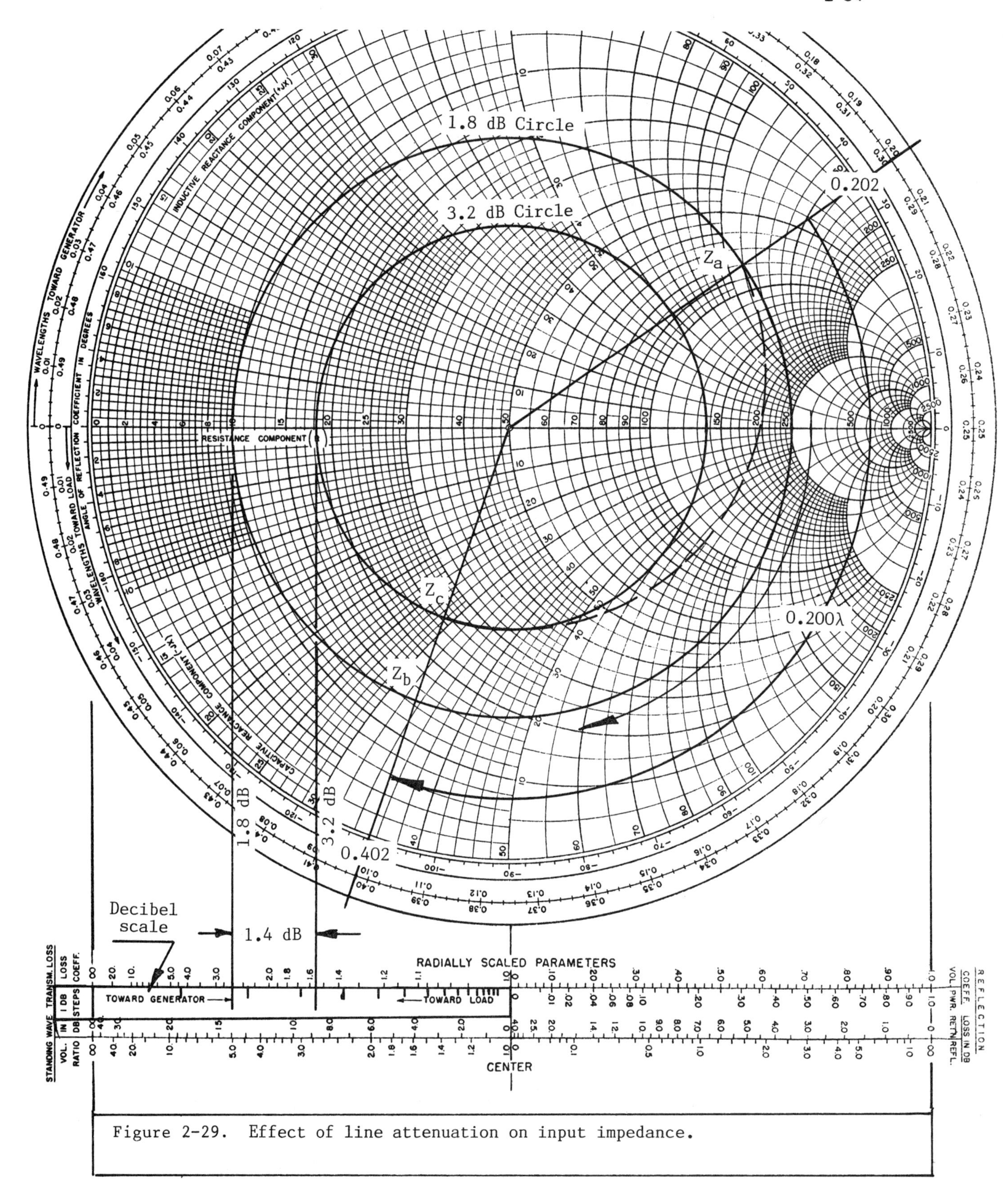

Figure 2-29. Effect of line attenuation on input impedance.

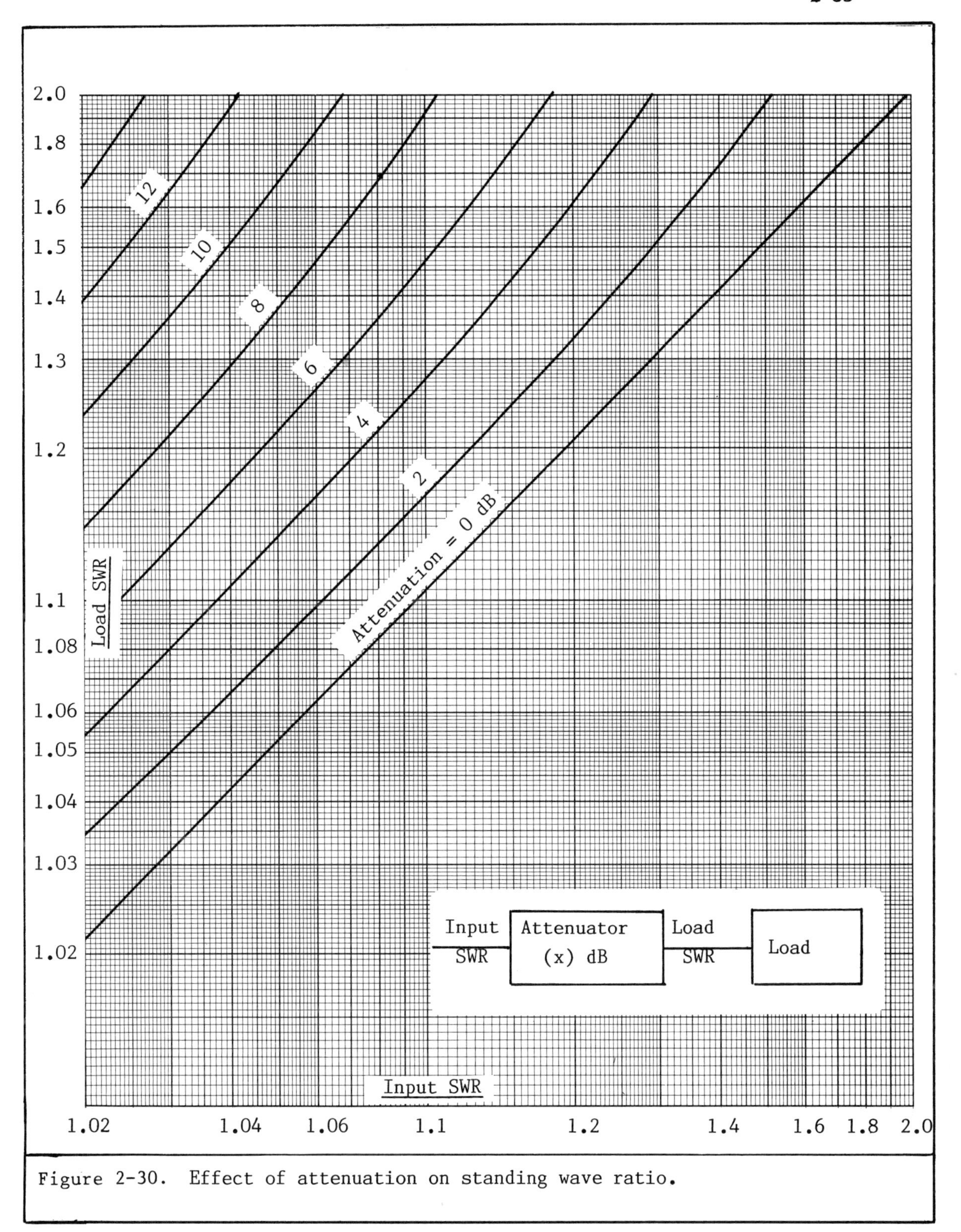

Figure 2-30. Effect of attenuation on standing wave ratio.

CHAPTER III

THE SMITH CHART

General.

Before we can proceed with impedance matching techniques it is important that we acquire an understanding of the various aids and charts, particularly the Smith chart, that are used to solve matching problems and to evaluate the performance of antennas and transmission systems. It has often been said that if one understands Smith charts, he understands transmission lines.

Many devices and charts have been invented to aid in visualizing, understanding, computing and measuring the various electrical parameters associated with transmission lines. These charts have taken many forms over the years from the complex hyperbolic function charts to the Cartesian coordinates, the Hudson chart, the Clement chart, the Z-Theta chart and, finally, the versatile Smith chart which was developed by P.H. Smith. The Smith chart made its debut in Electronics, January 1939, in an article entitled "Transmission Line Calculator." In the January 1944 issue of Electronics, Mr. Smith presented additional information in an article entitled "An Improved Transmission Line Calculator." The Smith chart is a device that facilitates the solution of complex transmission line problems. It is indispensable to the antenna engineer.

The R-X Diagram.

The impedance Z_a of an antenna at any given frequency may be expressed as a complex number $R_a + jX_a$ which may be plotted on a complex plane, called an R-X diagram or an Argand diagram, where the horizontal axis represents the real component R, and the vertical axis the imaginary component jX. The R-X diagram has a coordinate grid system that is arranged in such a fashion as to permit plotting of the impedance in rectangular form. The impedance can be shown as a function of frequency by plotting the impedance point determined for each frequency and connecting the points with a curve as shown in Figure 3-1. In this particular case, it can be seen that at one frequency the curve crosses the zero reactance axis. This corresponds to a pure resistive value for the impedance and hence resonance.

The Z-Theta Chart.

In the R-X diagram, impedances are expressed in rectangular form $R \pm jX$. It is possible, however, to devise an analogous chart in which the impedances are in polar form. That is, $R \pm jX = Z\angle\theta$. Such a chart is shown in Figure 3-2. The illustrated chart has a center value of 50 ohms (Z = 50 ohms) for direct use with 50-ohm systems. Other Z-θ charts may be obtained normalized with Z = 1.0 for use with other systems.

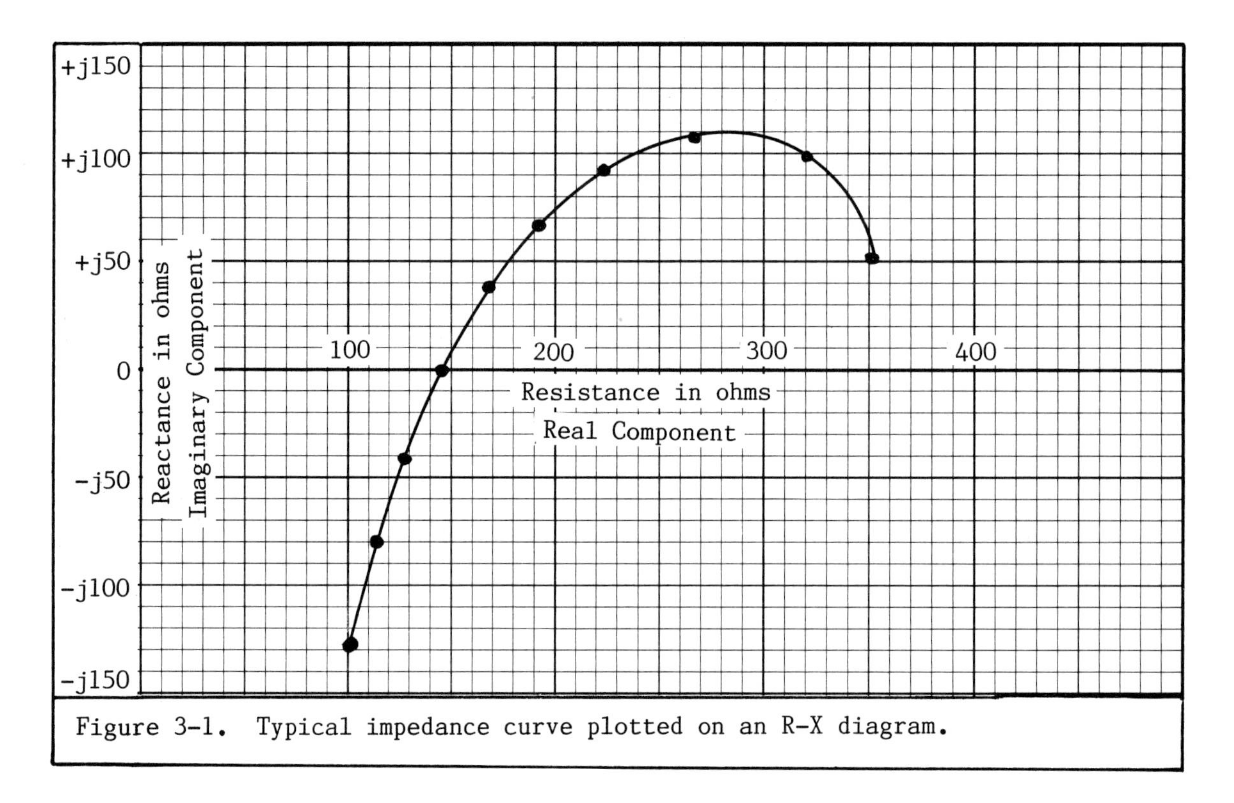

Figure 3-1. Typical impedance curve plotted on an R-X diagram.

Usually, the polar coordinates are converted to their equivalent rectangular coordinates and transferred to the Smith chart. If the $Z/\underline{\theta}$ and Smith charts are the same size, it is a simple procedure to overlay the charts, and directly transferring the impedance points to the Smith chart. Table 3-1 illustrates the conversion of the polar coordinates shown in Figure 3-2 to their equivalent R-X coordinates. The R-X values have been plotted on the Smith chart shown as Figure 3-3.

TABLE 3-1

CONVERSION OF $Z/\underline{\theta}$ DATA TO R-X DATA

Freq (mHz)	Z	θ	R = Z cos θ	X = Z sin θ
100	32.5	-22°	30.1	-12.2
110	35.0	-10°	34.5	-6.1
120	37.5	0°	37.5	0
130	42.0	$+10^{o}$	41.4	+7.3
140	47.5	+20	44.6	+16.2
150	55.0	+28	48.6	+25.8
160	70.0	+38	55.2	+43.1

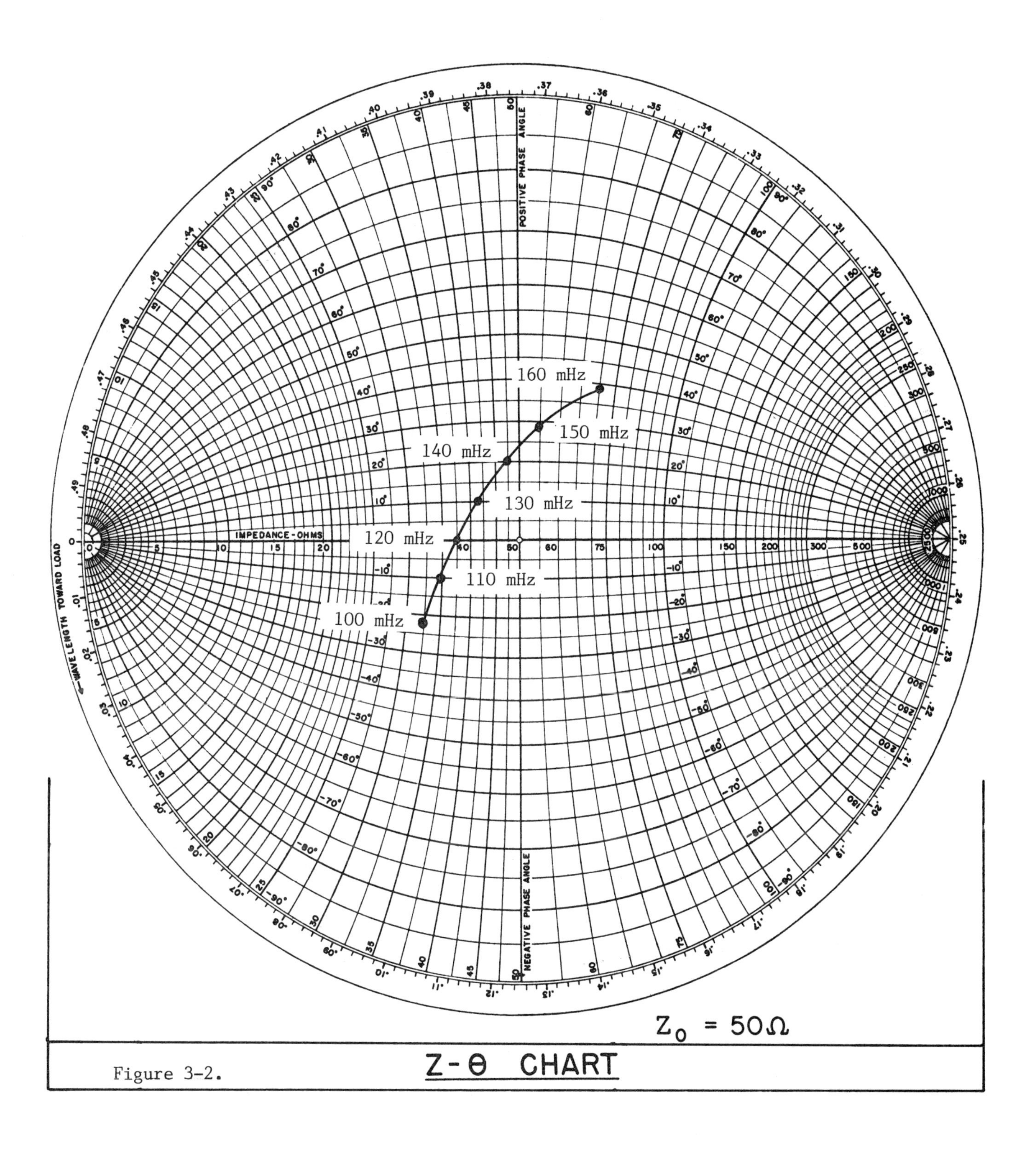

$Z_0 = 50\Omega$

Figure 3-2. **Z-θ CHART**

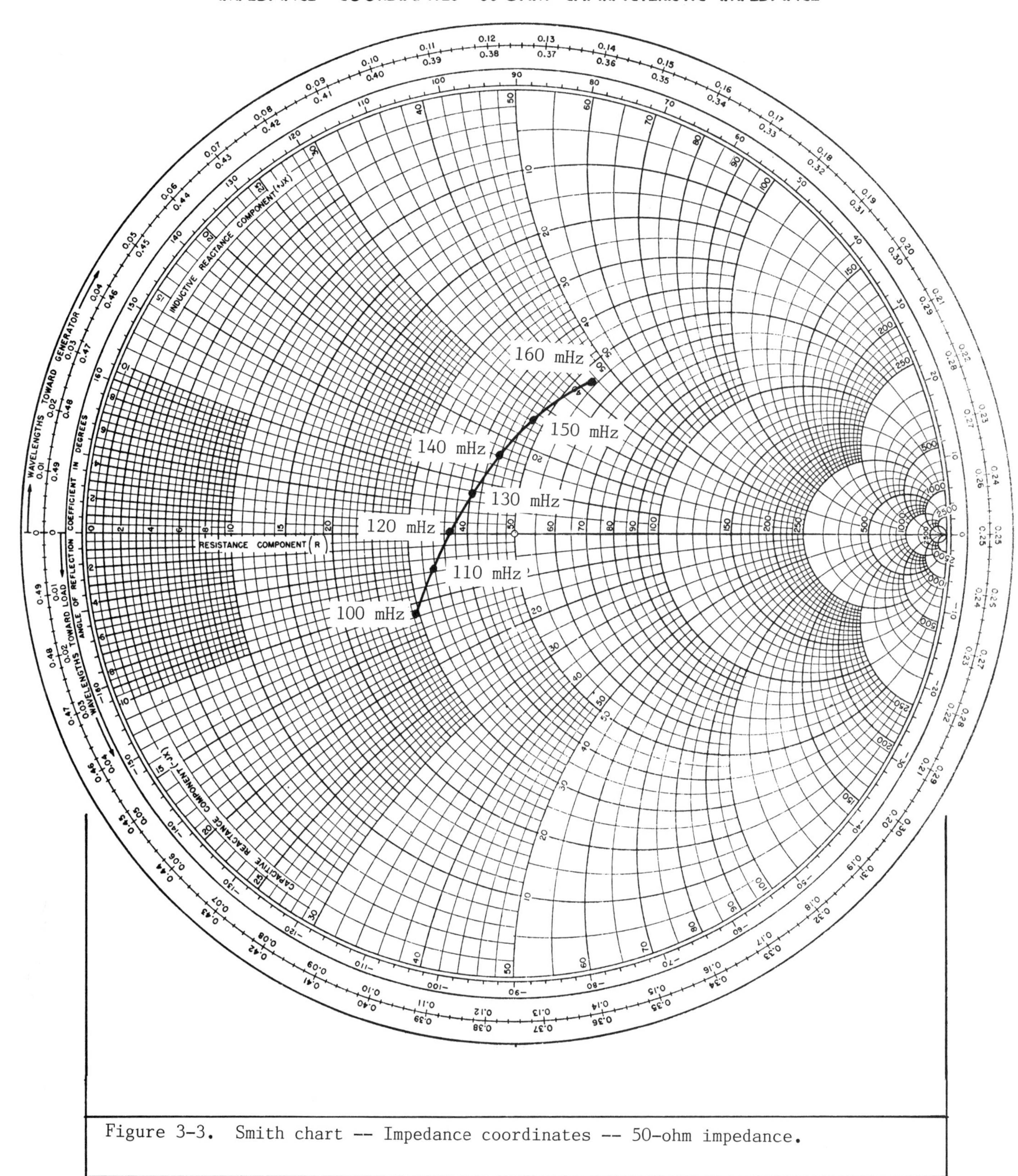

Figure 3-3. Smith chart -- Impedance coordinates -- 50-ohm impedance.

The Smith Chart.

Of all the various transmission-line charts that have evolved, the one in common usage is the Smith chart. The Smith chart shown in Figure 3-3 has a center value of 50 ohms for use with impedance bridges that measure directly in impedances. Frequently antenna measurements are obtained with admittance bridges such as the General Radio Model 1602. In this case, the recorded admittance can be plotted directly onto a Smith chart with admittance coordinates such as shown in Figure 3-4. Note that the conductance and susceptance components are the reciprocal of resistance and reactance components. The center of the admittance chart is the reciprocal of 50 ohms.

$$Y_o = 1/Z_o = 1/50 = 0.02 \text{ mho} = 20 \text{ millimhos}$$

The Smith chart consists of a family of circles and a family of arcs which intersect each other at right angles. The circles (see Figure 3-5(a)) are tangent at a common point at the right of the chart. Points along any of these circles represent the same value of resistance R. A circle whose diameter is one half that of the chart corresponds to a value of R = 50 ohms. Larger circles correspond to lower values of R, down to zero for a circle equal to the chart diameter. Smaller circles represent higher values of resistance, approaching infinity as the circle becomes smaller. The smallest circle of Figure 3-3 corresponds to R = 2500 ohms.

The family of arcs (see Figure 3-5(b)) represents constant values of the reactance +jX and -jX. These arcs all pass through the point at the right of the chart, and have their radii along a vertical line passing through that point. In Figure 2-3 the main scale for reading values of $\pm jX$ is just inside the outer circle, jX = 0 at the left of the chart and increases in both directions, inductive reactance +jX clockwise and capacitive reactance -jX counterclockwise. At the 90° counterclockwise, -jX = -50 ohms, and clockwise, +jX = +50 ohms. As the right of the chart is approached, both +jX and -jX increase to infinity, with the largest labeled value being 2500 ohms.

The Normalized Smith Chart.

In antenna measurements, resistances and reactances are expressed in terms of their relationship to the characteristic impedance of the associated transmission line. For example, if a complex impedance of 55.2 + j43.1 (160 mHz, Table 3-1) is being considered in a 50-ohm line system, the impedance will be referred to as 1.10 + j0.86 in the normalized coordinate system. Each component of this impedance has been divided by the characteristic impedance of the transmission line, 50 ohms in this case, as follows

$$Z' = \frac{Z_a}{Z_o} = \frac{R_a}{Z_o} \pm \frac{jX_a}{Z_o} = \frac{55.2}{50} + \frac{j43.1}{50} = 1.10 + j0.86 \qquad (3\text{-}1)$$

ADMITTANCE COORDINATES—20-MILLIMHO CHARACTERISTIC ADMITTANCE

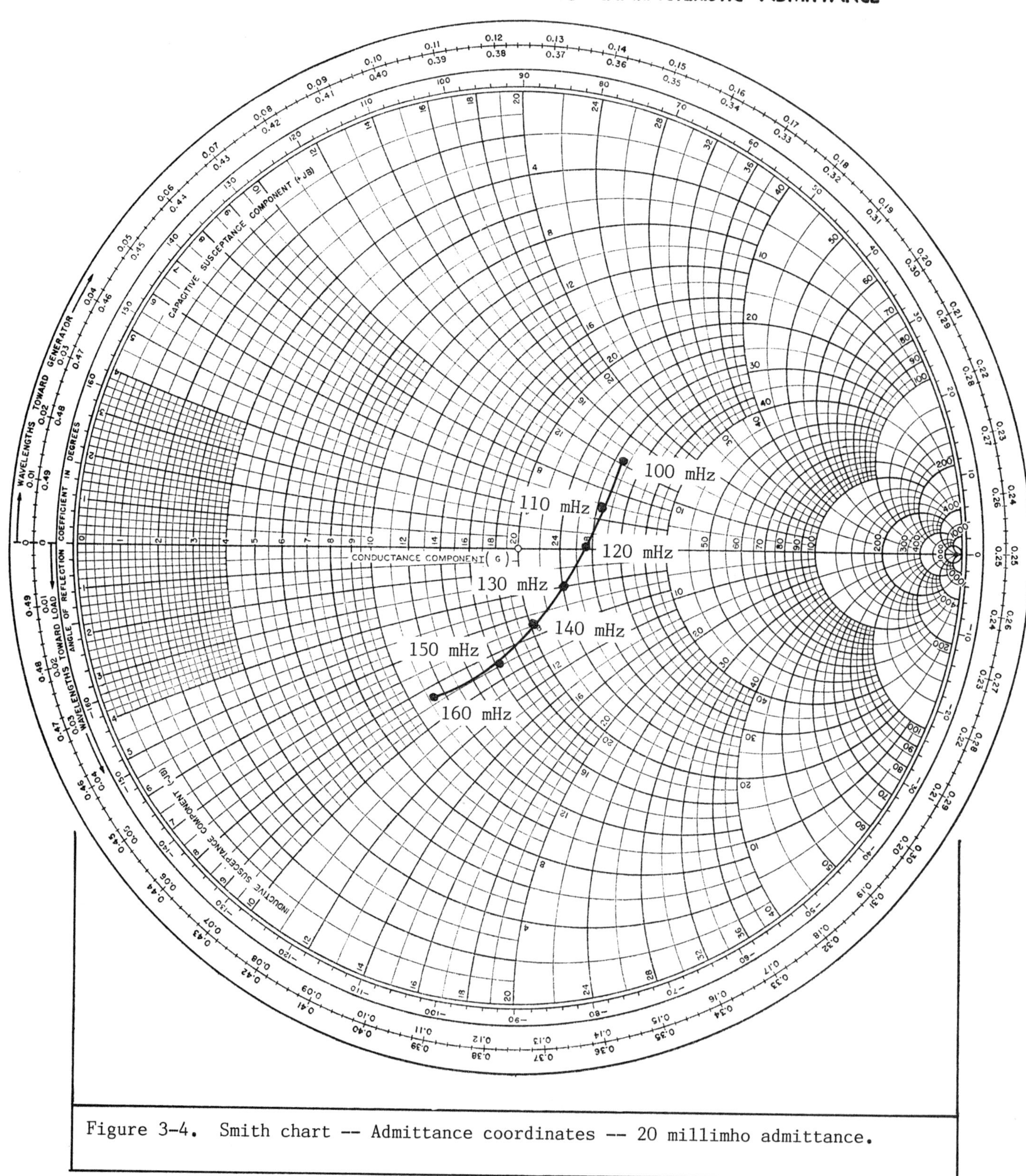

Figure 3-4. Smith chart -- Admittance coordinates -- 20 millimho admittance.

where

Z' = normalized impedance in ohms

Z_a = actual impedance in ohms

Z_o = transmission line characteristic impedance

R_a = actual resistance in ohms

X_a = actual reactance in ohms

This is known as normalizing the impedance. Normalized impedances are then plotted on a normalized Smith chart, Figure 3-6.

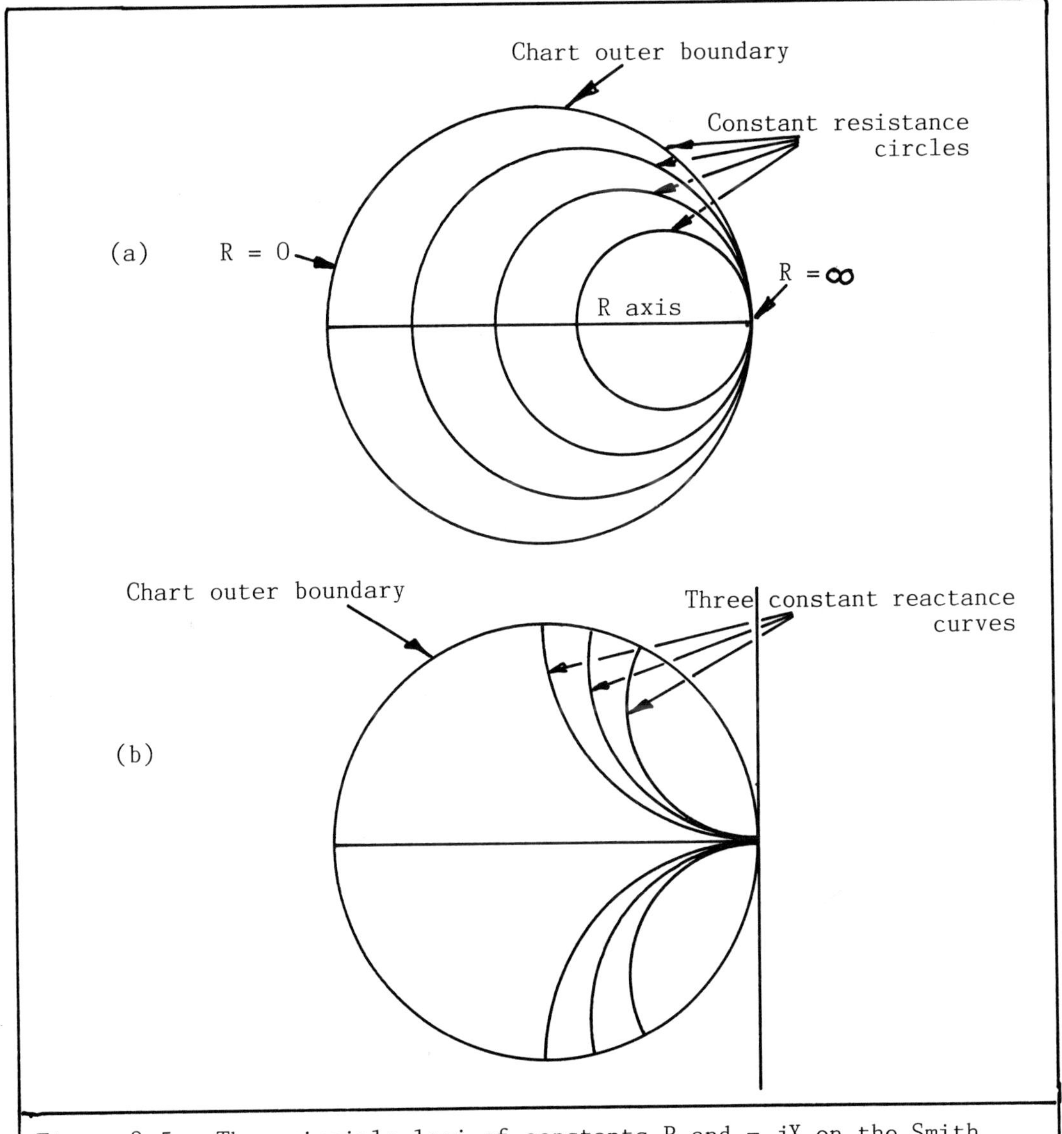

Figure 3-5. The principle loci of constants R and $\pm$ jX on the Smith chart. (a) Constant resistance circles. (b) Constant reactance curves.

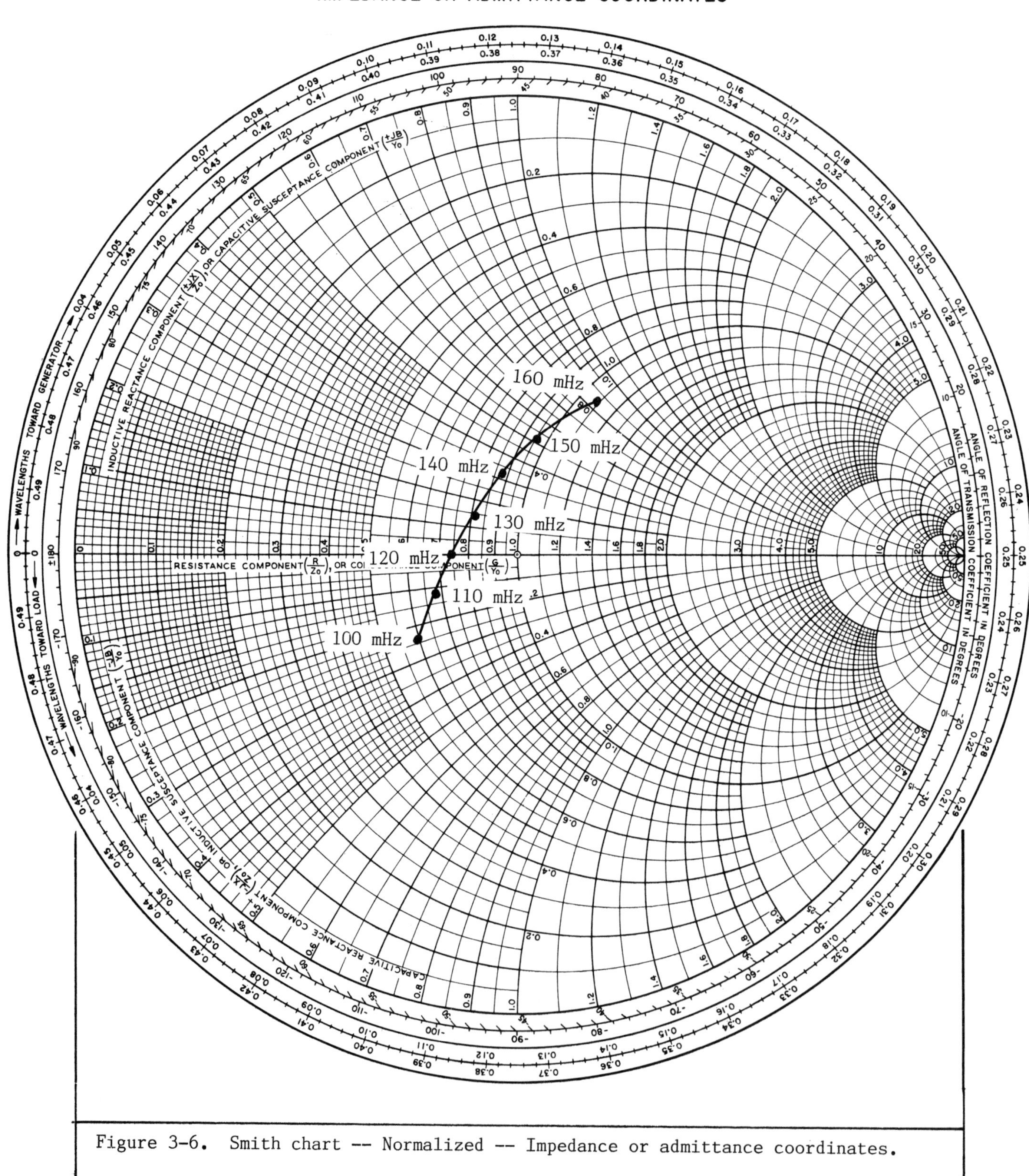

Figure 3-6. Smith chart -- Normalized -- Impedance or admittance coordinates.

The normalized Smith chart of Figure 3-6 can also be used for plotting normalized admittances. Admittance coordinates are normalized when their actual values are divided by the associated transmission characteristic admittance as follows

$$Y' = \frac{Y_a}{Y_o} = \frac{G_a}{Y_o} \pm \frac{jB_a}{Y_o} \quad (3\text{-}2$$

where

Y' = normalized admittance in mhos

Y_a = actual admittance in mhos

Y_o = transmission line characteristic admittance

G_a = actual conductance in mhos

B_a = actual susceptance in mhos

Example, a load admittance of 0.025 - j0.011 measured on a 50-ohm line is normalized to

$$Y' = \frac{0.025}{(1/50)} - \frac{j0.011}{(1/50)} = 1.25 - j0.55$$

Normalized coordinate values make the chart applicable to either impedance or admittance. Another example, The measured impedance of an antenna is determined to be

$$Z_a = R_a \pm jX_a = 30 + j20 \quad \text{ohms}$$

With respect to a 50-ohm line, the normalized antenna impedance is

$$Z' = \frac{Z_a}{50} = \frac{30}{50} + \frac{j20}{50} = 0.6 + j0.4 \quad \text{ohms}$$

which would then appear on the normalized Smith chart coordinates at the intersection of R/Z_o = 0.6 and $+jX/Z_o$ = 0.40.

The transmission line characteristic impedance (Z_o = 50 ohms) is equivalent to a characteristic admittance of $1/Z_o$ = 1/50 or 0.02 mho (20-millimho). In our example, the antenna impedance of Z_a = 30 + j20 is equivalent to an antenna admittance of

$$Y_a = 1/Z_a = \frac{1}{R_a + jX_a} = \frac{R_a}{R_a^2 + jX_a^2} - \frac{jX_a}{R_a^2 + jX_a^2} \qquad (3\text{-}3)$$

$$= \frac{30}{30^2 + 20^2} - \frac{j20}{30^2 + 20^2} = \frac{30}{1300} - \frac{j20}{1300}$$

$$= 0.023 - j0.015 \quad \text{mho}$$

The normalized antenna admittance for a 50-ohm line is then, by definition

$$Y' = \frac{Y_a}{0.02} = \frac{0.023}{0.02} - \frac{j0.015}{0.02} = 1.15 - j0.75 \text{ mho}$$

which, as previously described, is the reciprocal of the normalized complex antenna impedance, namely, $Z_a = 0.6 + j0.4$ ohms, and lies diametrically opposite the antenna impedance and at an equal distance from the center of the normalized Smith chart as shown in Figure 3-7.

Properties of the Smith Chart.

The Smith chart has many useful properties:

- Impedances repeat every half wavelength by virtue of the fact that the circumference around the Smith chart is one half wavelength.
- The impedance point lying anywhere within the limits of the Smith chart will have a corresponding admittance point that is diametrically opposite the impedance point and with an equal distance from the center of the chart (see Figure 3-7).
- The impedance and admittance points are separated by a circumferential distance that is equal to a quarter wavelength.
- Capacitive reactance $-X_c$, when added in series with the antenna reactance $\pm jX_a$, moves the antenna impedance point Z_a counterclockwise along circles of constant resistance. For example, $Z_a = R_a \left[\pm X_a + (-X_c)\right]$.

- o Inductive reactance $+X_L$, when added in series with the antenna reactance $\underline{+}jX_a$, moves the antenna impedance point Z_a clockwise along circles of constant resistance. For example, $Z_a = R_a \left[\underline{+}X_a + (+X_L)\right]$.
- o Capacitive susceptance $+B_c$, when added in shunt with the antenna susceptance $\underline{+}jB_a$, moves the antenna impedance point Z_a counterclockwise along circles of constant conductance. For example, $Y_a = G_a \left[\underline{+}B_a + (+B_c)\right]$.
- o Inductive susceptance $-B_L$, when added in shunt with the antenna susceptance $\underline{+}B_a$, moves the antenna impedance point Z_a clockwise along circles of constant conductance. For example, $Y_a = G_a \left[\underline{+}B_a + (-B_L)\right]$.

It is necessary when adding reactance or susceptance to an antenna's reactance or susceptance to make the addition algebraically. For example, if an impedance point has a reactance of, say, +100 ohms, and a capacitive element the reactance of which is -160 ohms is added to it in series, the resulting reactance becomes

$$X_{total} = +100 + (-160) = -60 \text{ ohms}$$

While this bit of algebra will provide the new impedance and/or admittance location on the Smith chart, it is important, when analyzing the overall procedure, to observe that the positive values in each case move the points clockwise along the constant circles of resistance or conductance on which the points are located, while negative values move the points counterclockwise. The constant circles can be visualized by overlaying a reversed transparent Smith chart on the top of another Smith chart so that the zero impedance region on one chart is over the infinite impedance region of the other chart.

Using The Smith Chart.

Most single frequency matching techniques require an L-type network consisting of two elements. Ordinarily, the solution to such networks require numerous impedance-admittance transformation and extensive mathematical manipulation. Obviously an overlay which performs the impedance-admittance (or visa versa) transformation would be a tremendous time saver. A practical way to go from one position to another while using this overlay is by means of a board or tracing box of convenient size with a pivot inserted in its center. The Smith chart is then placed on the board and carefully centered on the pivot. (The pivot is made from a pin or thumb tack).

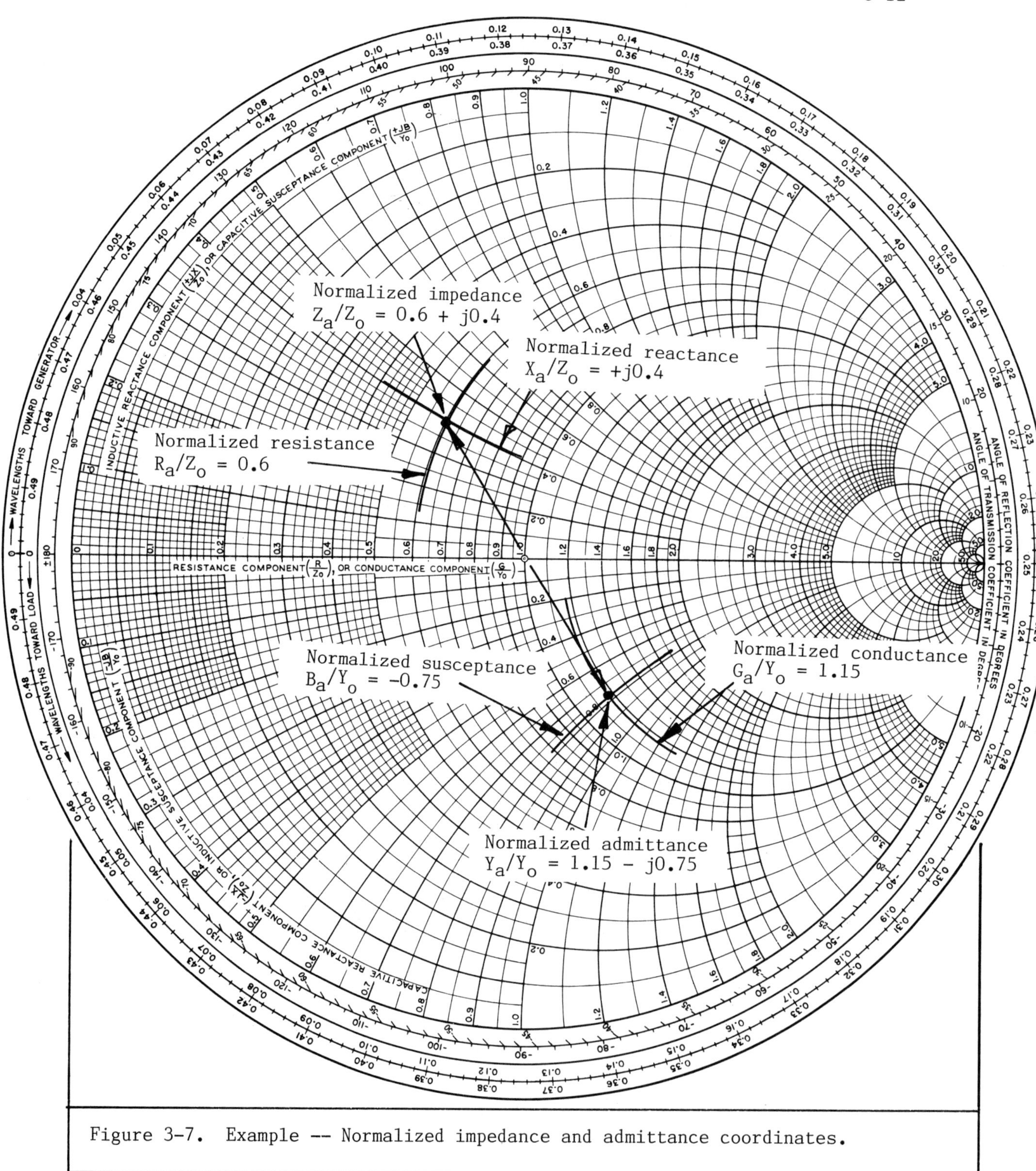

Figure 3-7. Example -- Normalized impedance and admittance coordinates.

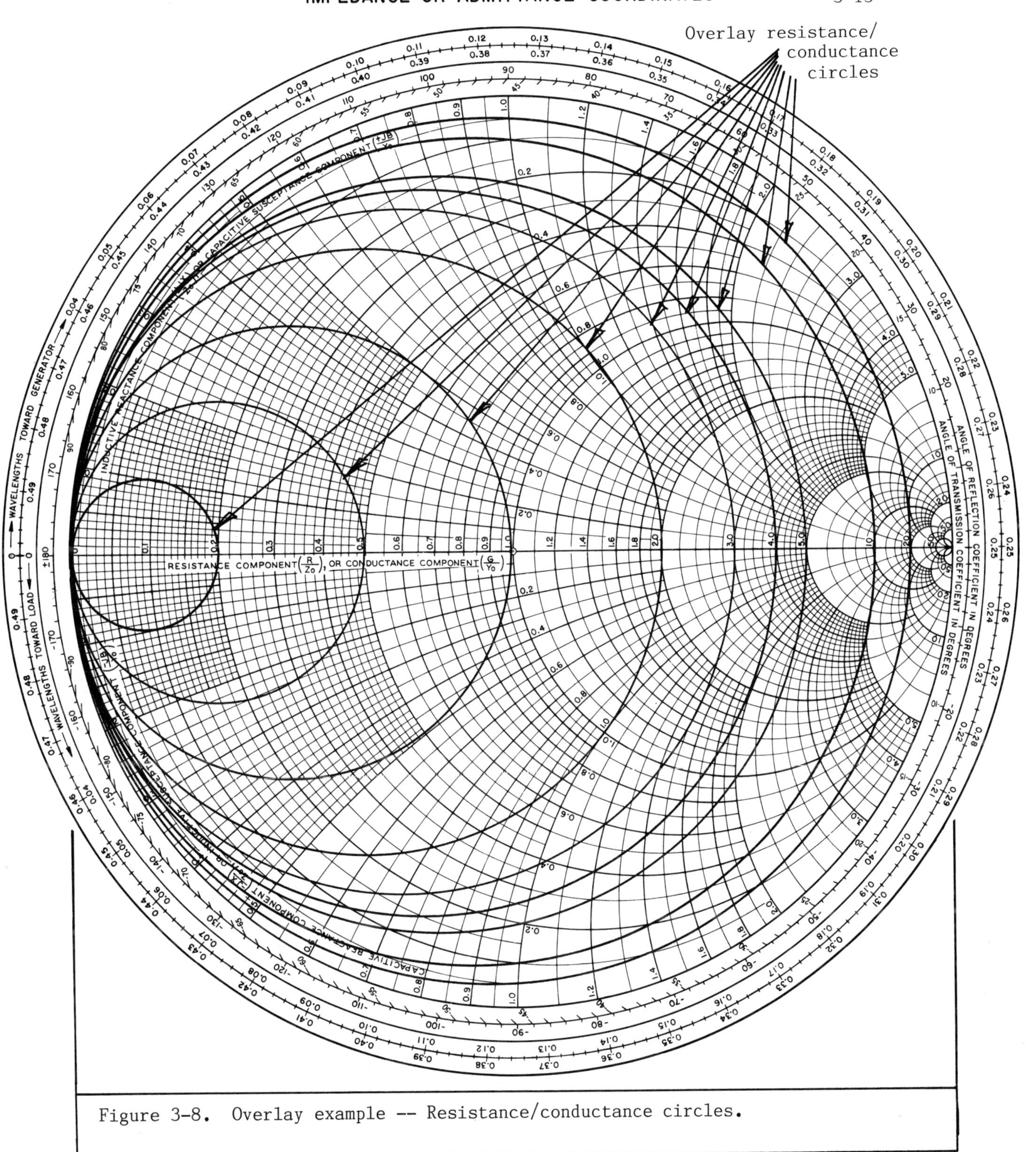

Figure 3-8. Overlay example -- Resistance/conductance circles.

Finally, the overlay, another Smith chart is laid over the first. An impedance point plotted on this overlay can now be rapidly changed to an admittance position (or vice versa) by simply rotating the overlay 180 degrees. The selection of a matching element and its arrangement at the antenna feed point are made easier by being able to use the new impedance and/or admittance positions as required.

The development of the overlay technique permits easy visualization of each step required to match an antenna to the transmission line. Figure 3-8 shows the overlay in skeletal form, only a few of the constant conductance circles have been drawn for clarity.

Line Length and the Smith Chart.

The Smith chart can be of assistance in determining the load impedance where it is impossible to connect the load directly to the terminals of the impedance measuring device, but rather the load must be separated from the device by a length of line $\beta\ell$ long as shown in Figure 3-9.

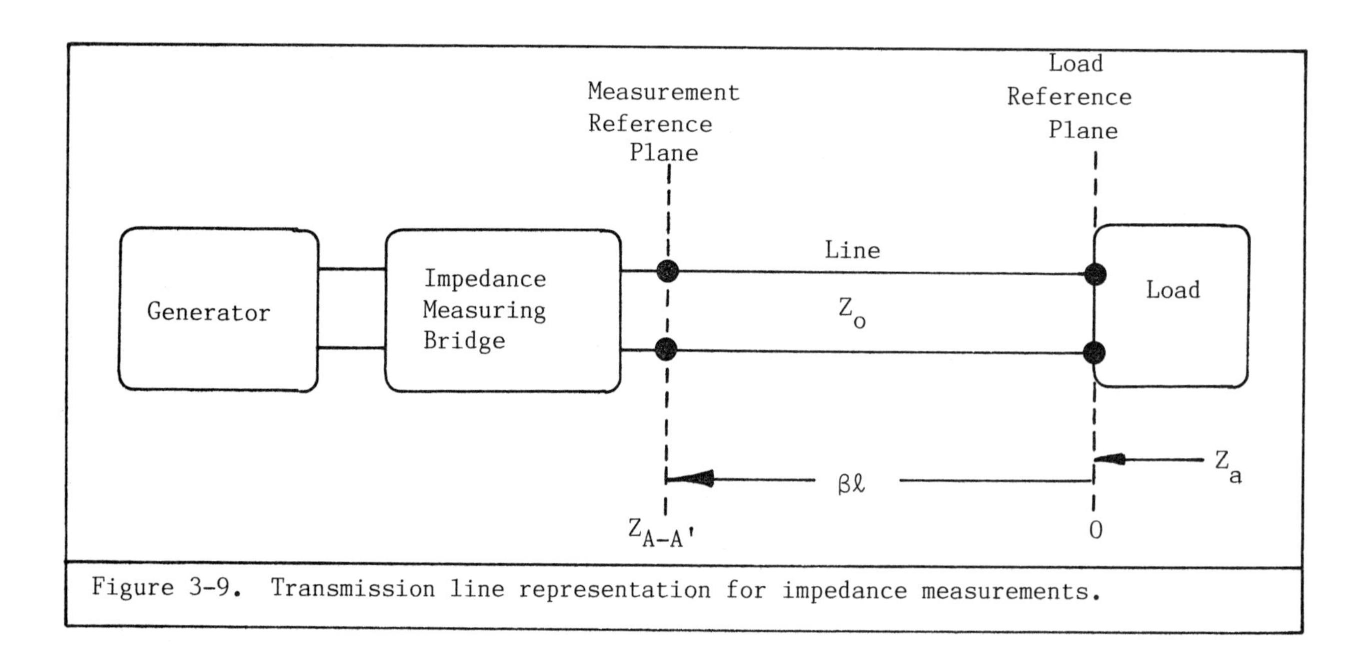

Figure 3-9. Transmission line representation for impedance measurements.

The measured impedance $Z_{A-A'}$ at some distance $\beta\ell$ from the location of the load impedance Z_a is given by

$$Z_{A-A'} = Z_o \frac{Z_a + jZ_o \tan \beta\ell}{Z_o + jZ_a \tan \beta\ell} \tag{2-1}$$

where

$Z_{A-A'}$ = measured impedance

Z_a = load impedance

Z_o = characteristic impedance of the line

$\beta\ell$ = electrical length of the line

The Smith chart has two circular scales "Wavelengths toward load" and "Wavelengths toward generator" which are calibrated in hundredths of a wavelength. One complete revolution of either scale corresponds to a half-wavelength. These scales are used to determine the impedance at any point along an interconnecting cable after the impedance for one specific point has been determined.

With reference to Figure 3-10, an impedance point is shown as $Z_{A-A'}$ = 30 -j80. If $Z_{A-A'}$ is the impedance measured at the bridge terminals and one wishes to determine the impedance at the opposite end of a 0.120 wavelength long line, point $Z_{A-A'}$ is simply rotated counterclockwise about the center of the chart (along a constant SWR circle, SWR = 6.5 to 1) a distance of 0.120 wavelength. If $Z_{A-A'}$ lies at the scale reading of 0.168 wavelength on the "Wavelengths toward load" scale, then the new reading will be on a radial from the center of the chart cutting the scale at

$$0.168\lambda + 0.120\lambda = 0.288\lambda$$

The impedance at the load end of the line is determined to be Z_a = 100 + j143.

Determining SWR With the Smith Chart.

Any circle drawn about the center of the Smith chart is a circle of constant SWR. Perhaps the best way for determining SWR is by plotting an impedance point on a normalized Smith chart as shown in Figure 3-11. A circle is then drawn through that point. The circle crosses the resistance line at two points: at the left of center and at the right of center. The SWR is obtained from the normalized resistance scale at the right of center. In this case, for a normalized load impedance of Z_a = 1.8 + j2.2, the SWR is 4.9 to 1.

It has become customary in many areas to refer VSWR (voltage standing wave ratio) in terms of dB, where

$$\text{VSWR(dB)} = 20 \log_{10} \text{VSWR} \quad (3\text{-}4)$$

Since VSWR is the ratio of the maximum voltage to the minimum voltage, it is not exactly correct to express VSWR in terms of dB. The only time

$$\text{dB} = 20 \log \frac{V_1}{V_2} \quad (3\text{-}5)$$

is when the two voltages are measured across the same value of resistance. On a transmission line, the impedance is highest at the point of maximum voltage and lowest at the point of minimum voltage and the ratio of the

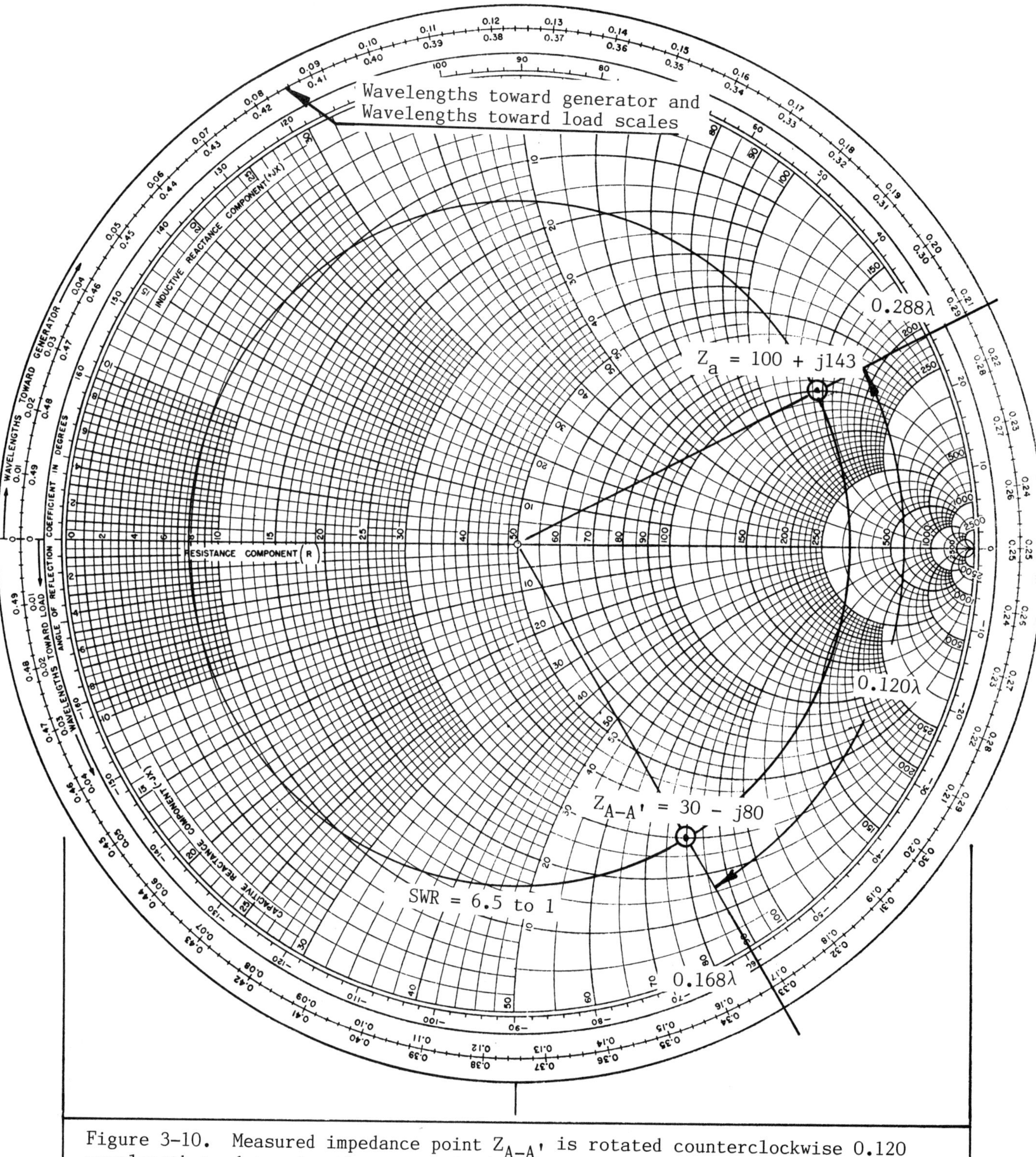

Figure 3-10. Measured impedance point $Z_{A-A'}$ is rotated counterclockwise 0.120 wavelength to determine the actual load impedance.

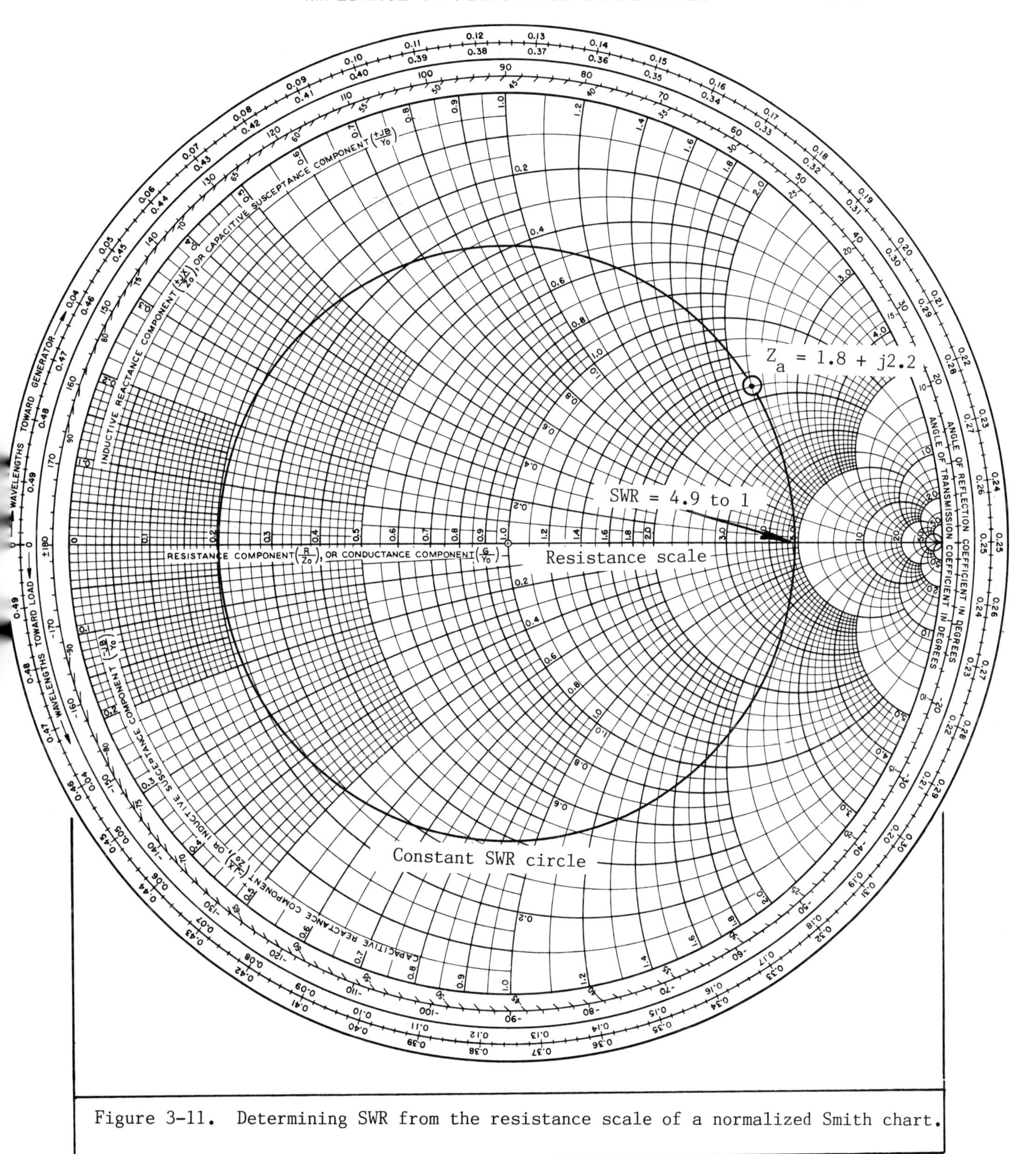

Figure 3-11. Determining SWR from the resistance scale of a normalized Smith chart.

impedances is exactly equal to the square of the voltage ratios. Therefore what is normally called VSWR in dB is a misnomer. The use of the term "volt-logit" would be more appropriate

$$1 \text{ volt-logit} = 10 \log_{10} \frac{V_1}{V_2} \qquad (3\text{-}6)$$

when the resistance across which the voltages are measured are disregarded. the use of the terms "volt-logit," "current-logit," etc. was proposed by J.W. Horton in "fundamental Considerations Regarding the Uses of Relative Magnitudes," Proc. IRE, April 1952, pp. 440-444.

Since standing wave ratios are often measured in dB, some manufacturers have calibrated their test equipment in accordance with Eq. (3-5) which perpetuates the misnomer of the term VSWR(dB).

CHAPTER IV

IMPEDANCE MATCHING TECHNIQUES

General.

Most of the antenna impedance matching problems encountered in practice can easily be handled with an L-type matching network. The L-network was first described by P.H. Smith, in an article that appeared in Electronics, March 1942, entitled "L-Type Impedance Transformation Circuits." In his disclosure, Smith developed eight matching networks that used only two pure reactances at a time: one in series with the antenna to be matched and the other either shunting the antenna alone, or shunting the parallel combination of the first reactance and the antenna. These networks are illustrated in Figure 4-1. The following is a brief description of each of these L-networks. It must be remembered that each network is only capable of transforming a complex antenna impedance to a pure resistive match at a single frequency.

Choice of Reactive Combinations.

The combination of reactances used to match a complex antenna impedance to a pure resistive match is governed by the nature of the antenna impedance, that is, where the antenna impedance position occurs on the Smith chart. An impedance in regions 1, 2, 3, or 4 in Figure 4-2 can be matched to a pure resistance only through the use of two reactances as indicated by the appropriate letters, i.e., (a) through (h). The choice of matching network depends on the availability of inductors or capacitors and their size, the convenience of line sections, the need for dc biasing, the need for grounding, etc. The eight Smith chart overlays illustrated in Figure 4-3 (a) through (h), summarize the matching capabilities of the eight possible L-type circuit combinations.

Matching With a Single Element.

Matching with a single element presents certain restrictions. Since a single element, series or shunt, moves the impedance or admittance point only along circles of constant resistance or conductance, optimum matching cannot be achieved. There are regions on the Smith chart that cannot be matched to any specified SWR. Figure 4-4 illustrates the limits of matching possibilities for a SWR of 2.0 to 1. If a SWR of 1.5 to 1 or less is desired the matching possibilities are further limited.

There is one way to circumvent the matching limitations imposed by a single matching element and that is by the use of a short section of transmission line. A transmission line can move an impedance or admittance point to a more favorable region where optimum matching is made possible with one matching element. This procedure is illustrated in Figure 4-5. In this figure the normalized load impedance is $Z_a = 1.7 - j5.0$. By using a short section of line of length $0.288\lambda - 0.278\lambda = 0.01\lambda$, Z_a is transformed to a new impedance point, $Z_n = 1.0 - j3.9$. A single element, a series inductor

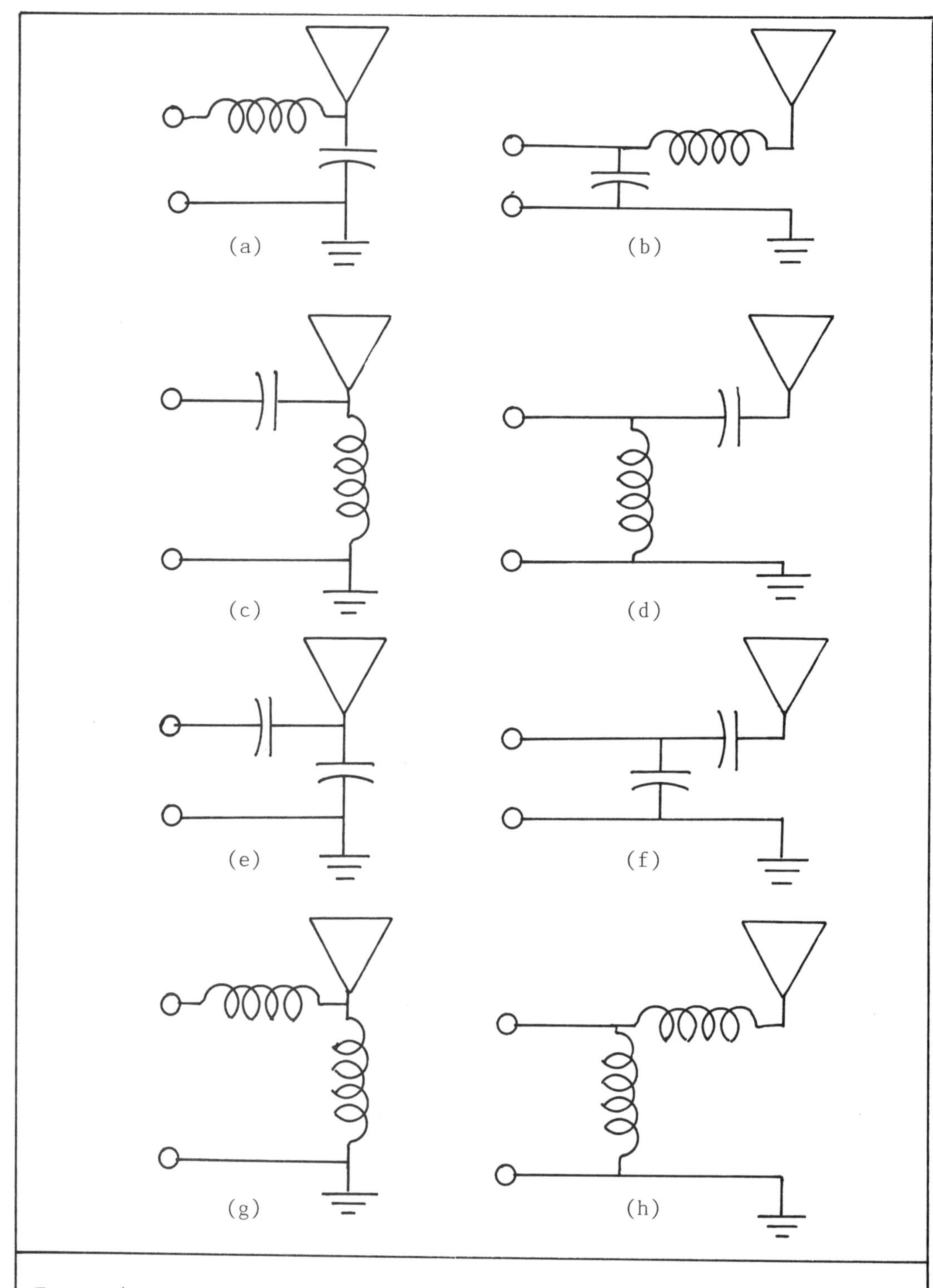

Figure 4-1. Eight possible L-type circuits.

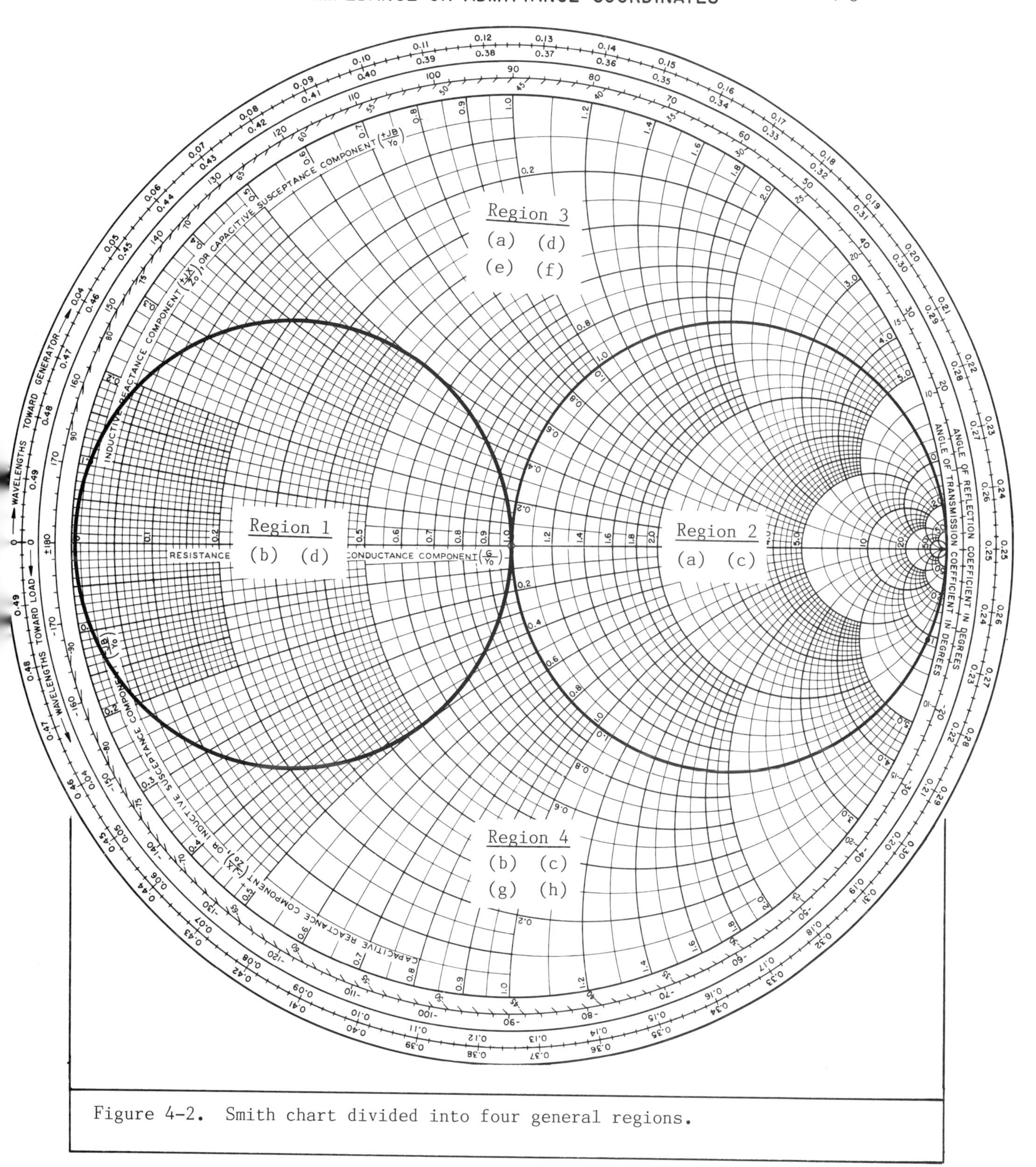

Figure 4-2. Smith chart divided into four general regions.

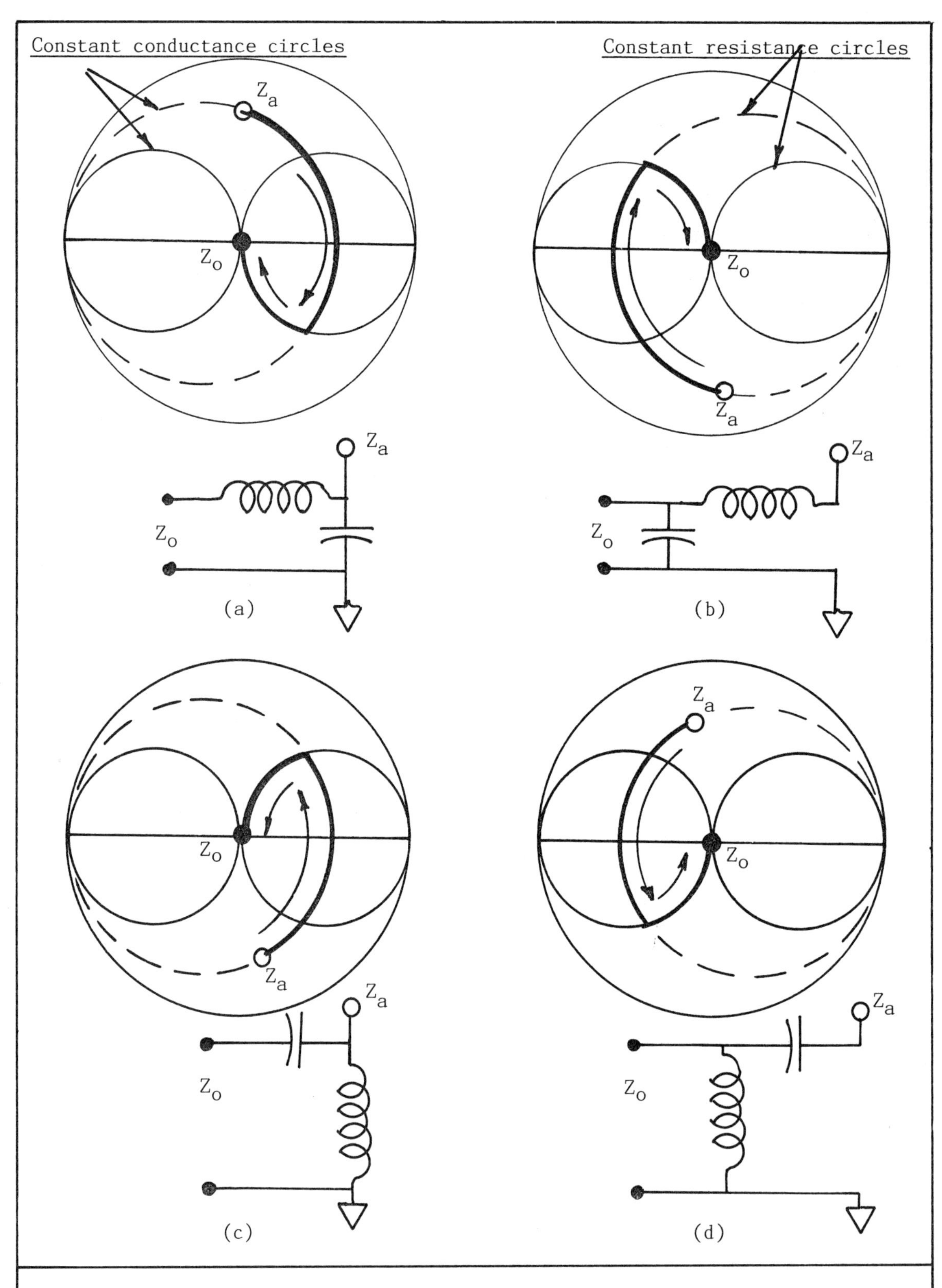

Figure 4-3. Matching solutions for typical L-type circuits.

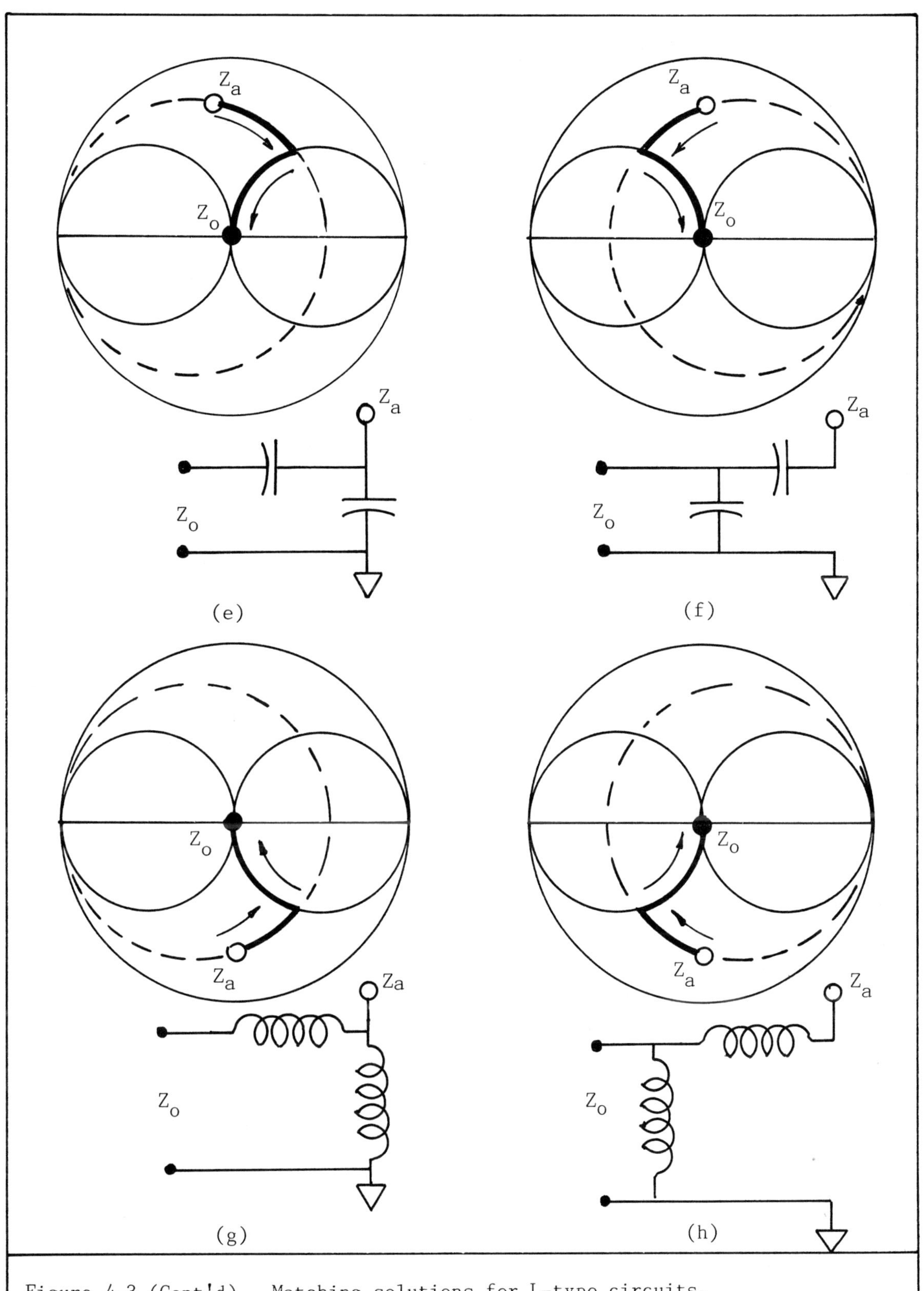

Figure 4-3 (Cont'd). Matching solutions for L-type circuits.

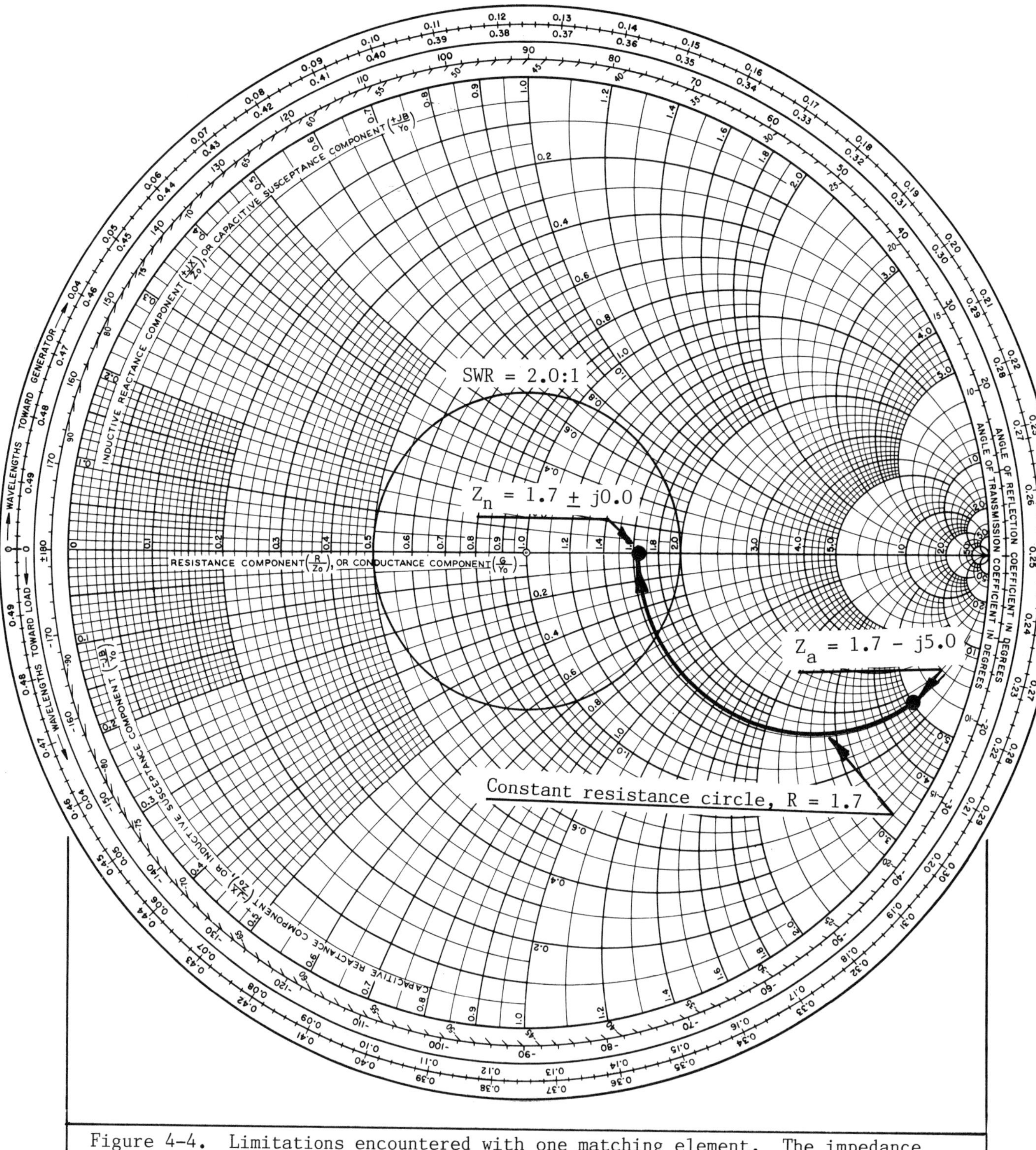

Figure 4-4. Limitations encountered with one matching element. The impedance point can only follow the circle of constant resistance.

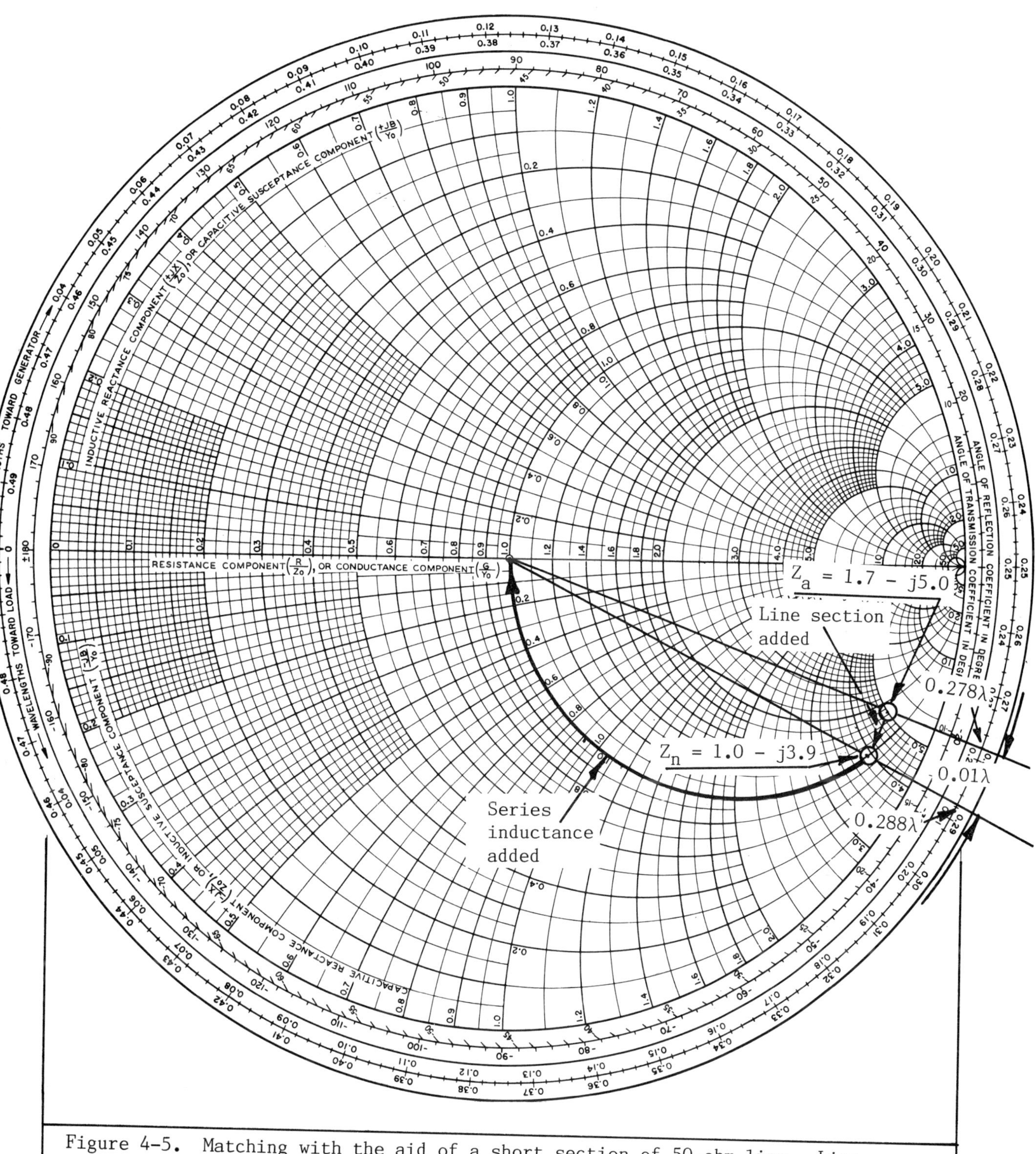

Figure 4-5. Matching with the aid of a short section of 50-ohm line. Line section moves the impedance point to a more favorable circle of constant resistance.

with a reactance of +3.9 x 50 = 195 ohms, can now be used to move Z_n to the center of the chart for an optimum match, Z = 1.0 + j0. Figure 4-7 illustrates the limitations encountered with one-element matching. The objective, in this case, is a SWR circle of 2.0 to 1. The restrictions are even greater for smaller SWR circles.

The technique of using a short section of line as described is called "line matching." The noted difference between the line transformer and the short line is that the short line is considerably less than one-quarter wavelength long. Any transmission line impedance can be used for this application, however, the Smith chart must be normalized to the line's characteristic impedance before performing the first move.

A similar single-element matching arrangement is the shunt stub. A shunt stub consists of a short-circuited or open-circuited transmission line in parallel with the antenna. This arrangement is illustrated in Figure 4-6.

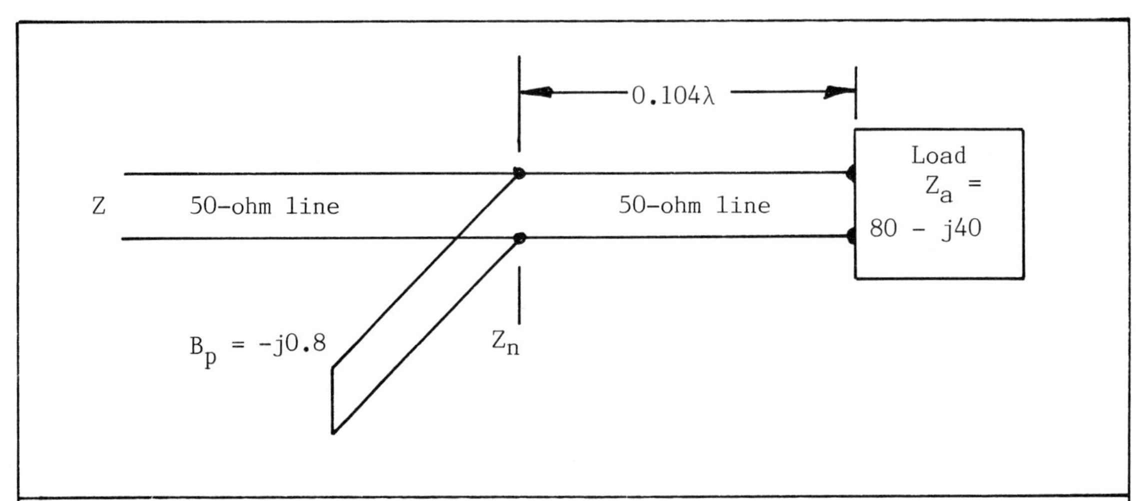

Figure 4-6. A parallel-connected stub and a short line are used to match an impedance of 80 - j40 to a 50-ohm system.

Note that, as in the example shown in Figure 4-5, a short section of line is interposed between the antenna terminals and the stub position. The effect of the short-circuited shunt stub of parallel reactance $+X_p$ on the new impedance Z_n may be determined by subtracting the susceptance $-B_p$ of the shunt stub from the new admittance Y_n as in equation

$$Y_n = G_n + j(B_n - B_p) \tag{4-1}$$

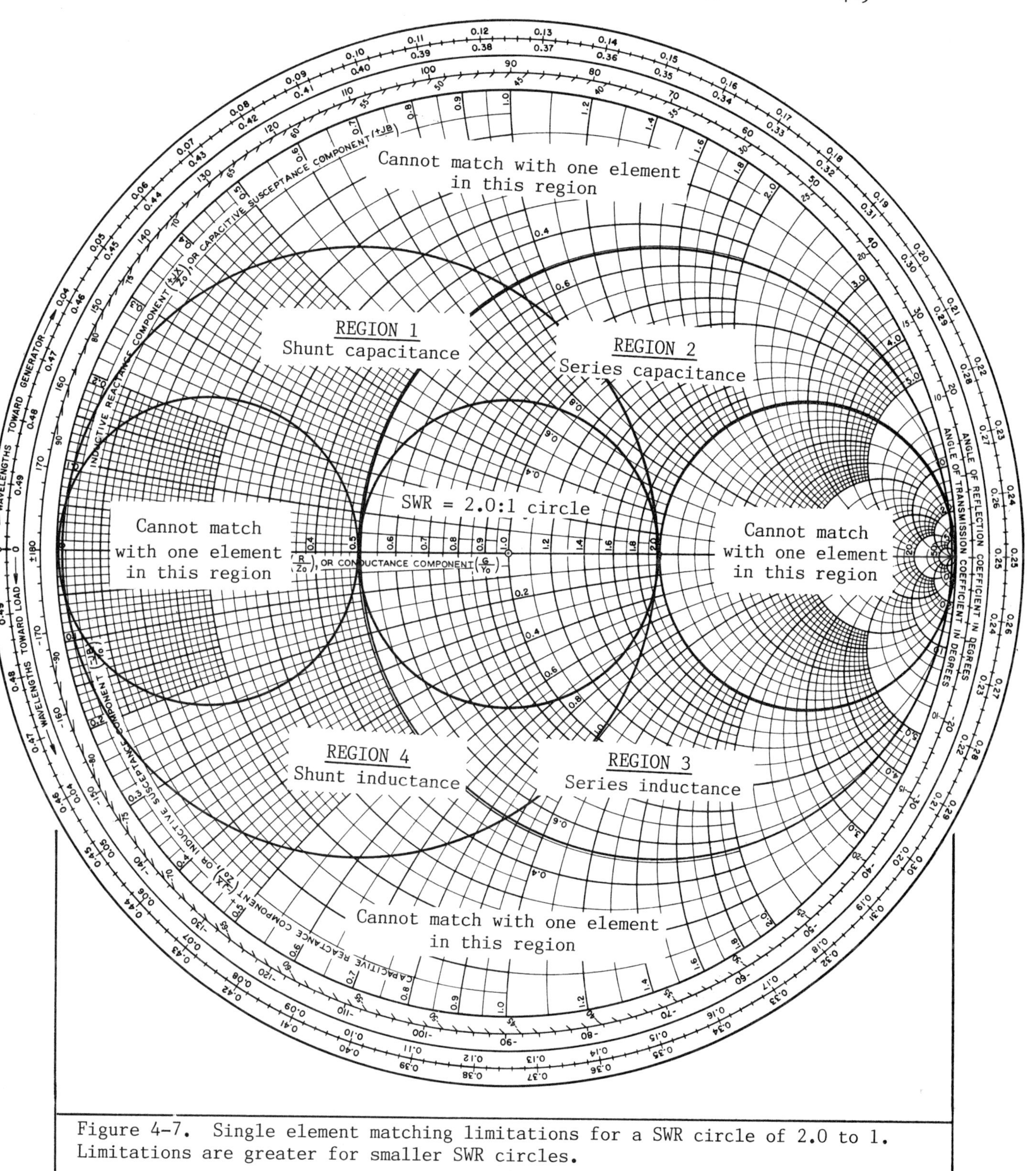

Figure 4-7. Single element matching limitations for a SWR circle of 2.0 to 1. Limitations are greater for smaller SWR circles.

where

Y_n = new admittance

G_n = new conductance

B_n = new susceptance

B_p = parallel stub susceptance

With reference to Figures 4-6 and 4-8, the antenna impedance $Z_a = 80 - j40$ is to be matched to a 50-ohm system. On the Smith chart (Fig. 4-8) are plotted the normalized Z_a point $(80 - j40)/50 = 1.6 - j0.8$ and Y_a, which is diametrically opposite Z_a, $Y_a = 0.5 + j0.26$.

To move Y_a to the constant conductance circle $G = 1.0$ requires that Z_a be moved to a new impedance point $Z_n = 0.62 - j0.48$. This is accomplished by adding a short section of 50-ohm line 0.104λ long to the antenna. The parallel stub susceptance $B_p = -j0.8(50) = -j40$ will transform the new admittance point Y_n to the center of the chart where $G = 1.0$ and $B = j0$, and the antenna will be matched as desired.

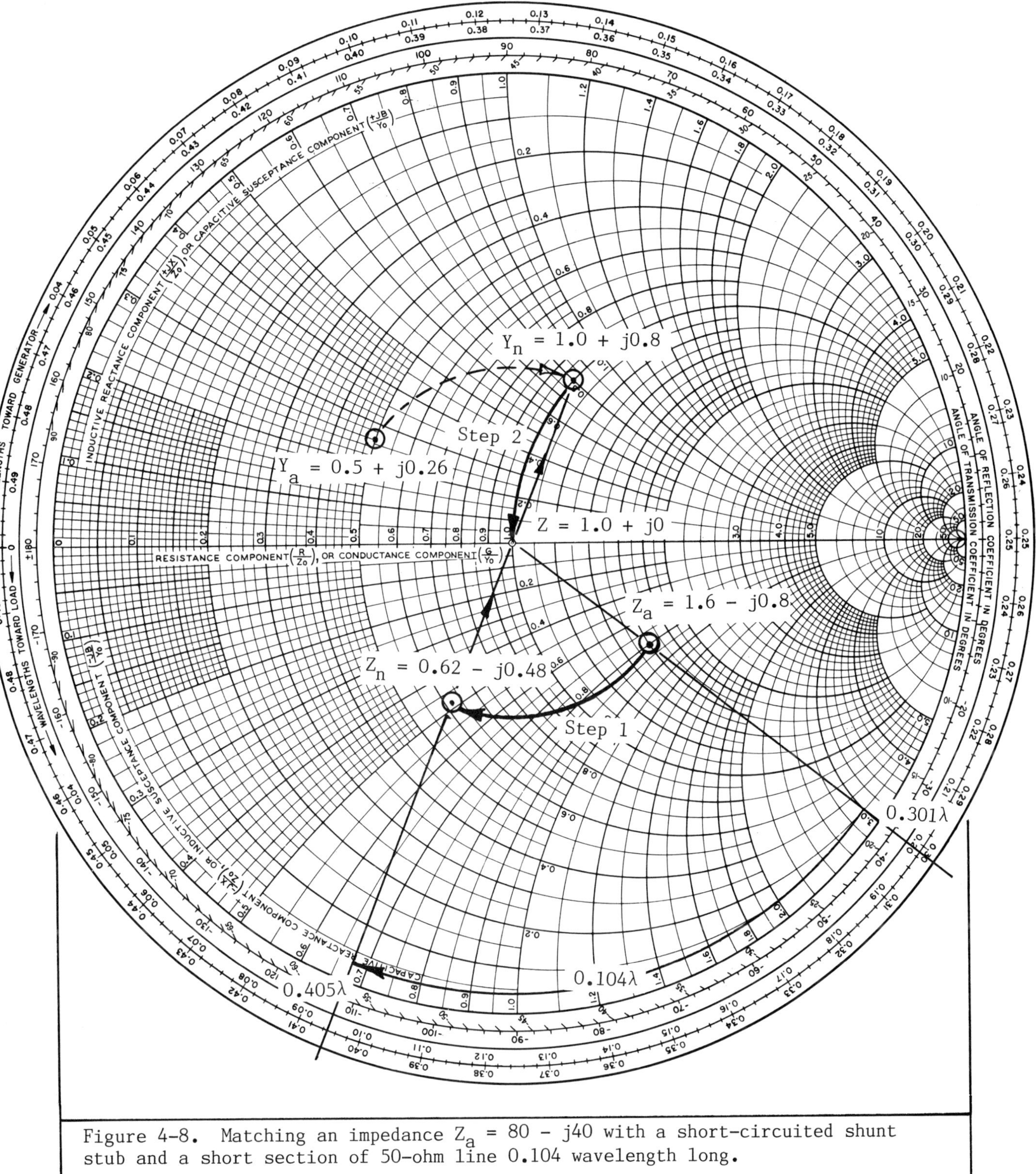

Figure 4-8. Matching an impedance Z_a = 80 - j40 with a short-circuited shunt stub and a short section of 50-ohm line 0.104 wavelength long.

CHAPTER V

MATCHING OVER A BAND OF FREQUENCIES

General.

Single frequency impedance matching is relatively simple. If there is a bandwidth to be matched, the problem becomes more difficult. The first situation encountered is that it is not possible to match a band of frequencies to an optimum SWR of 1.0 to 1. Instead we try to place the bandwidth of interest to within a specified SWR circle. Typically, SWR levels of up to 2.0 to 1 are specified for transmitting systems and up to 5.0 to 1 and sometimes greater for receiving systems.

Bandwidth is a relative term that can be made definite by specifying the maximum value of the SWR not to be exceeded within the band specified. Broadband, like bandwidth, is also relative. The term "broadband" is reserved for antenna systems that have bandwidths of over fifteen percents. Systems that have bandwidths of less than fifteen percents are considered narrowband systems.

When matching over a band of frequencies it must be realized that the impedance points do not move the same amount for different frequencies. A single series or shunt matching element will do the following:

- o Shunt capacitance moves the high frequencies more than the low frequencies. $+B_{ref}\frac{f_x}{f_{ref}}$
- o Shunt inductance moves the low frequencies more than the high frequencies. $-B_{ref}\frac{f_{ref}}{f_x}$
- o Series capacitance moves the low frequencies more than the high frequencies. $-X_{ref}\frac{f_{ref}}{f_x}$
- o Series inductance moves the high frequencies more than the low frequencies. $+X_{ref}\frac{f_x}{f_{ref}}$

where

B_{ref} = susceptance at reference frequency

f_{ref} = reference frequency

f_x = other frequency

To illustrate, if the difference in reactance is -2.5 chartohms* (normalized reactance) at, say, 6.2 mHz, what is the change at 12.4 mHz? The minus sign in front of 2.5 indicates that the reactance is "capacitive."

* For clarity the terms "chartohm" will be used to denote normalized reactance and "chartmho" to denote normalized susceptance.

From

$$X_c = \frac{1}{2\pi fC} \qquad (5\text{-}1)$$

it is seen that the change at other frequencies (f_x) will be

$$-2.5 \times \frac{6.2}{f_x}$$

and, specially, for 12.4 mHz

$$-2.5 \times \frac{6.2}{12.4} = -1.25 \text{ chartohms}$$

What has just been said about reactances and their dependence on the frequency applies to susceptances as well. Thus, if +3.0 is a change in capacitive susceptance of a point, the change at other frequencies will be proportional to these other frequencies, as indicated by the expression

$$B_c = 2\pi fC \qquad (5\text{-}2)$$

Signs of Reactances and Susceptances.

Perhaps the most difficult aspect of impedance matching is keeping track of signs, direction of travel and to make the necessary additions and subtractions correctly. For instance, if a point has a susceptance of +0.35 chartmho and an inductive element with a susceptance of -0.6 chartmho is added in parallel, the resultant susceptance would be

$$B = 0.35 + (-0.6) = -0.25 \text{ chartmho}$$

While this bit of algebra will provide the new location of the point without difficulty, it is important that the proper direction of each move be observed. The following should aid in visualizing the effect of adding or subtracting reactances or susceptances to the original point:

- Shunt capacitance (+B) moves the admittance point clockwise along constant conductance lines.
- Shunt inductance (-B) moves the admittance point counterclockwise along constant conductance lines.
- Series capacitance (-X) moves the impedance point counterclockwise along constant resistance lines.
- Series inductance (+X) moves the impedance point clockwise along constant resistance lines.

The following tables should clearly illustrate the effect of each matching element upon the signs and directions.

TABLE 5-1

Shunt capacitive susceptance (B = +2.0 chartmhos) added at 3 mHz					$+2 \frac{f_x}{3\ mHz}$
f_{mHz}	Old Position	+	Difference	=	New Position
1	+j10.0		(+0.667)		+j10.667
2	+j4.0		(+j1.33)		+j5.330
3	+j0		(+j2.00)		+j2.000
4	-j1.0		(+j2.667)		+j1.667
5	-j3.2		(+j3.33)		+j0.130
6	-j6.4		(+j4.00)		-j2.400

TABLE 5-2

Shunt inductive susceptance (B = -2.0 chartmhos) added at 3 mHz					$-2 \frac{3\ mHz}{f_x}$
f_{mHz}	Old Position	+	Difference	=	New Position
1	+j10.0		(-j6.0)		+j4.000
2	+j4.00		(-j3.0)		+j1.000
3	+j0		(-j2.0)		-j2.000
4	-j1.00		(-j1.5)		-j2.500
5	-j3.20		(-j1.2)		-j4.400
6	-j6.40		(-j1.0)		-j7.400

TABLE 5-3

Series capacitive reactance (X = -2.0 chartohms)added at 3.0 mHz					$-2 \frac{3\ mHz}{f_x}$
f_{mHz}	Old Position	+	Difference	=	New Position
1	+j6.0		(-j6.0)		+j0
2	+j2.0		(-j3.0)		-j1.0
3	-j1.0		(-j2.0)		-j3.0
4	-j3.0		(-j1.5)		-j4.5
5	-j9.0		(-j1.2)		-j10.2
6	+j2.0		(-j1.0		+j1.0

TABLE 5-4

Series inductive reactance (X = +2.0 chartohms) added at 3.0 mHz					$+2 \frac{f_x}{3.0 \text{ mHz}}$
f_{mHz}	Old Position	+	Difference	=	New Position
1	+j6.0		(+j0.667)		+j6.667
2	+j2.0		(+j1.330)		+j3.330
3	-j1.0		(+j2.000)		+j1.000
4	-j3.0		(+j2.667)		-j0.333
5	-j9.0		(+j3.330)		-j5.670
6	-j9.5		(+j4.000)		-j5.500

The Smith Chart Overlay.

To combine a shunt element with an impedance the impedance must be inverted to its admittance position and the shunt element must also be inverted from reactance to susceptance. The load susceptance and the shunt susceptance must then be added together. This sum must again be inverted to obtain the impedance. This process, however simple, can be time consuming if several impedance points must be compensated and evaluated. Hence, the impedance points are plotted on an overlay. A practical way to go from one position to another using this overlay is by means of a shadow box with a frosted pane. A thumbtack is fastened to the pane and a Smith chart is carefully centered on the thumbtack and taped to the pane. Finally, the overlay, consisting of another Smith chart, is centered over the first. An impedance curve plotted on this overlay can now be rapidly changed to an admittance curve or vice versa by simply turning the overlay 180 degrees.

Eight Matching Examples.

The effect that each matching element, series reactance and shunt susceptance, has upon an impedance plot representing a band of frequencies can be seen by the examples shown as Figures 5-1 throught 5-8 and associated work tables. An explanation of the legends used in these figures is perhaps necessary. For simplicity, only three frequencies are used: 30 mHz, 31 mHz and 32 mHz. These frequencies were selected as a matter of convenience and do not represent any special case. The initial impedance point is represented by the symbol Z and the frequencies by the numbers 1, 2 and 3 (1 = 30 mHz, 2 = 31 mHz, and 3 = 32 mHz). The result of adding series reactance to the load impedance is denoted by the symbols Z_{11}, Z_{22} and Z_{33}. The diametrically opposite admittance positions are represented by Y_{11}, Y_{22} and Y_{33}. The result of adding shunt susceptance to Y_{11}, Y_{22} and Y_{33} is shown as Y_{111}, Y_{222} and Y_{333}. Sometimes these final admittance points are converted to their diametrically opposite impedances Z_{111}, Z_{222} and Z_{333}. It should be noted that although the center frequency was used for the initial calculations, it may not be the best frequency to use. Also, the amount of correction required for achieving a matched condition at the center frequency will determine the amount of divergence or "blossoming" of the final impedance or admittance curve.

Matching Procedures for 4-3(a) Through 4-3(h).

TABLE 5-5

Problem: Match center frequency impedance Z_2 to center of Smith chart using L-type matching network shown in Figure 4-1(a).

Given: $Z_1 = 1.0 + j2.0$, $Z_2 = 1.4 + j2.4$, $Z_3 = 2.0 + j3.0$					
Step 1: Determine admittance points from impedance points using overlay.					
Step 2: Add capacitive shunt susceptance to Y_2 to move Z_2 to R = 1.0 line.					
f_{mHz}	Old Position	+	Correction	=	New Position
30	$Y_1 = 0.190 - j0.400$		+0.668		$Y_{11} = 0.190 + j0.268$
31	$Y_2 = 0.180 - j0.310$		+0.690		$Y_{22} = 0.180 + j0.380$
32	$Y_3 = 0.150 - j0.230$		+0.712		$Y_{33} = 0.150 + j0.482$
Step 3: Add series inductive reactance to move Z_{22} to $Z_{222} = 1.0 + j0$.					
f_{mHz}	Old Position	+	Correction	=	New Position
30	$Z_{11} = 1.70 - j2.500$		+2.253		$Z_{111} = 1.700 - j0.247$
31	$Z_{22} = 1.000 - j2.180$		+2.180		$Z_{222} = 1.000 + j0$
32	$Z_{33} = 0.580 - j1.900$		+2.112		$Z_{333} = 0.580 + j0.212$

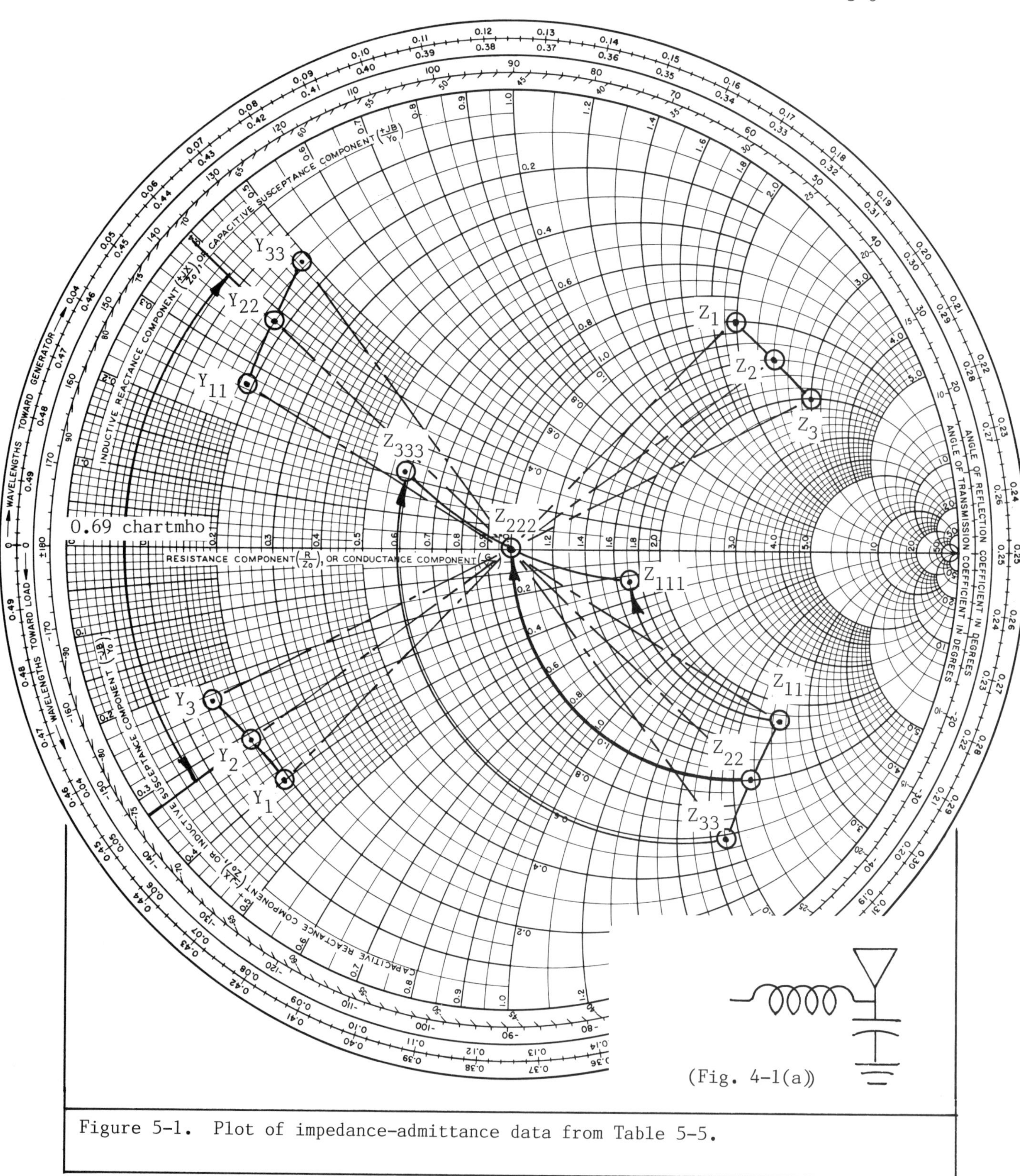

Figure 5-1. Plot of impedance-admittance data from Table 5-5.

TABLE 5-6

Problem: Match center frequency impedance Z_2 to center of Smith chart using L-type matching network shown in Figure 4-1(b).

Given: $Z_1 = 0.100 - j\,0.400$, $Z_2 = 0.160 - j0.340$, $Z_3 = 0.200 - j0.300$					
Step 1: Add inductive reactance to Z_2 to move Z_2 to a point that will cause Y_{22} to be placed on the G = 1.0 line. Use overlay to locate Z_{22} and Y_{22} points.					
f_{mHz}	Old Position	+	Correction	=	New Position
30	$Z_1 = 0.100 - j0.400$		+0.677		$Z_{11} = 0.100 + j0.277$
31	$Z_2 = 0.160 - j0.340$		+0.700		$Z_{22} = 0.160 + j0.360$
32	$Z_3 = 0.200 - j0.300$		+0.723		$Z_{33} = 0.200 + j0.423$
Step 2: Plot admittance points Y_{11}, Y_{22} and Y_{33} from Z_{11}, Z_{22} and Z_{33}.					
Step 3: Add capacitive shunt susceptance to Y_{22} to move Y_{22} to G = 1.0 & B=0.					
f_{mHz}	Old Position	+	Correction	=	New Position
30	$Y_{11} = 1.200 - j3.200$		+2.260		$Y_{111} = 1.2 - j0.940$
31	$Y_{22} = 1.000 - j2.300$		+2.300		$Y_{222} = 1.0 + j0$
32	$Y_{33} = 0.900 - j1.900$		+2.374		$Y_{333} = 0.900 + j0.474$

TABLE 5-7

Problem: Match the center frequency impedance Z_2 to center of Smith chart using L-type matching network shown in Figure 4-1(c).

Given: $Z_1 = 1.0 - j1.85$, $Z_2 = 0.8 - j1.60$, $Z_3 = 0.6 - j1.40$					
Step 1: Invert impedance to admittance using overlay.					
Step 2: Add to Y_2 shunt susceptance to move Y_2 to Y_{22} to place Z_{22} on R = 1.0.					
f_{mHz}	Old Position	+	Correction	=	New Position
30	$Y_1 = 0.225 + j0.420$		(-0.961)		$Y_{11} = 0.225 - j0.541$
31	$Y_2 = 0.250 + j0.500$		(-0.930)		$Y_{22} = 0.250 - j0.430$
32	$Y_3 = 0.260 + j0.600$		(-0.901)		$Y_{33} = 0.260 - j0.301$
Step 3: Add series capacitive reactance to Z_{22} to move Z_{22} to center of chart.					
f_{mHz}	Old Position	+	Correction	=	New Position
30	$Z_{11} = 0.620 + j1.600$		(-1.777)		$Z_{111} = 0.620 - j0.177$
31	$Z_{22} = 1.000 + j1.720$		(-1.720)		$Z_{222} = 1.000 + j0$
32	$Z_{22} = 1.600 + j1.900$		(-1.666)		$Z_{333} = 1.600 + j0.234$

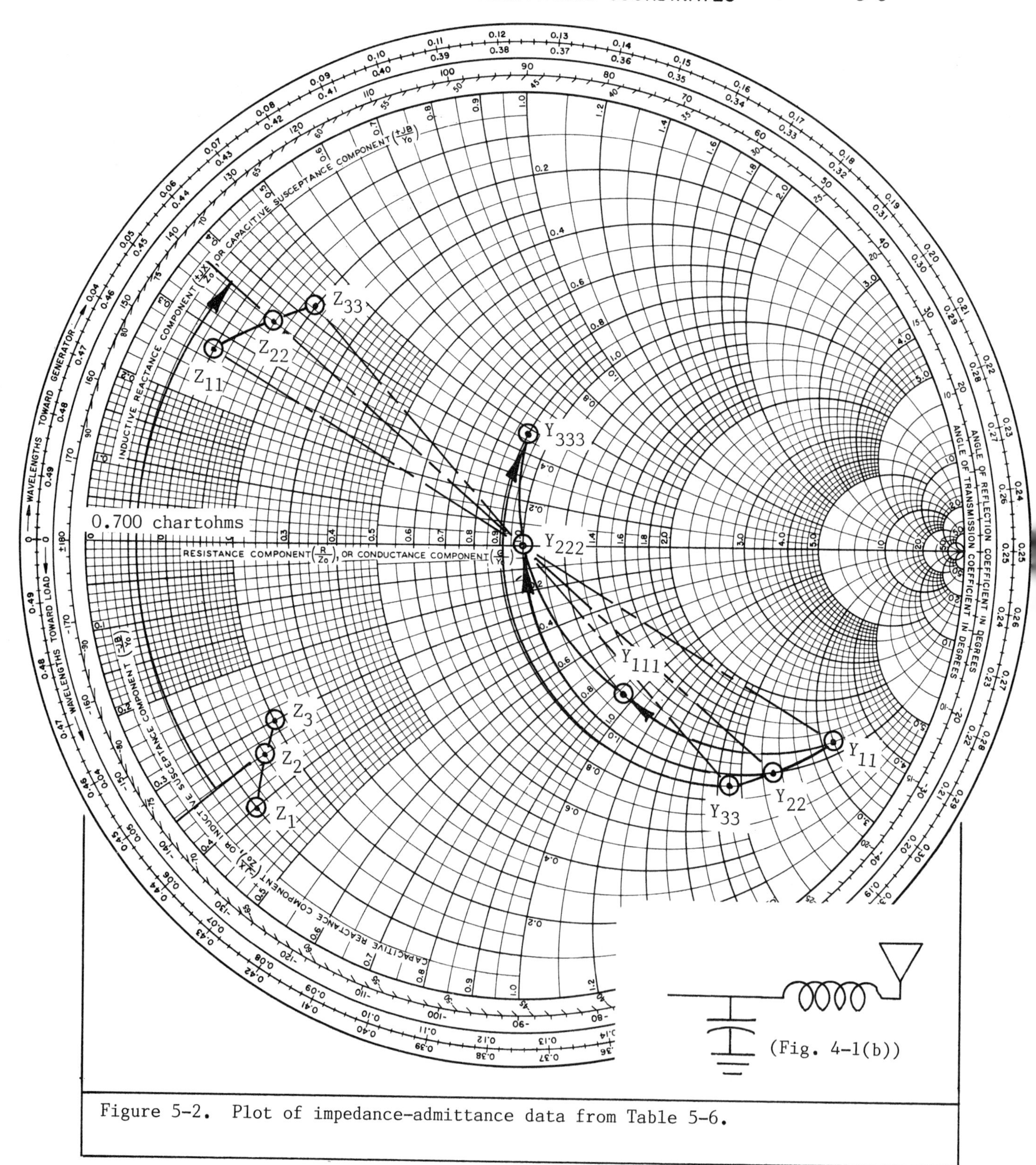

Figure 5-2. Plot of impedance-admittance data from Table 5-6.

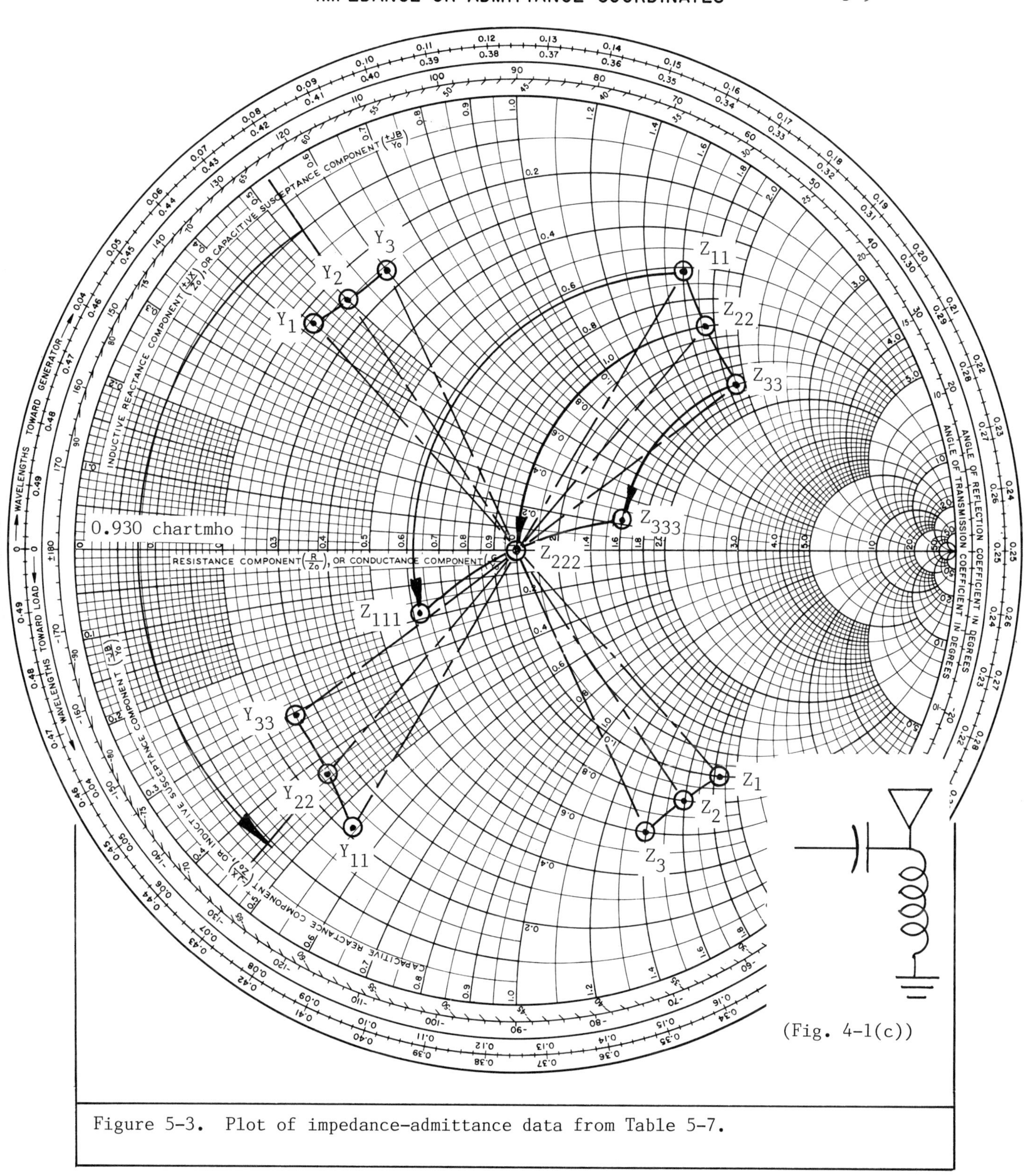

Figure 5-3. Plot of impedance-admittance data from Table 5-7.

TABLE 5-8

Problem: Match center frequency impedance to center of Smith chart using L-type matching network shown in Figure 4-1(d).

Given: $Z_1 = 0.200 + j0.200$, $Z_2 = 0.160 + j0.310$, $Z_3 = 0.100 + j0.400$					
Step 1: Add capacitive reactance to Z_2 to move Z_2 to a point that will cause Y_{22} to be placed on the G = 1.0 line. Use overlay to locate Z_{22} and Y_{22}.					
f_{mHz}	Old Position	+	Correction	=	New Position
30	$Z_1 = 0.200 + j0.200$		(-0.682)		$Z_{11} = 0.200 - j0.482$
31	$Z_2 = 0.160 + j0.310$		(-0.660)		$Z_{22} = 0.160 - j0.350$
32	$Z_3 = 0.100 + j0.400$		(-0.639)		$Z_{33} = 0.100 - j0.239$
Step 2: Plot admittance points Y_{11}, Y_{22} and Y_{33} from Z_{11}, Z_{22} and Z_{33}.					
Step 3: Add inductive shunt susceptance to Y_{22} to move Y_{22} to G = 1.0 and jB= 0.					
f_{mHz}	Old Position	+	Correction	=	New Position
30	$Y_{11} = 0.700 + j1.750$		(-2.273)		$Y_{111} = 0.7000 - j0.523$
31	$Y_{22} = 1.000 + j2.200$		(-2.200)		$Y_{222} = 1.000 + j0$
32	$Y_{33} = 1.400 + j3.600$		(-2.131)		$Y_{333} = 1.400 + j1.469$

TABLE 5-9

Problem: Match center frequency impedance to center of Smith chart using L-type matching network shown in Figure 4-1(e).

Given: $Z_1 = 0.200 + j0.800$, $Z_2 = 0.200 + j0.900$, $Z_3 = 0.200 + j1.000$					
Step 1: Determine admittance points from impedance points. Use overlay.					
Step 2: Add capacitive shunt susceptance to Y2 to move Z_2 to R = 1.0 line.					
f_{mHz}	Old Position	+	Correction	=	New Position
30	$Y_1 = 0.300 - j1.180$		+0.629		$Y_{11} = 0.300 - j0.551$
31	$Y_2 = 0.240 - j1.080$		+0.650		$Y_{22} = 0.240 - j0.430$
32	$Y_3 = 0.190 - j0.975$		+0.671		$Y_{22} = 0.190 - j0.304$
Step 3: Add series capacitive reactance to move Z_{22} to $Z_{222} = 1.0 + j0$.					
f_{mHz}	Old Position	+	Correction	=	New Position
30	$Z_{11} = 0.720 + j1.400$		(-1.839)		$Z_{111} = 0.720 - j0.439$
31	$Z_{22} = 1.000 + j1.780$		(-1.780)		$Z_{222} = 1.000 + j0$
32	$Z_{33} = 1.420 + j2.300$		(-1.724)		$Z_{333} = 1.420 + j0.576$

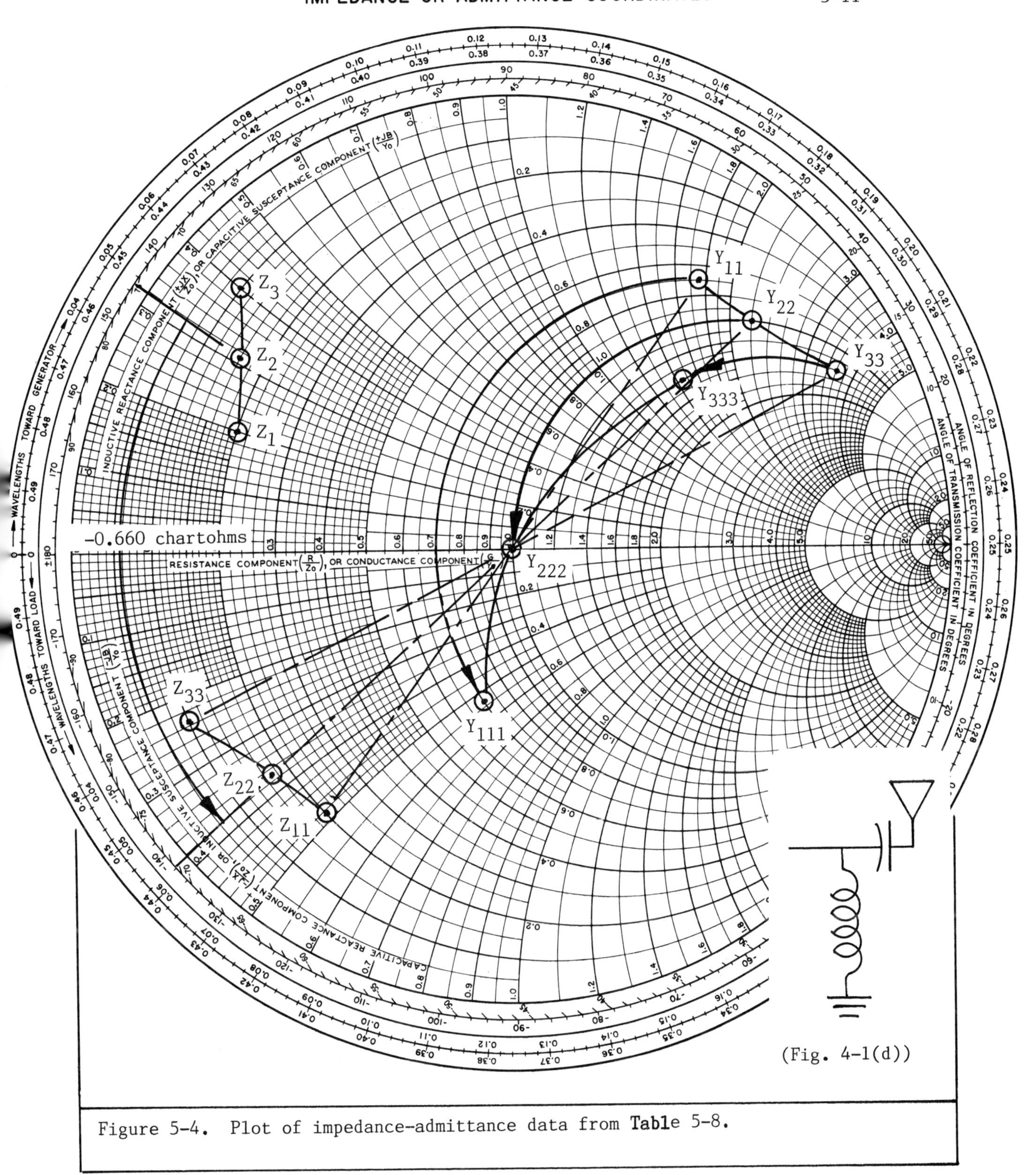

Figure 5-4. Plot of impedance-admittance data from Table 5-8.

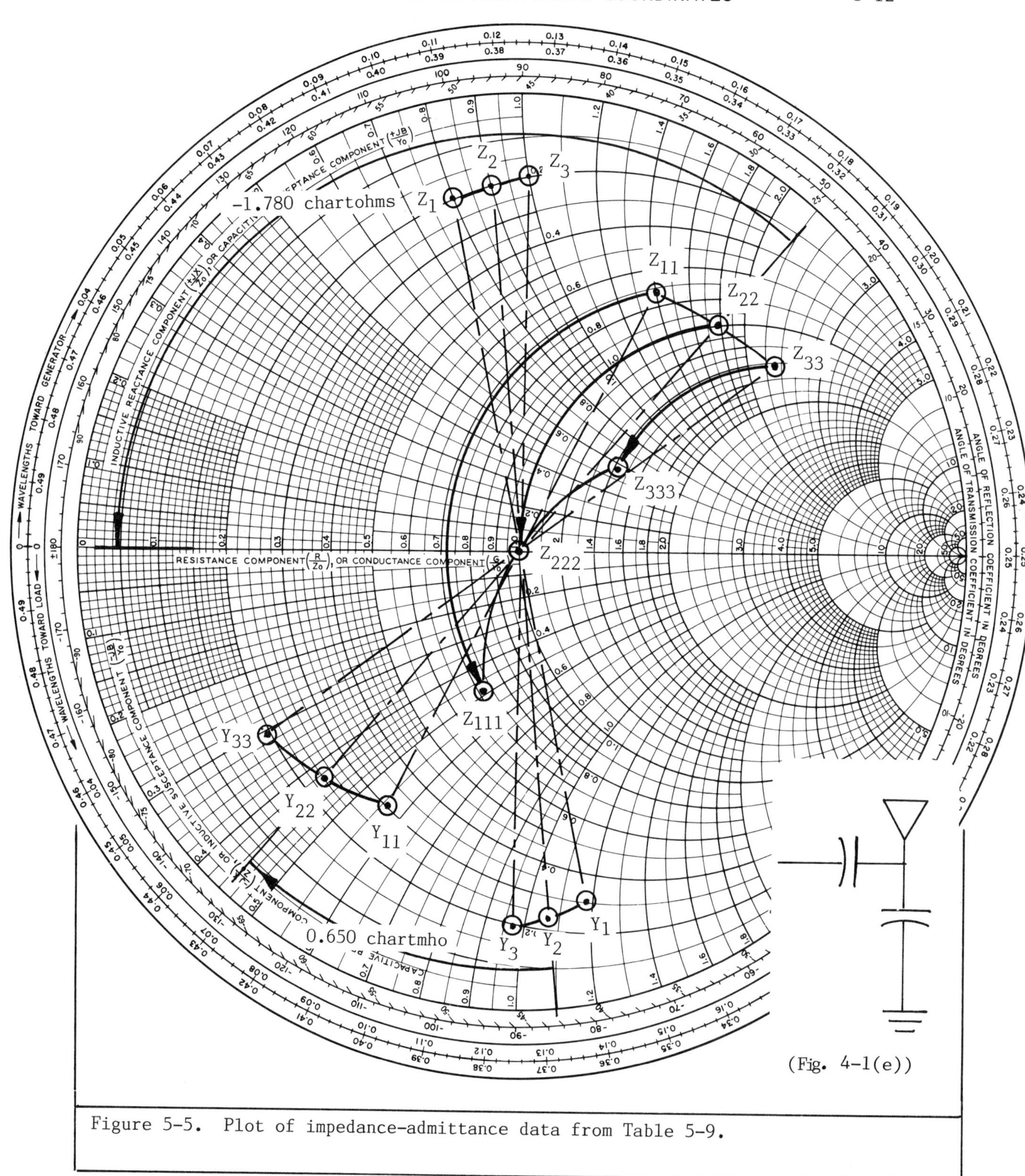

Figure 5-5. Plot of impedance-admittance data from Table 5-9.

TABLE 5-10

Problem: Match center frequency impedance to center of Smith chart using L-type matching network shown in Figure 4-1(f).

Given: $Z_1 = 0.400 + j1.000$, $Z_2 = 0.300 + j1.200$, $Z_3 = 0.200 + j1.400$

Step 1: Add capacitive reactance to Z_2 to move Z_2 to a point that will cause Y_{22} to be placed on the G = 1.0 line. Use overlay to locate Z_{22} and Y_{22}.

f_{mHz}	Old Position	+	Correction	=	New Position
30	$Z_1 = 0.400 + j1.000$		(-0.765)		$Z_{11} = 0.400 + j0.235$
31	$Z_2 = 0.300 + j1.200$		(-0.740)		$Z_{22} = 0.300 + j0.460$
32	$Z_3 = 0.200 + j1.400$		(-0.717)		$Z_{33} = 0.200 + j0.683$

Step 2: Plot admittance points Y_{11}, Y_{22} and Y_{33} from Z_{11}, Z_{22} and Z_{33}.

Step 3: Add capacitive shunt susceptance to Y_{22} to move Y_{22} to G = 1.0 and B = 0

f_{mHz}	Old Position	+	Correction	=	New Position
30	$Y_{11} = 1.900 - j1.100$		+1.490		$Y_{111} = 1.900 + j0.390$
31	$Y_{22} = 1.000 - j1.540$		+1.540		$Y_{222} = 1.000 + j0$
32	$Y_{33} = 0.400 - j1.350$		+1.590		$Y_{333} = 0.400 + j0.240$

TABLE 5-11

Problem: Match center frequency impedance to center of Smith chart using L-type matching network shown in Figure 4-1(g).

Given: $Z_1 = 0.200 - j0.700$, $Z_2 = 0.200 - j0.600$, $Z_3 = 0.200 - j0.500$

Step 1: Determine admittance points from impedance points. Use overlay.

Step 2: Add inductive shunt susceptance to Y_2 to move Z_2 to R = 1.0 line.

f_{mHz}	Old Position	+	Correction	=	New Position
30	$Y_1 = 0.380 + j1.320$		(-1.023)		$Y_{11} = 0.380 + j0.297$
31	$Y_2 = 0.500 + j1.500$		(-0.990)		$Y_{22} = 0.500 + j0.510$
32	$Y_3 = 0.670 + j1.720$		(-0.959)		$Y_{33} = 0.670 + j0.761$

Step 3: Add inductive reactance to Z_{22} to move Z_{22} to $Z_{333} = 1.0 + j0$.

f_{mHz}	Old Position	+	Correction	=	New Position
30	$Z_{11} = 1.660 - j1.320$		+0.968		$Z_{111} = 1.660 - jo.352$
31	$Z_{22} = 1.000 - j1.000$		+1.000		$Z_{222} = 1.000 + j0$
32	$Z_{33} = 0.650 - j0.750$		+1.032		$Z_{333} = 0.650 + j0.282$

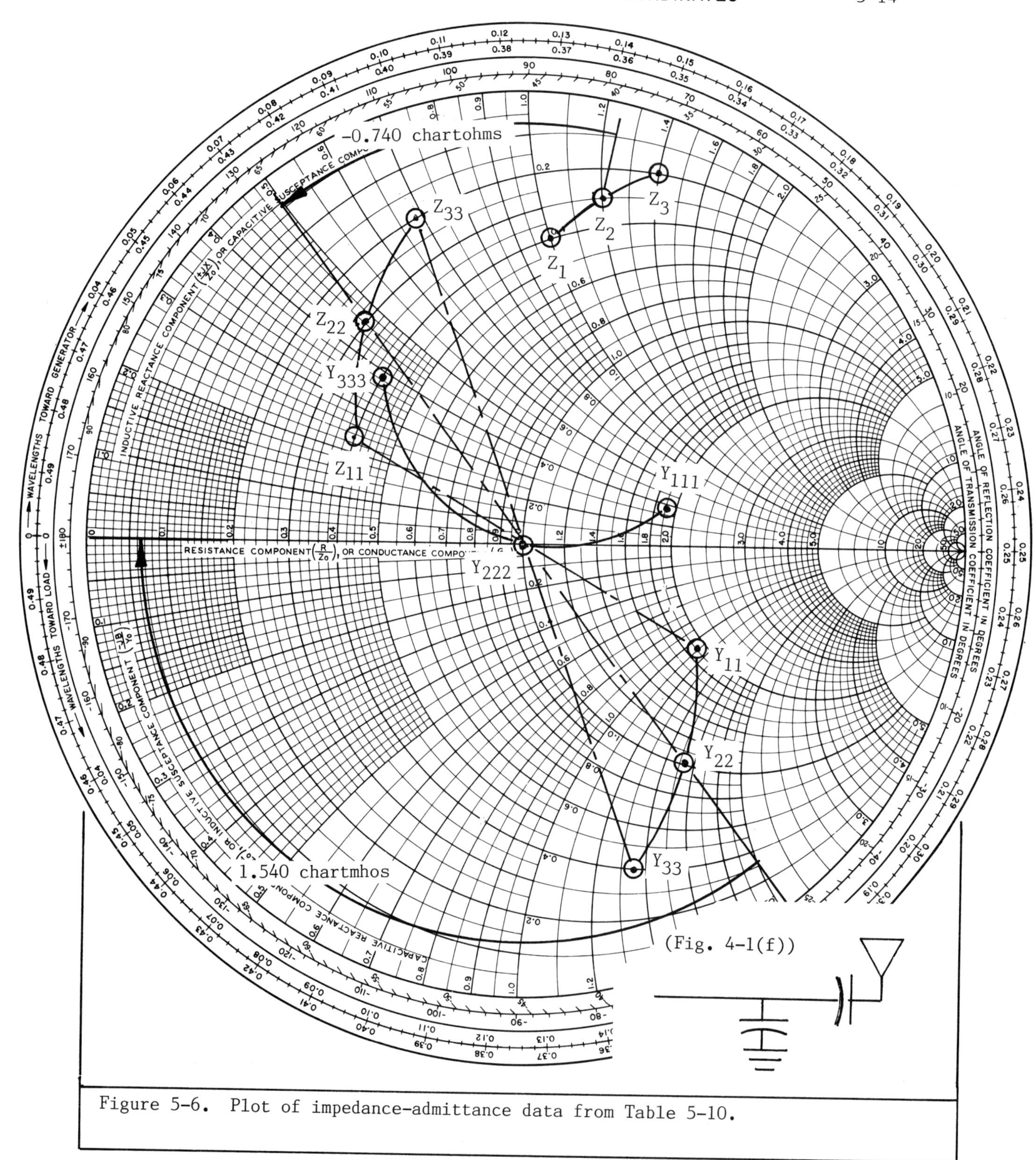

Figure 5-6. Plot of impedance-admittance data from Table 5-10.

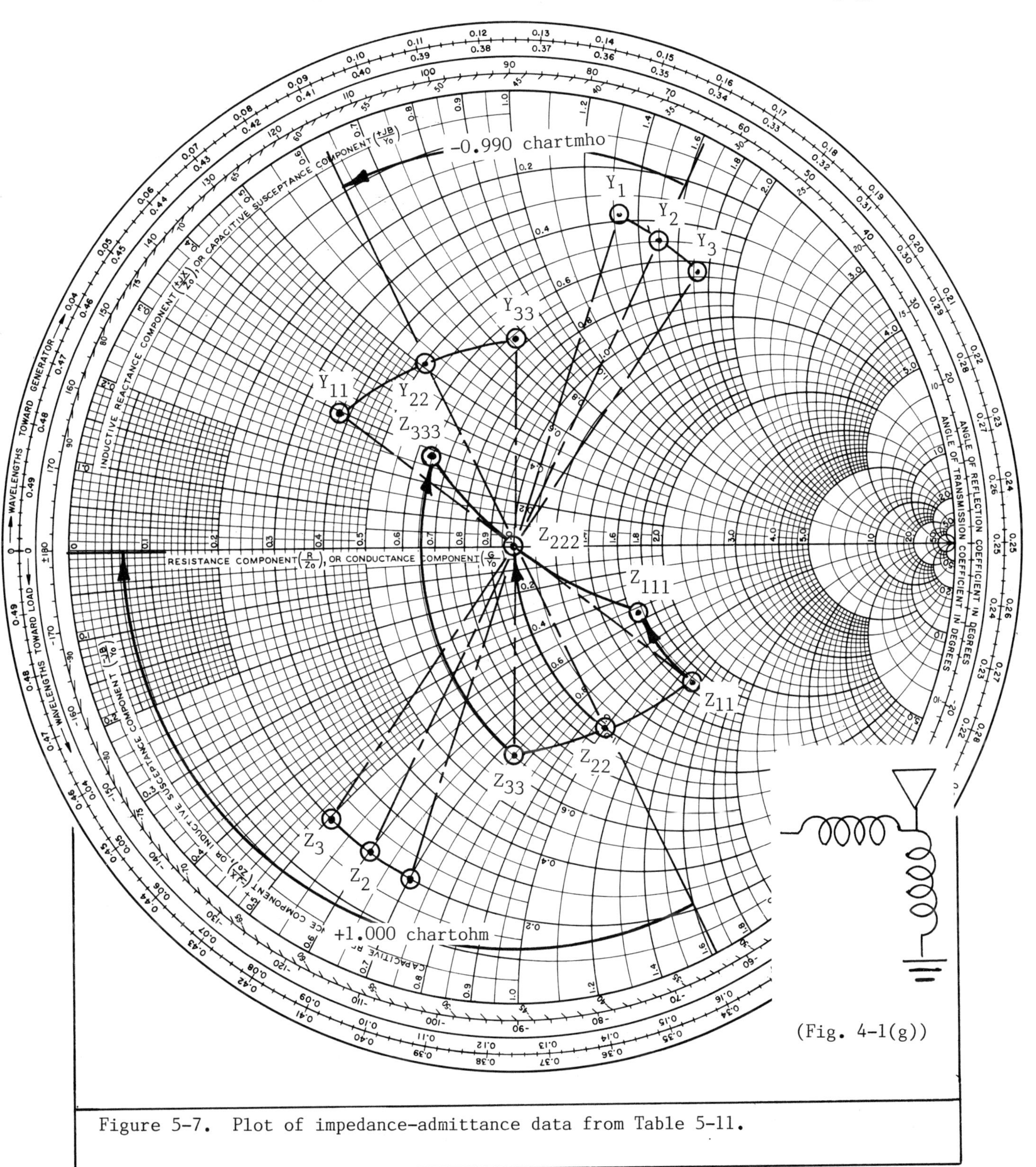

Figure 5-7. Plot of impedance-admittance data from Table 5-11.

TABLE 5-12

Problem: Match center frequency impedance to center of Smith chart using L-type matching network shown in Figure 4-1(h).

Given: $Z_1 = 0.200 - j1.200$, $Z_2 = 0.300 - j1.100$, $Z_3 = 0.400 - j1.000$					
Step 1: Add inductive reactance to Z_2 to move Z_2 to a point that will cause Y_{22} to be placed on the G = 1.0 line. Use overlay to locate Z_{22} and Y_{22}.					
f_{mHz}	Old Position	+	Correction	=	New Position
30	$Z_1 = 0.200 - j1.200$		+0.629		$Z_{11} = 0.200 - j0.571$
31	$Z_2 = 0.300 - j1.100$		+0.650		$Z_{22} = 0.300 - j0.450$
32	$Z_3 = 0.400 - j1.000$		+0.671		$Z_{33} = 0.400 - j0.329$
Step 2: Plot admittance points Y_{11}, Y_{22} and Y_{33} from Z_{11}, Z_{22} and Z_{33}.					
Step 3: Add inductive shunt susceptance to move Y_{22} to G = 1.0 and jB = 0.					
f_{mHz}	Old Position	+	Correction	=	New Position
30	$Y_{11} = 0.550 + j1.550$		(-1.550)		$Y_{111} = 0.550 + j0$
31	$Y_{22} = 1.000 + j1.500$		(-1.500)		$Y_{222} = 1.000 + j0$
32	$Y_{33} = 1.500 + j1.250$		(-1.453)		$Y_{333} = 1.500 - j0.203$

<u>Summary.</u>

It has been demonstrated that antenna impedance matching, using any of the eight L-type matching circuits, can be accomplished quite easily at one frequency. In the examples presented the center frequency, 31 mHz, was matched to the center of the Smith chart. Of particular interest is the behavior of the impedance at the other frequencies, 30 and 32 mHz. Although no attemptwas made to match the band of frequencies into any definite SWR circle, each frequency was reasonably matched to an acceptable level. Of particular interest is the "blossoming of the final impedance or admittance points. An antenna impedance that requires little correction will not blossom as much as one that requires much correction. This is one aspect that must be observed when it is required to match to a specific definition circle. The challenge can be a great deal of fun. Of course, the secret is to have an initial antenna impedance that is either close to the center of the Smith chart or one that is tightly clustered. The examples in the following chapter will be matched to within definite SWR circles.

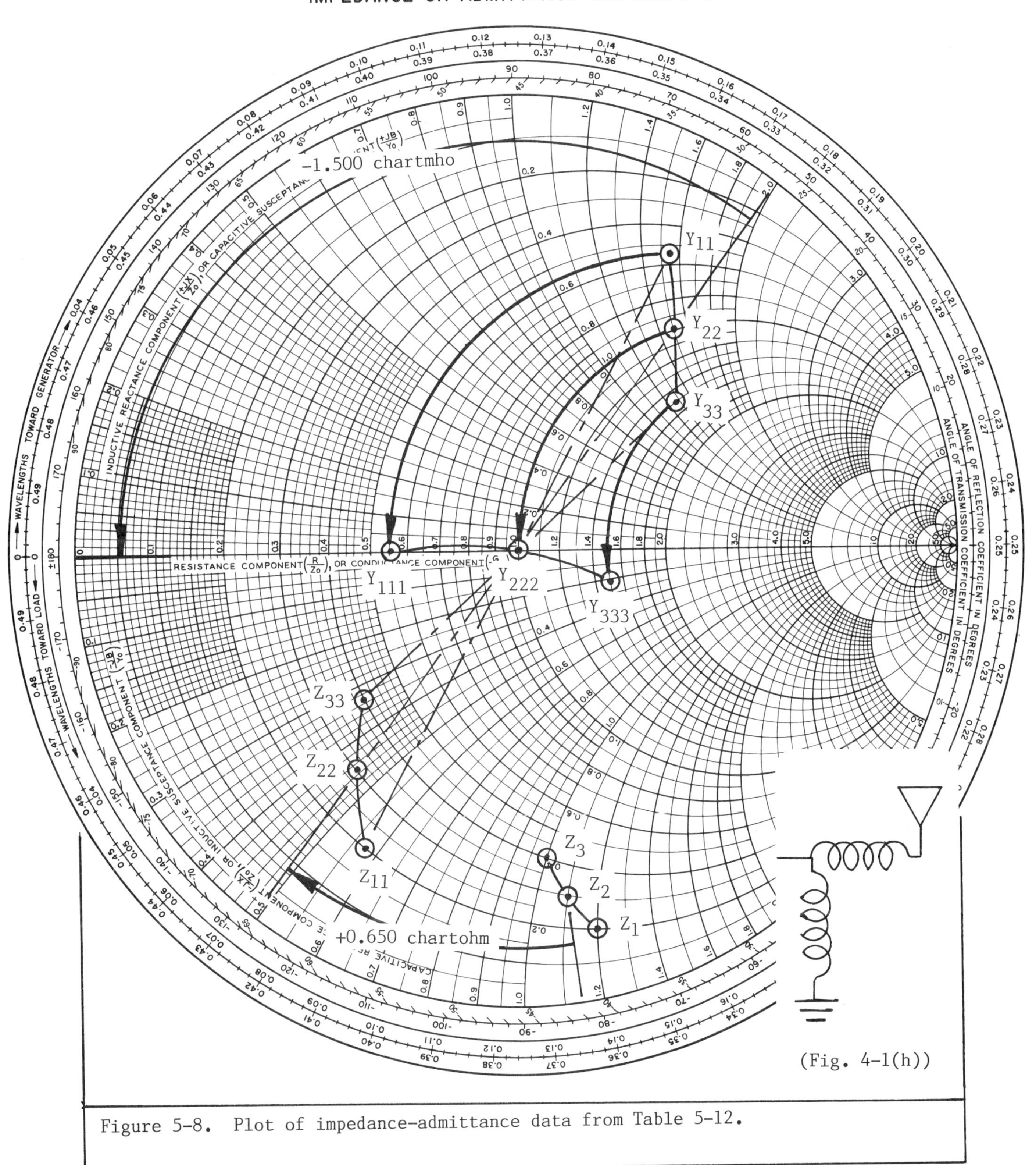

Figure 5-8. Plot of impedance-admittance data from Table 5-12.

CHAPTER VI

MATCHING SOLUTIONS

General.

The examples chosen to show various narrowband and broadband matching techniques are typical. The first group of examples deal with narrowband matching and the second group with broadband matching. These examples differ from those previously described in that the impedances are placed within a definite SWR circle. The only time impedance matching becomes difficult is when broadband matching is necessary or when the SWR circle is small. In such cases, optimum matching may require three or four matching networks. Sometimes even these are not sufficient and the antenna configuration or design must be modified to tighten up the impedance points or to move them into an area that is more favorable to matching. It is often desirable to incorporate impedance compensation within the antenna structure itself but this approach is beyond the scope of this discussion.

Narrowband Matching.

Example No. 1. Problem: Match the following antenna impedance points to a SWR of 2.0 to 1 or better.

f_{mHz}	Impedance	Normalized Impedance
12.0	Z_1 = 10.0 - j60	Z_1 = 0.200 - j1.200
12.2	Z_2 = 16.5 - j55	Z_2 = 0.330 - j1.100
12.4	Z_3 = 20.0 - j50	Z_3 = 0.400 - j1.000

Step 1. Enter normalized impedance on the Smith chart as shown in Figure 6-1.

Step 2. Draw a SWR circle centered on the Smith chart with its radius passing through 2.0 on the R/Z_o axis. The objective is to move the impedance or admittance points into this circle with a minimum of correction.

Step 3. An examination of Figures 4-2 and 4-3 indicates that the impedance points are in region 4 and that (b), (c), (g) and (h) are possible matching solutions. Solution (g) appears to require less correction, therefore, it is our initial choice.

Step 4. The first matching element is a shunt inductor. Using an overlay, invert the impedance points to their equivalent admittance points.

f_{mHz}	Normalized Admittance
12.0	$Y_1 = 0.140 + j0.815$
12.2	$Y_2 = 0.250 + j0.830$
12.4	$Y_3 = 0.345 + j0.860$

Step 5. Determine the amount of shunt inductive susceptance required to move the mid frequency admittance to the G = 1.0 line. A susceptance Of 0.830 - 0.430 = 0.400 chartmho is required. Since the move is counterclockwise to reach the G = 1.0 line, the correction required is negative.

Step 6. Compute for the new admittance positions.

f_{mHz}	Old Position	+	Correction	=	New Position
12.0	$Y_1 = 0.140 + j0.815$		(-0.407)		$Y_{11} = 0.140 + j0.408$
12.2	$Y_2 = 0.250 + j0.830$		(-0.400)		$Y_{22} = 0.250 + j0.430$
12.4	$Y_3 = 0.345 + j0.860$		(-0.395)		$Y_{33} = 0.345 + j0.465$

Step 7. The second matching element is a series inductor. Invert the admittance points to their equivalent impedances and compute the amount of series inductive reactance required to move the mid frequency point to the center of the Smith chart. The reactance at the mid frequency is -j1.760 chartohms. A reactance of +1.760 chartohms is required to move the mid frequency to the jX = 0 line. Determine the final impedance for all frequencies.

f_{mHz}	Old Position	+	Correction	=	New Position
12.0	$Z_{11} = 0.750 - j2.250$		+1.731		$Z_{111} = 0.750 - j0.519$
12.2	$Z_{22} = 1.000 - j1.760$		+1.760		$Z_{222} = 1.000 + j0$
12.4	$Z_{33} = 1.050 - j1.400$		+1.789		$Z_{333} = 1.050 + j0.389$

It can be seen that the initial approach to matching the impedances within a SWR circle of 2.0 places the impedance point Z_{111} just outside the circle. It appears that an additional series reactance of about 0.100 will move Z_{111} well within the circle. Caution must be exercised so as not to push the Z_{333} point outside the circle.

Step 8. Add a reactance of 0.100 to 1.731 at 12.0 mHz and recompute. Plot the new impedance positions.

f_{mHz}	Old Position	+	Correction	=	New Position
12.0	$Z_{11} = 0.750 - j2.250$		+1.831		$Z_{111} = 0.750 - j0.419$
12.2	$Z_{22} = 1.000 - j1.760$		+1.923		$Z_{222} = 1.000 + j0.163$
12.4	$Z_{33} = 1.050 - j1.400$		+2.014		$Z_{333} = 1.050 + j0.614$

Step 9. Determine the size of inductor required for the shunt element.

$$L = \frac{1}{2\pi f B_L Y_o}$$

where $B_L Y_o = 0.400 \times 1/50 = 0.008$ mho
$f = 12.2 \times 10^6$ Hz/sec

Substituting

$$L = \frac{1}{(6.28)(12.2 \times 10^6)(0.008)}$$

$$L = 1.63 \times 10^{-6} \text{ Henrys or } 1.63\ \mu\text{H}$$

Step 10. Determine the size of inductor required for the series element.

$$L = \frac{X_L}{2\pi f}$$

where $X_L = 1.923 \times 50 = 96.15$ ohms
$f = 12.2 \times 10^6$ Hz/sec

Substituting

$$L = \frac{96.15}{(6.28)(12.2 \times 10^6)}$$

$$L = 1.255 \times 10^{-6} \text{ Henrys or } 1.255\ \mu\text{H}$$

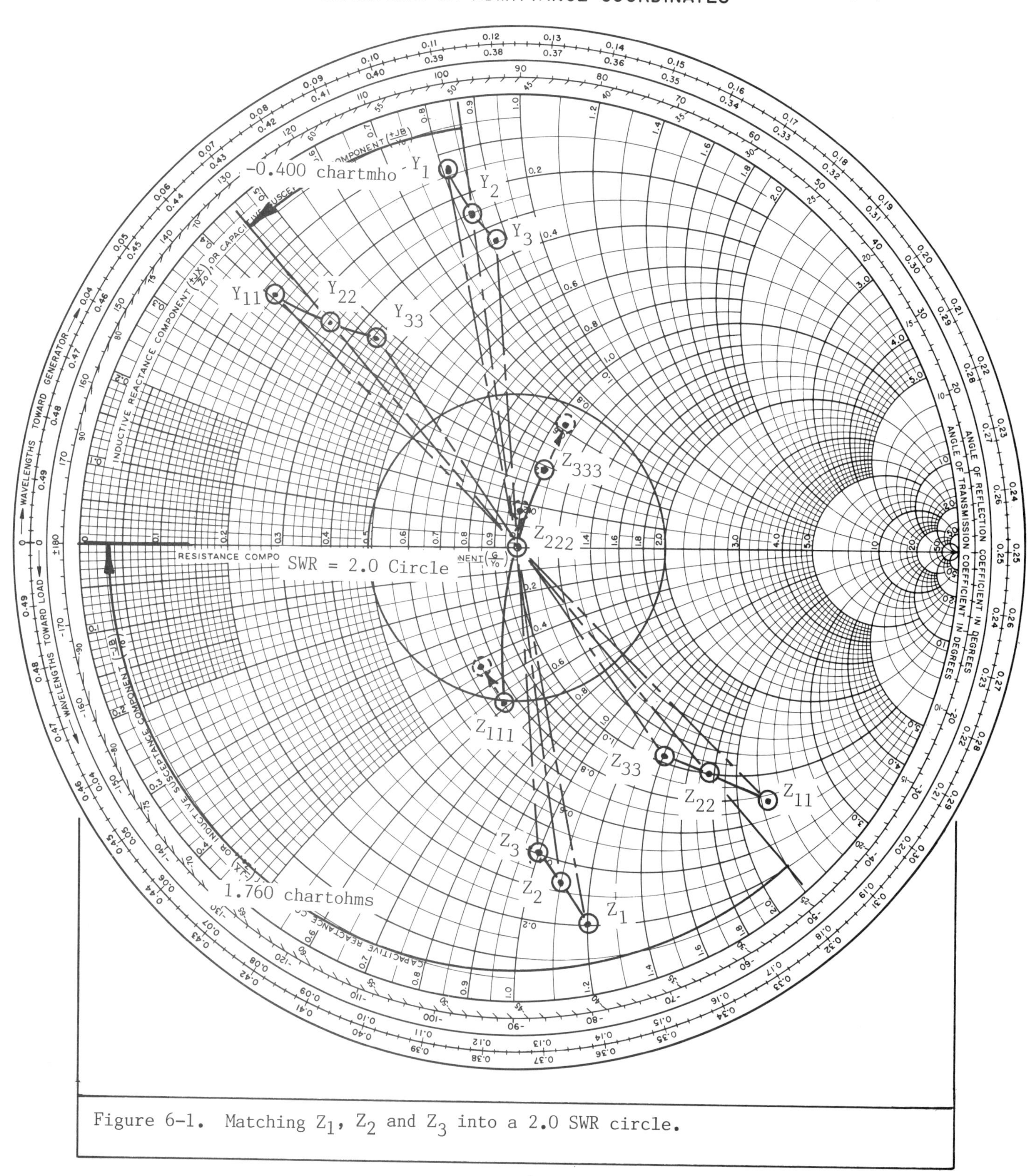

Figure 6-1. Matching Z_1, Z_2 and Z_3 into a 2.0 SWR circle.

Example 2. Problem: Match the following impedance points to a 50-ohm line. The desired SWR is 1.5 to 1 or better. A line transformer is required.

f_{mHz}	Impedance	Normalized Impedance
50	Z_1 = 52 - j45	Z_1 = 1.040 - j0.900
51	Z_2 = 67.5 - j32.5	Z_2 = 1.350 - j0.650
52	Z_3 = 87 - j20	Z_3 = 1.740 - j0.400
53	Z_4 = 120 - j26	Z_4 = 2.400 - j0.052
54	Z_5 = 110 - j70	Z_5 = 2.200 - j1.400

Step 1. Enter the above normalized data on a normalized Smith chart as shown in Figure 6-2(a). This type of curve, where the high frequency end loops downward, is almost ideal for matching with a line transformer.

Step 2. Draw a SWR circle on the Smith chart with its radius passing through 1.5 on the R/Z_o axis. The objective is to move all of the impedance points within the circle.

Step 3. Since we are using a line transformer we must first determine the characteristic impedance Z_o' of the transformer. Draw an outer boundary circle that is tangent to the SWR circle and in such a way as to include all of the impedance points. The SWR and outer boundary circles are shown in Figure 6-2(a).

Step 4. Determine the line transformer characteristic impedance from the minimum and maximum of the boundary circle.

$$Z_o' = \sqrt{\text{Min x Max}}$$

where Min = 0.675 x 50 = 33.75 ohms
Max = 4.100 x 50 = 205 ohms

Substituting

$$Z_o' = \sqrt{33.75 \times 205} = 83 \text{ ohms}$$

Step 5. Normalize the impedance points and the SWR circle to the line transformer impedance, 83 ohms. Figure 6-2(b) illustrates the new normalized positions.

f_{mHz}	R x 50/83 jX x 50/83
50	Z_1 = 0.627 - j0.542
51	Z_2 = 0.813 - 0.392
52	Z_3 = 1.048 - j0.241
53	Z_4 = 1.446 - j0.313
54	Z_5 = 1.325 - j0.843
	SWR min. = 0.407
	SWR max. = 0.904

Step 6. The impedance points must now be rotated clockwise into the SWR circle. The 53 mHz frequency appears to be critical, therefore, this frequency will be used to establish the length of the line transformer. We only need to place this impedance point just within the circle. Draw a line through the 53 mHz point to the Wavelength Toward Generator scale. A wavelength of 0.288 is intercepted on the scale. To rotate the 53 mHz point just into the circle requires a rotation of 0.147 wavelength.

$$0.435\lambda - 0.288\lambda = 0.147\lambda$$

Step 7. Determine the extent of rotation required at other frequencies. Since the higher frequencies rotate a greater distance than the lower frequencies, the amount of rotation is determined as follows

$$\lambda_{f_x} = 0.147\lambda \times \frac{f_x}{f_{53}}$$

f_{mHz}	λ_{f_x}
50	0.139
51	0.141
52	0.144
53	0.147
54	0.150

Step 8. Rotate each impedance point the specified amount of rotation as indicated in the following table.

f_{mHz}	Wavelength to load	+	Rotation	=	New Position	
50	0.398		0.139		0.537	(0.037)
51	0.393		0.141		0.534	(0.034)
52	0.349		0.144		0.493	
53	0.288		0.147		0.435	
54	0.319		0.150		0.469	

Step 9. Convert the impedance points of Figure 6-2(b) to their normalized impedance relative to 50 ohms as shown in Figure 6-2(c).

f_{mHz}	Normalized 83 ohms	Normalized 50 ohms
50	$Z_{11} = 0.480 + j0.180$	$Z_{11} = 0.797 + j0.299$
51	$Z_{22} = 0.650 + j0.130$	$Z_{22} = 1.079 + j0.216$
52	$Z_{33} = 0.790 - j0.040$	$Z_{33} = 1.311 - j0.066$
53	$Z_{44} = 0.690 - j0.250$	$Z_{44} = 1.145 - j0.515$
54	$Z_{55} = 0.480 - j0.145$	$Z_{55} = 0.797 - j0.241$

Summary. It has been demonstrated that a line transformer is an effective impedance matching device. The impedance points of this example Z_{11}, Z_{44} and Z_{55} are critical. It does not appear that any adjustment can be made to the line transformer to improve the final impedance matching.

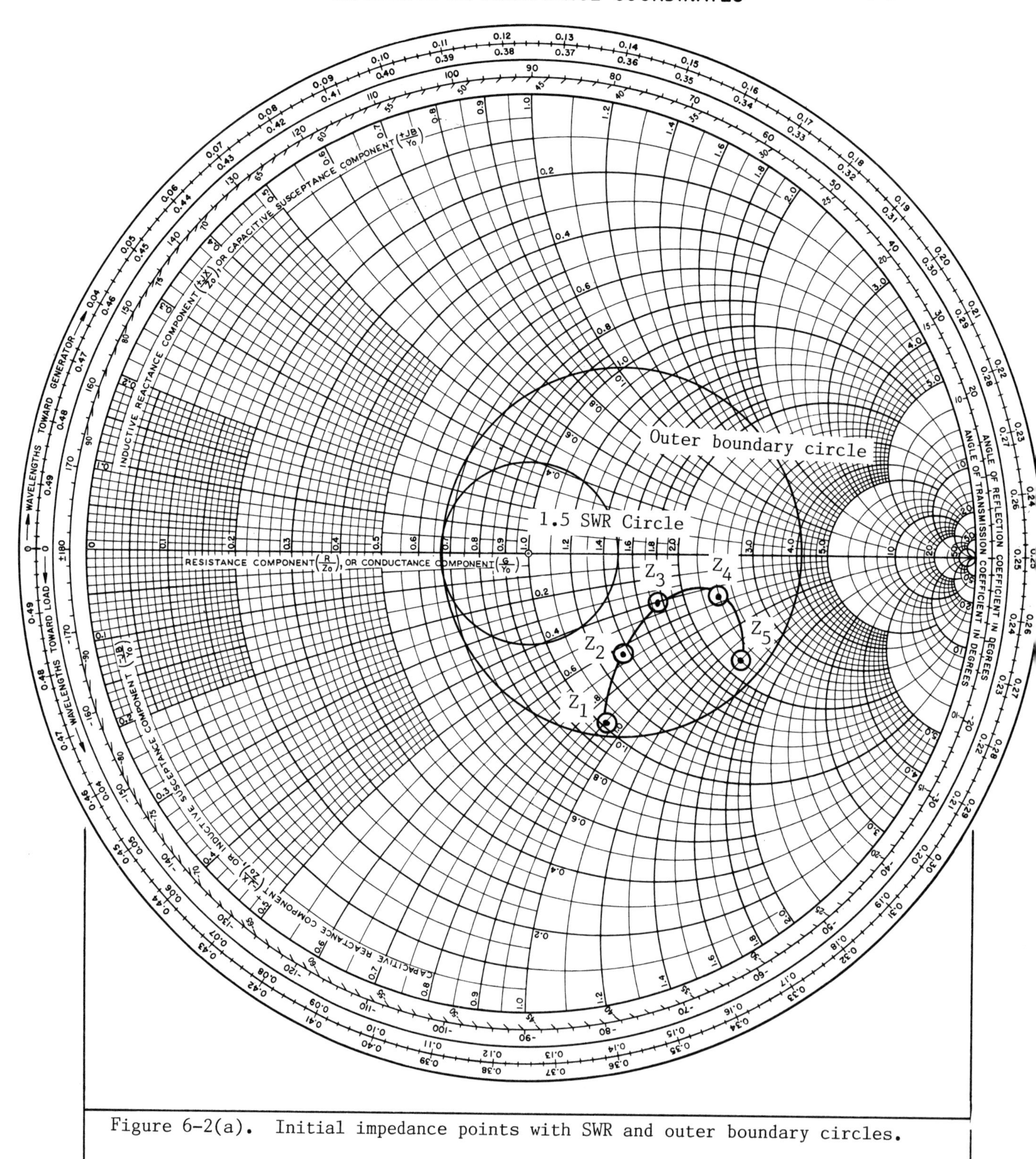

Figure 6-2(a). Initial impedance points with SWR and outer boundary circles.

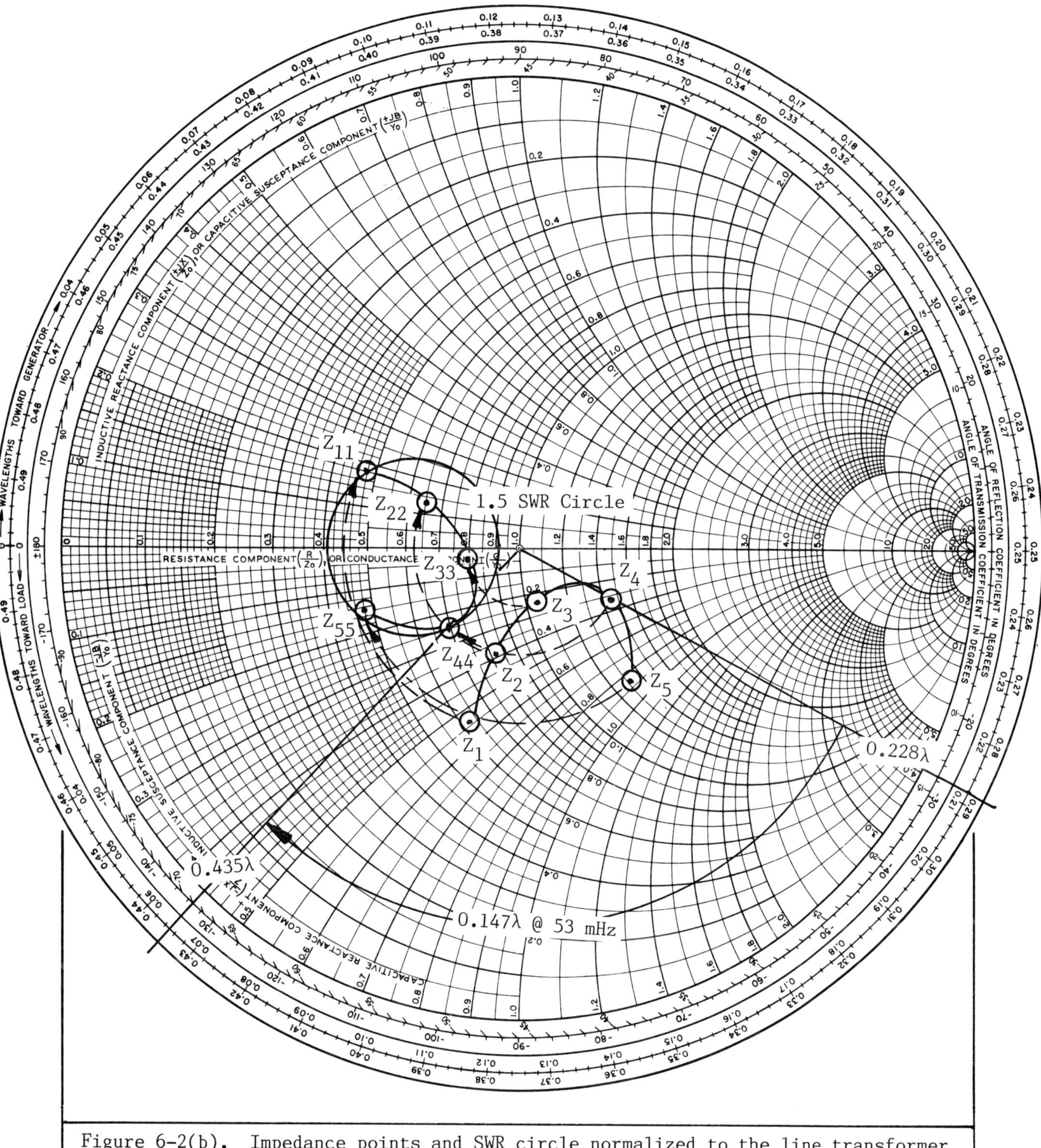

Figure 6-2(b). Impedance points and SWR circle normalized to the line transformer impedance of 83 ohms and rotated into the circle.

IMPEDANCE OR ADMITTANCE COORDINATES

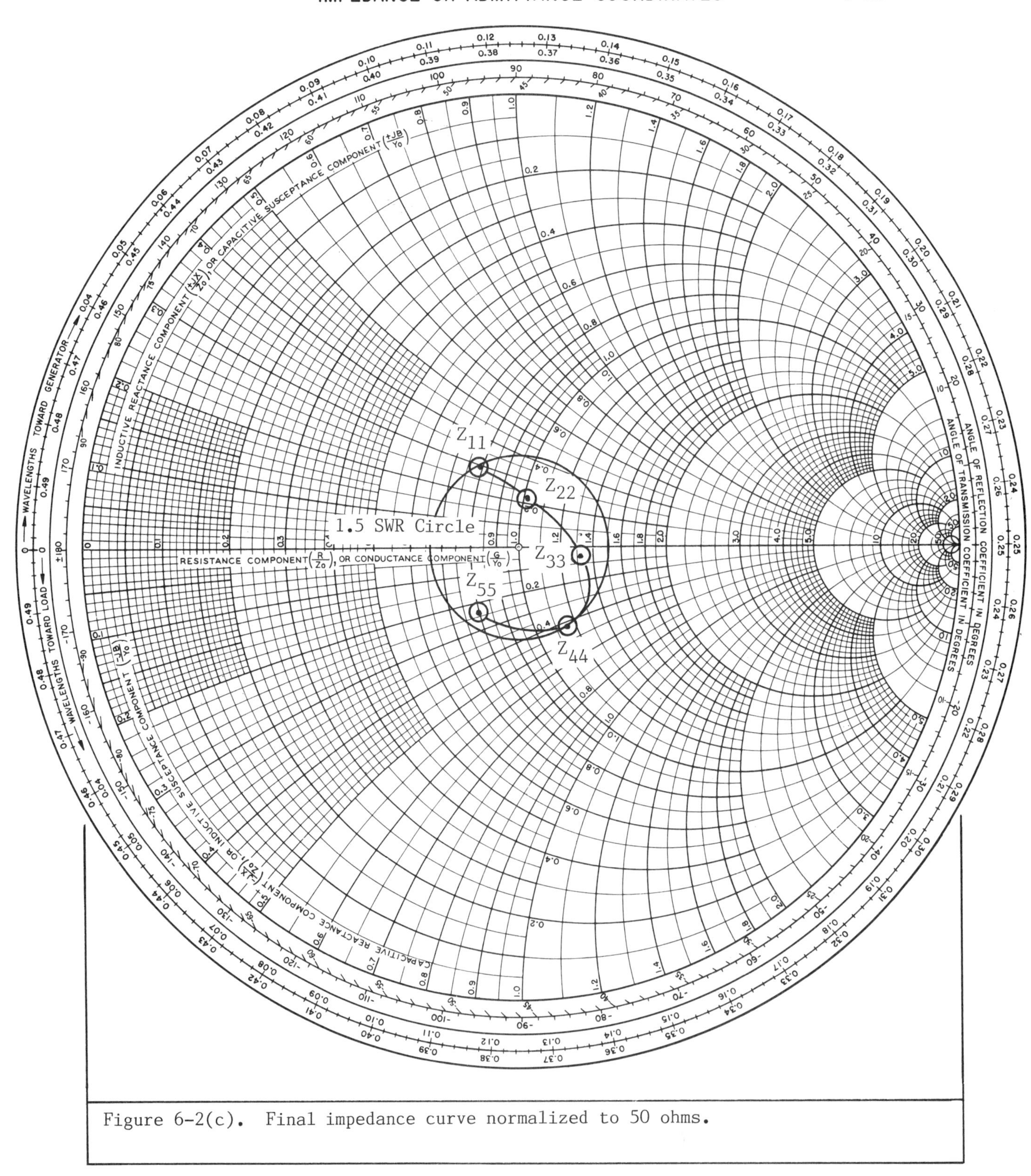

Figure 6-2(c). Final impedance curve normalized to 50 ohms.

Example No. 3. Problem: A half-wave dipole antenna operating on 80 meters and constructed of #14 wire has the following impedance. Match this impedance to a SWR of 2 to 1 or better.

f_{mHz}	Impedance	Normalized Impedance
3.5	Z_1 = 60.0 - j115	Z_1 = 1.20 - j2.30
3.6	Z_2 = 65.0 - j52.5	Z_2 = 1.3 - j1.05
3.7	Z_3 = 67.5 - j10.0	Z_3 = 1.35 - j0.20
3.8	Z_4 = 70.0 + j35.0	Z_4 = 1.40 + j0.70
3.9	Z_5 = 72.5 + j85.0	Z_5 = 1.45 + j1.70
4.0	Z_6 = 75.0 + j150	Z_6 = 1.50 + j3.00

Step 1. Enter the normalized impedance data on a normalized Smith chart as shown in Figure 6-3(a).

Step 2. Invert the normalized impedance to its admittance position (see Fig. 6-3(a)).

Step 3. An analysis of the admittance curve indicates that a resonant short-circuited shunt stub will close up the admittance curve. An initial try using a 50-ohm stub proved to be inadequate; a 25-ohm stub is favored. Determine the susceptance of a resonant stub 90 degrees long at 3.75 mHz.

f_{mHz}	θ	$\tan\theta$	$25\tan\theta$	$25\tan\theta/50$	Susceptance
3.5	84°	9.51	238 ohms	+4.8	-0.21
3.6	86.4^o	15.89	397 ohms	+8.0	-0.16
3.7	88.8^o	47.74	1194 ohms	+24.0	-0.04
3.75	90°	∞	∞	∞	0
3.8	91.2^o	-47.74	-1194 ohms	-24.0	+0.04
3.9	93.6^o	-15.89	-397 ohms	-8.0	+0.16
4.0	96.0^o	-9.51	-238 ohms	-4.8	+0.21

Step 4. Add above susceptance to admittance curve and plot new admittance position (see Fig. 6-3(b)).

f_{mHz}	Old Position	+	Correction	=	New Position
3.5	$Y_1 = 0.180 + j0.342$		(-0.21)		$Y_{11} = 0.180 + j0.132$
3.6	$Y_2 = 0.450 + j0.380$		(-0.16)		$Y_{22} = 0.450 + j0.220$
3.7	$Y_3 = 0.750 + j0.125$		(-0.04)		$Y_{33} = 0.750 + j0.085$
3.8	$Y_4 = 0.575 - j0.270$		+0.04		$Y_{44} = 0.575 - j0.230$
3.9	$Y_5 = 0.280 - j0.340$		+0.16		$Y_{55} = 0.280 - j0.180$
4.0	$Y_6 = 0.140 - j0.270$		+0.21		$Y_{66} = 0.140 - j0.06$

Step 5. Invert the new admittance curve into its equivalent impedance curve (see Fig. 6-3(b)).

Step 6. Draw a circle around the impedance curve with the curve centered within the circle while making the circle as small as possible. The curve shown in Figure 6-3(b) is centered on the R/Z_o axis = 2.7. The average resistance of the impedance curve is 2.7 x 50 = 135 ohms.

Step 7. A two-section line transformer will be used to match the 135-ohm average resistance to 50 ohms. Determine the impedances of a two-section line transformer as follows:

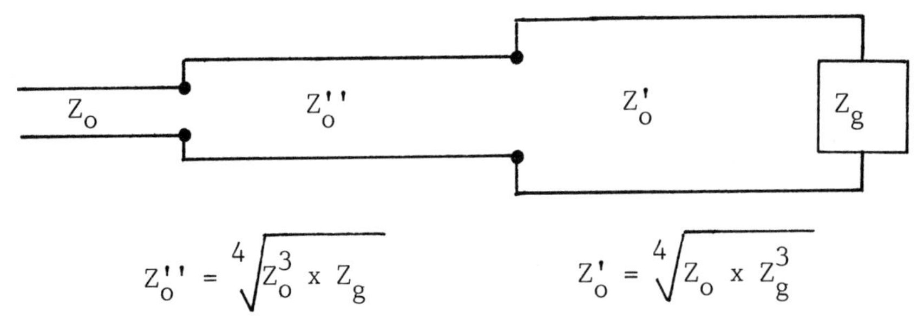

$$Z_o'' = \sqrt[4]{Z_o^3 \times Z_g} \qquad Z_o' = \sqrt[4]{Z_o \times Z_g^3}$$

where Z_o = 50 ohms and Z_g = 135 ohms

Substitution

$$Z_o'' = \sqrt[4]{50^3 \times 135} \qquad Z_o' = \sqrt[4]{50 \times 135^3}$$

$$= 64 \text{ ohms} \qquad = 105 \text{ ohms}$$

Step 8. Normalize the impedance curve of Figure 6-3(b) to 105 ohms and enter on the Smith chart (see Fig. 6-3(c)).

f_{mHz}	R50/105	jX50/105
3.5	Z_{11} = 1.714	-j1.238
3.6	Z_{22} = 0.857	-j0.405
3.7	Z_{33} = 0.657	-j0.071
3.8	Z_{44} = 0.714	+0.286
3.9	Z_{55} = 1.190	+j0.714
4.0	Z_{66} = 2.905	+j1.190

Step 9. The length of the first transformer is one-quarter wavelength long at the resonant frequency (about 3.725 mHz). Determine its length at other frequencies from

$$\lambda_{f_x} = 0.250\lambda \times \frac{f_x}{3.725}$$

f_{mHz}	λ_{f_x}
3.5	0.235
3.6	0.242
3.7	0.248
3.725	0.250
3.8	0.255
3.9	0.262
4.0	0.268

Step 10. Starting at 3.5 mHz, determine the new Wavelength Toward Generator position by drawing a straight line from the center of the chart, through the 3.5 mHz impedance point, to the Wavelength Toward Generator scale. The line intercepts 0.298 wavelength on the scale. Determine the amount of clockwise rotation from

$$0.298\lambda + \lambda_{f_x} = 0.298\lambda + 0.235\lambda = 0.533\ (0.033)$$

Repeat for all other frequencies.

f_{mHz}	Old λ	λ_{f_x}	New λ
3.5	0.298	0.235	0.533(0.033)
3.6	0.382	0.242	0.624(0.124)
3.7	0.480	0.248	0.728(0.228)
3.8	0.072	0.255	0.327
3.9	0.170	0.262	0.432
4.0	0.229	0.268	0.497

Step 11. Plot the new rotated impedance points on the Smith chart (see Fig. 6-3(c)).

Step 12. The rotated impedance points of Figure 6-3(c) must now be matched to 50 ohms with the 64-ohm line transformer. Normalize the rotated impedance points to 64 ohms and plot on the Smith chart (see Fig. 6-3(d)).

f_{mHz}	R105/64	jX105/64
3.5	Z_{11} = 0.574	+j0.312
3.6	Z_{22} = 1.477	+j0.719
3.7	Z_{33} = 2.543	+j0.295
3.8	Z_{44} = 1.969	-j0.788
3.9	Z_{55} = 0.952	-j0.509
4.0	Z_{66} = 0.484	-j0.033

Step 13. The second line transformer length is 0.250 wavelength at 3.725 mHz. Determine its length at the other frequencies. This is a repeat of Step 9.

Step 14. Starting at 3.5 mHz, determine the new Wavelength Toward Generator position by drawing a straight line from the center of the chart, through the 3.5 mHz impedance point, to the Wavelength Toward Generator scale. The line intercepts the scale at 0.066 wavelength. Determine the amount of clockwise rotation from

$$0.066\lambda + \lambda_{f_x} = 0.066\lambda + 0.235\lambda = 0.301\lambda$$

Repeat for all other frequencies.

f_{mHz}	Old λ	$λf_x$	New λ
3.5	0.066	0.235	0.301
3.6	0.192	0.242	0.434
3.7	0.242	0.248	0.490
3.8	0.282	0.255	0.537(0.037)
3.9	0.362	0.262	0.624(0.124)
4.0	0.494	0.268	0.762(0.262)

Step 15. Normalize to 50 ohms and plot on the Smith chart. This is the final step (see Fig. 6-3(e)).

f_{mHz}	R64/50	jX64/50
3.5	2.000	-j0.858
3.6	0.730	-j0.410
3.7	0.499	-j0.064
3.8	0.563	+0.256
3.9	1.114	+j0.640
4.0	2.690	-j0.307

Summary. This has been a particularly difficult example. It took one shunt stub and two line transformers to arrive at the results shown in Figure 6-3(e). High Q wire antennas such as this one are difficult to match over their entire operational frequency bands. However, we have managed to place most of the impedance curve with a 2.0 to 1 SWR circle. It does not appear that any additional matching can improve the curve other than reducing the Q of the antenna by increasing the wire diameter thus reducing its length-to-diameter ratio.

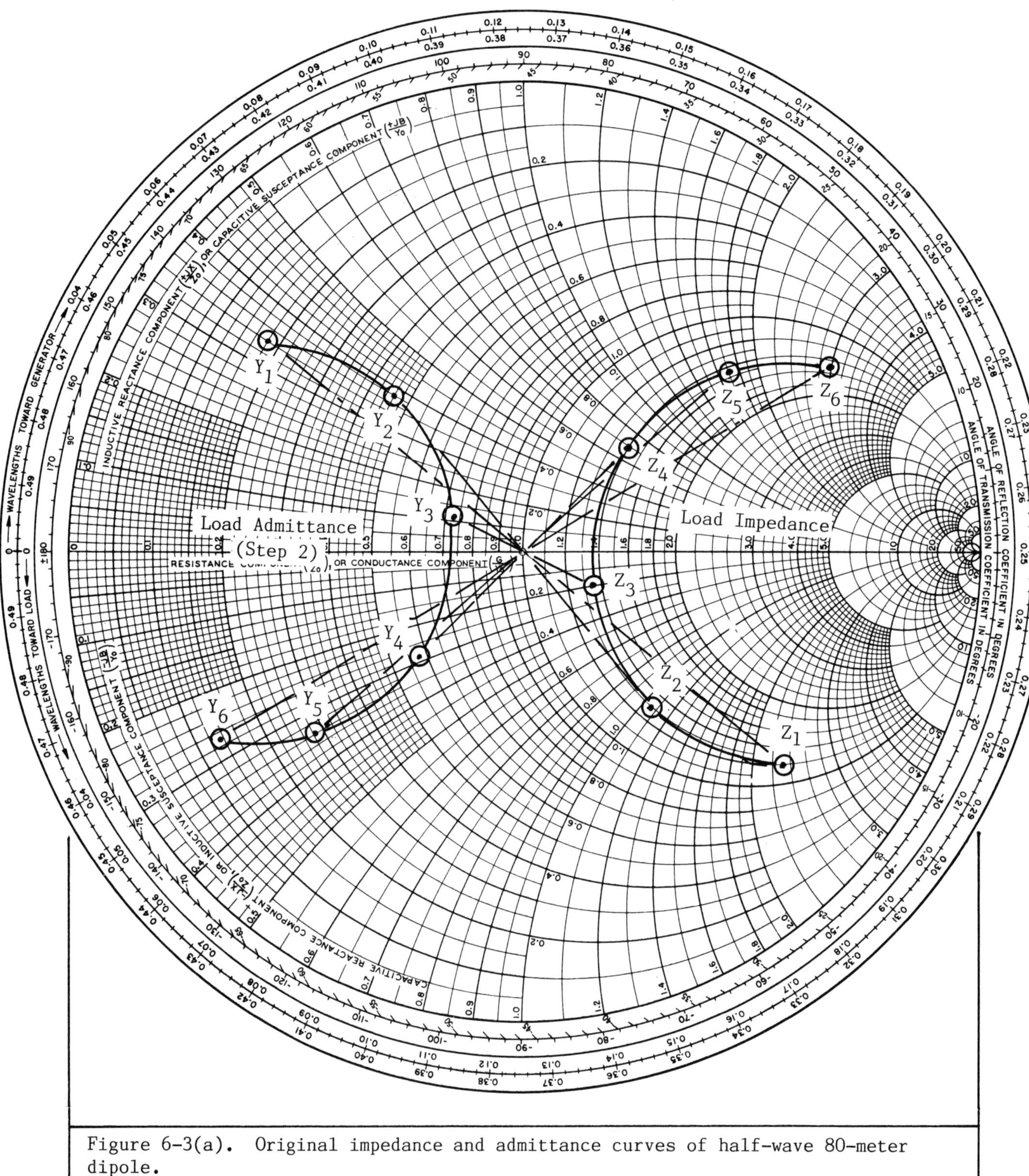

Figure 6-3(a). Original impedance and admittance curves of half-wave 80-meter dipole.

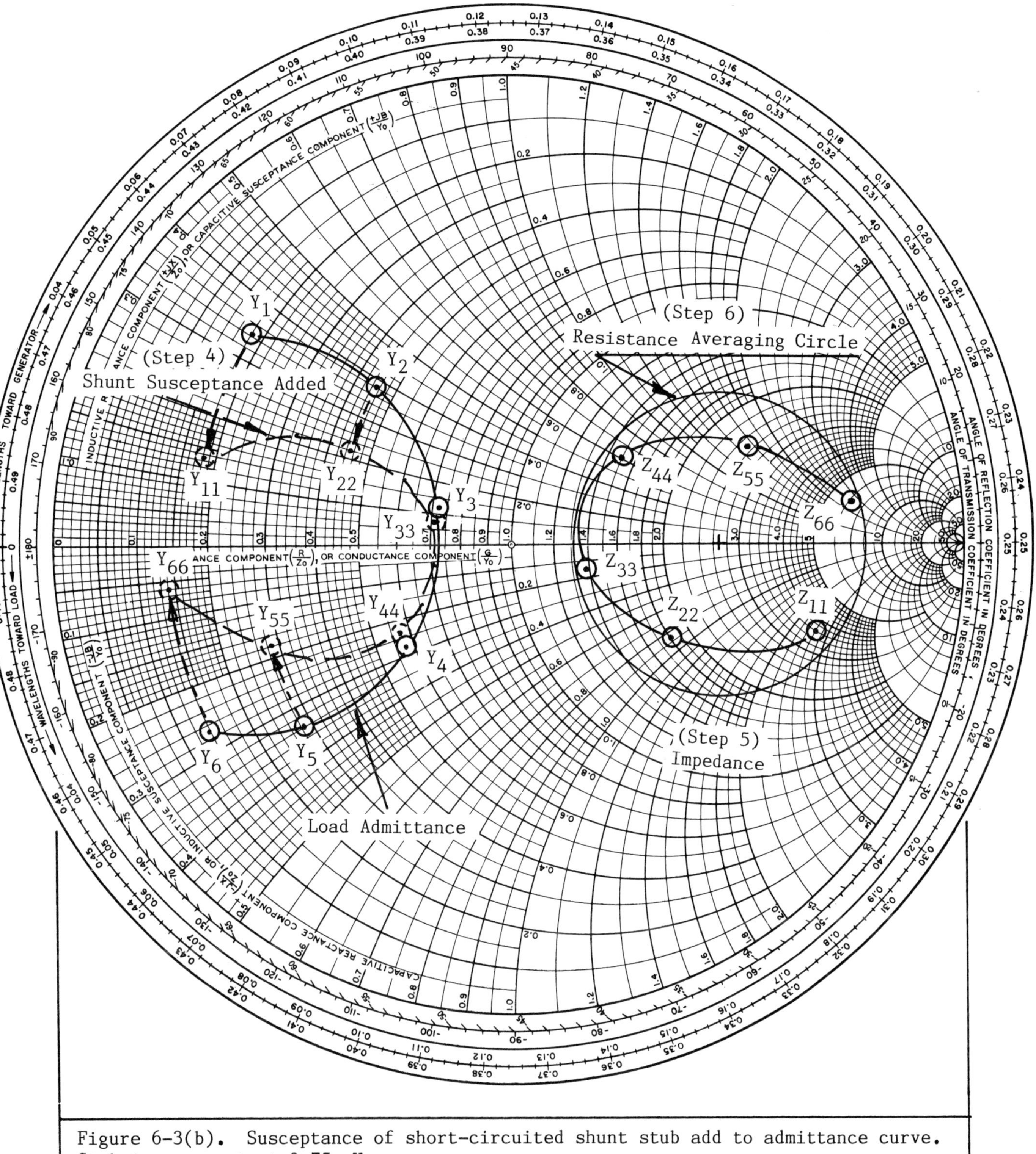

Figure 6-3(b). Susceptance of short-circuited shunt stub add to admittance curve. Stub is resonant at 3.75 mHz.

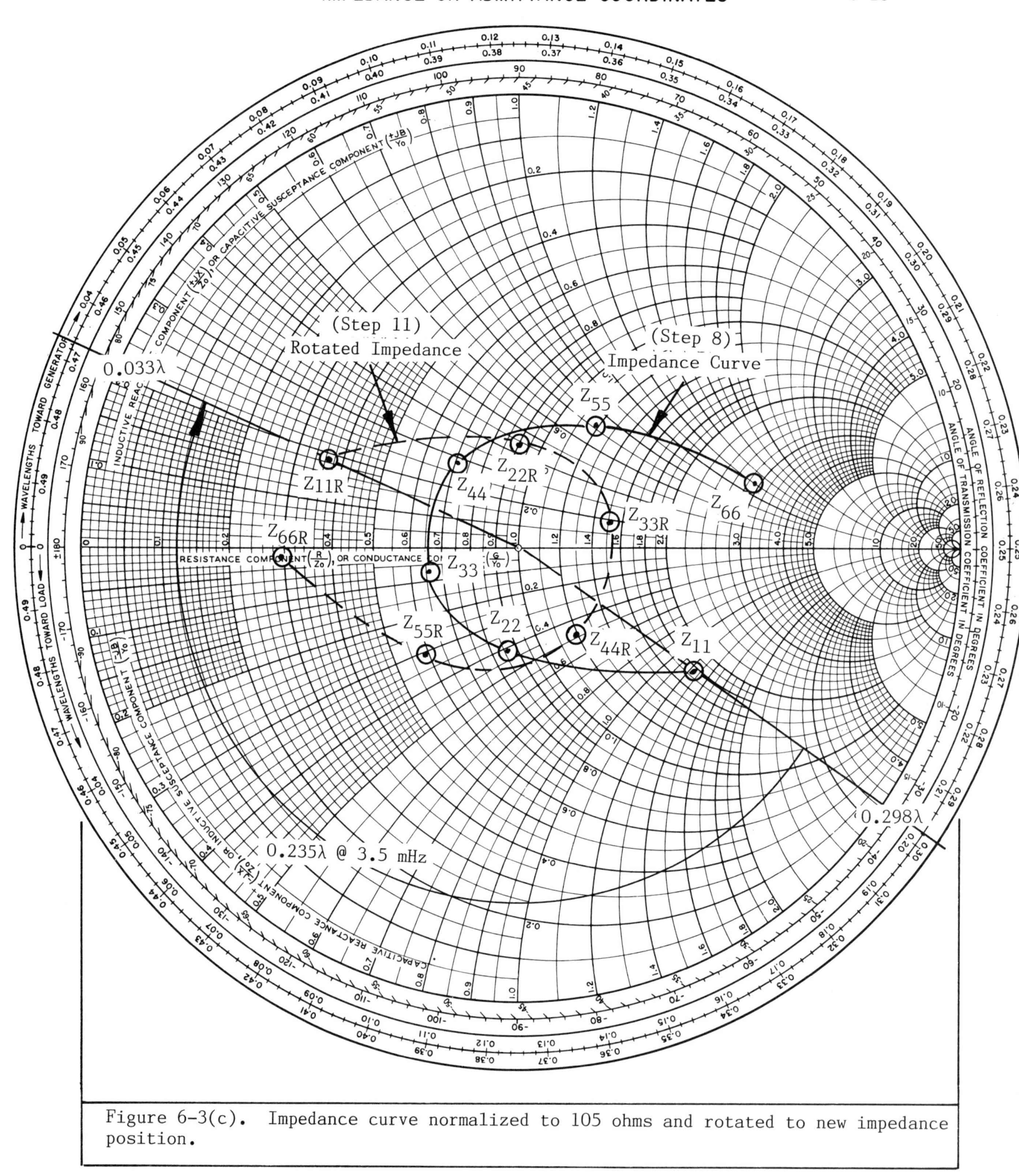

Figure 6-3(c). Impedance curve normalized to 105 ohms and rotated to new impedance position.

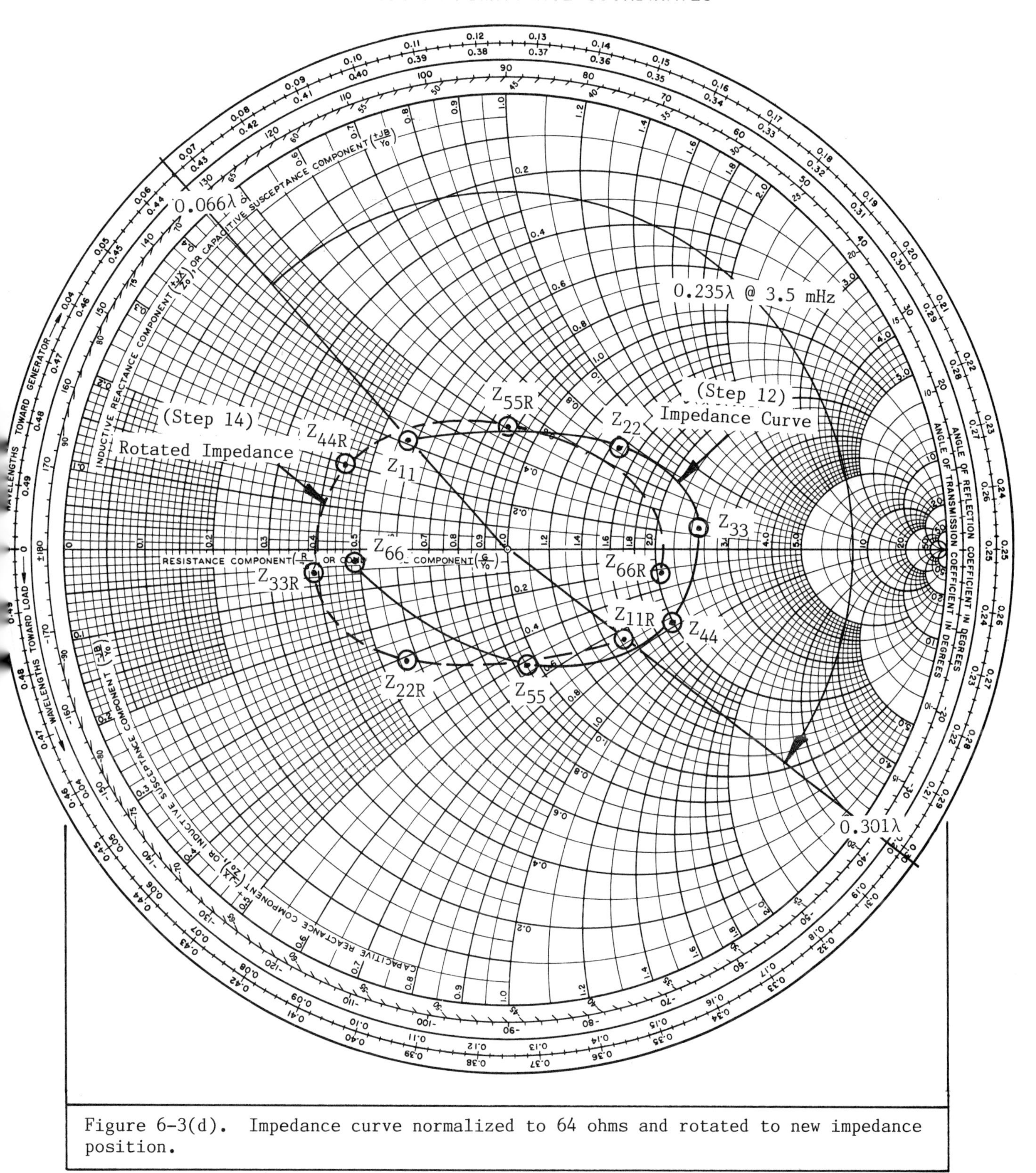

Figure 6-3(d). Impedance curve normalized to 64 ohms and rotated to new impedance position.

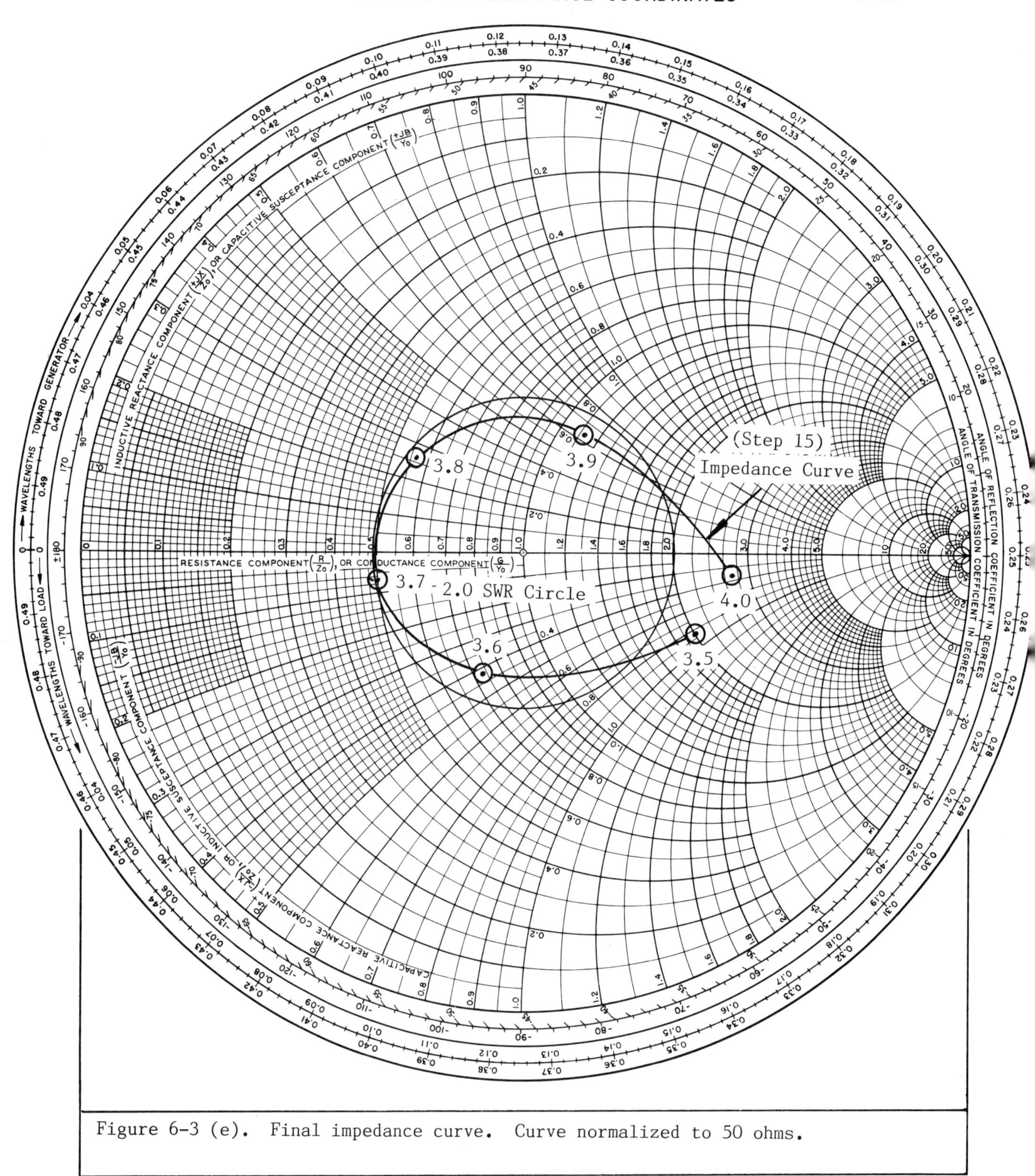

Figure 6-3 (e). Final impedance curve. Curve normalized to 50 ohms.

Example 4. Problem: A vertical 80-meter colinear antenna consisting of a one quarter wavelength section and a half wavelength section exhibits a horrible impedance. What is the best match that can be realized between 3.5 and 4.0 mHz?

f_{mHz}	Impedance	Normalized Impedance
3.5	Z_1 = 9.500 + j 94.450	Z_1 = 0.190 + j1.889
3.6	Z_2 = 9.750 + j97.550	Z_2 = 0.195 + j1.951
3.7	Z_3 = 10.00 + j101.25	Z_3 = 0.200 + j2.025
3.8	Z_4 = 10.50 + j103.05	Z_4 = 0.210 + j2.061
3.9	Z_5 = 11.00 + j108.50	Z_5 = 0.220 + j2.170
4.0	Z_6 = 12.00 + j115.00	Z_6 = 0.240 + j2.300

Step 1. Enter the impedance data on a normalized Smith chart (see Fig. 6-4(a)). Draw a 2.0 to 1 SWR circle. Draw a boundary circle tangent to the SWR circle. The first move will be to rotate the impedance curve to the left along lines of constant resistance with a series capacitor. The purpose of this move is to place the center frequency (3.750 mHz) on the boundary circle.

Step 2. Determine the amount of reactance required to place the center frequency on the boundary circle. The reactance required is 1.445 chartohms (see Fig. 6-4(a)). Compute for the reactance required at the other frequencies f_x from

$$X_{f_x} = 1.445 \times \frac{3.750}{f_x}$$

f_{mHz}	X_{f_x}
3.5	-1.548
3.6	-1.505
3.7	-1.465
3.75	-1.445
3.8	-1.426
3.9	-1.389
4.0	-1.355

Step 3. Add the series capacitive reactance to the load impedance and plot its new position (see Fig. 6-4(a)).

f_{mHz}	Old Position	+	Correction	=	New Position
3.5	Z_1 = 0.190 + j1.889		(-1.548)		Z_{11} = 0.190 + j0.341
3.6	Z_2 = 0.195 + j1.951		(-1.505)		Z_{22} = 0.195 + j0.446
3.7	Z_3 = 0.200 + j2.025		(-1.465)		Z_{33} = 0.200 + j0.560
3.8	Z_4 = 0.210 + j2.061		(-1.426)		Z_44 = 0.210 + j0.635
3.9	Z_5 = 0.220 + j2.170		(-1.389)		Z_{55} = 0.220 + j0.781
4.0	Z_6 = 0.240 + j2.300		(-1.355)		Z_{66} = 0.240 + j0.945

Step 4. Invert the impedance curve to its admittance equivalence in preparation for the next move (see Fig. 6-4(a)). Determine the amount of shunt capacitive susceptance required to move the center frequency to the G/Y_o axis. The amount of susceptance required is 1.500 chartmhos (see Fig. 6-4(b)). Compute the amount of susceptance required at the other frequencies f_x from

$$B_{f_x} = 1.500 \times \frac{f_x}{3.750}$$

f_{mHz}	B_{f_x}
3.5	1.400
3.6	1.440
3.7	1.480
3.75	1.500
3.8	1.520
3.9	1.560
4.0	1.600

Step 5. Determine the new admittance position and plot on the Smith chart (see Fig. 6-4(b)).

f_{mHz}	Old Position	+	Correction	=	New Position
3.5	Y_{11} = 1.250 - j2.200		+1.400		Y_{111} = 1.250 - j0.800
3.6	Y_{22} = 0.810 - j1.840		+1.440		Y_{222} = 0.810 - j0.400
3.7	Y_{33} = 0.580 - j1.580		+1.480		Y_{333} = 0.580 - j0.100
3.8	Y_{44} = 0.450 - j1.410		+1.520		Y_{444} = 0.450 + j0.110
3.9	Y_{55} = 0.320 - j1.190		+1.560		Y_{555} = 0.320 + j0.370
4.0	Y_{66} = 0.240 - j1.010		+1.600		Y_{666} = 0.240 + j0.590

Step 6. Invert the new admittance position to its equivalent impedance position (see Fig. 6-4(b)). What we now have is an impedance curve that is amenable to being folded into a 2.0 SWR circle. The Z_{444} (3.8 mHz) point is on the R = 2.10 constant resistance line and cannot be matched into the 2.0 SWR circle.

Step 7. An examination of the impedance curve of Figure 6-4(b) shows that an addition of about -0.35 chartohm at 3.5 mHz and about +1.500 chartohms at 4.0 mHz are needed. The task is to select the proper series resonant circuit that will provide the necessary reactance above and below resonance. Unfortunately, there are countless combinations of L-C ratios that can be resonated at a particular frequency, most of which will not satisfy the matching requirements.

As a rough approximation, the following equation can be used to determine the value of inductor required for the series resonant L-C circuit:

$$L = \frac{X_x}{2\pi}\left[\frac{f_x}{f_x^2 - f_r^2}\right]$$

where L = inductance required in μH

X_x = inductance required at f_x

f_x = other frequency

f_r = resonant frequency of L-C circuit

Substituting X_x = 1.5 x 50 = 75 ohms

f_x = 4.0 mHz

f_r = 3.60 mHz*

* Resonating the series L-C circuit at 3.6 mHz (Z_{222}) will prevent that impedance point from moving. Point Z_{111} will move towards the left because it is below resonance and all other points will move toward the right with the largest move with point Z_{666}.

Solving

$$L = \frac{75}{6.28}\left[\frac{4.0}{4.0^2 - 3.6^2}\right]$$

$$= 11.94\ (1.3158) = 15.71\ \mu H$$

At resonance $X_L = X_C$, therefore

$$X_L = 6.28 \times 3.6 \times 15.71 = 355 \text{ ohms}$$

and

$$C = 1/6.28 \times 3.6 \times 355 = 125 \text{ pF}$$

To obtain the reactance at 3.5 mHz

$$X_L = 6.28 \times 3.5 \times 15.71 = 345.3 \text{ ohms}$$

$$X_C = 1/6.28 \times 3.5 \times 125 = 364 \text{ ohms}$$

$$X_{total} = 345.3 - 364 = -18.7 \text{ ohms} = -0.374 \text{ chartohm}$$

It appears that -0.374 chartohm will move the 3.5 mHz point well into the SWR circle. Let us now look at the 4.0 mHz point

$$X_L = 6.28 \times 4.0 \times 15.71 = 394.6 \text{ ohms}$$

$$X_C = 1/6.28 \times 4.0 \times 125 = 318.5 \text{ ohms}$$

$$X_{total} = 394.6 - 318.5 = +86.1 \text{ ohms} = +1.722 \text{ chartohms}$$

It appears that +1.722 chartohms will move the 4.0 mHz (Z_{666}) point well into the SWR circle. Compute for other frequencies in a like manner

f_{mHz}	X_L	-	X_C	=	Ohms	Chartohms
3.5	285.7		302.3		-16.6	-0.332
3.6	Resonance				0	0
3.7	365		344.3		+20.7	+0.414*
3.8	Not computed					
3.9	Not computed					
4.0	394.6		318.5		+86.1	+1.722

* The 3.7 mHz point is in trouble because the 0.414 chartohm, when added to 0.500 chartohm, puts the 3.7 mHz point outside the circle. Try again with a smaller inductor, i.e., 13.0 μH.

$$X_{L_{3.6}} = 6.28 \times 3.6 \times 13.0 = 293.9 \text{ ohms}$$

$$C = 1/6.28 \times 3.6 \times 293.9 = 150.5 \text{ pF}$$

f_{mHz}	X_L	-	X_c	=	Ohms	Chartohms
3.5	285.7		302.3		-16.6	-0.332
3.6		Resonance			0	0
3.7	302.1		286		+16.1	+0.322
3.8	310.2		278.4		+31.8	+0.636
3.9	318.4		271.3		+47.1	+0.942
4.0	326.6		264.5		+62.1	+1.242

Step 8. Add the reactance obtained in Step 7 to the impedance curve of Figure 6-4(b).

f_{mHz}	Old Position	+	Correction	=	New Position
3.5	Z_{111} = 0.550 + j0.350		(-0.332)		0.550 + j 0.018
3.6	Z_{222} = 0.975 + j0.480		0		0.975 + j0.480
3.7	Z_{333} = 1.500 + j0.500		+0.322		1.500 + j0.822
3.8	Z_{444} = 2.100 - j0.500		+0.636		2.100 + j0.136
3.9	Z_{555} = 1.350 - j1.550		+0.942		1.350 - j0.608
4.0	Z_{666} = 0.600 - j1.460		+1.242		0.600 - j0.218

Plot the new impedance position on a Smith chart (see Fig. 6-4(c)).

Summary. The 3.7 mHz point proved to be the critical point. Perhaps a resonance at 3.65 mHz instead of 3.600 mHz would limit the travel of the 3.7 mHz point. In any event, we have done quite well matching the entire 80-meter band into a SWR circle of 2.2 to 1. The matching arrangement is illustrated below.

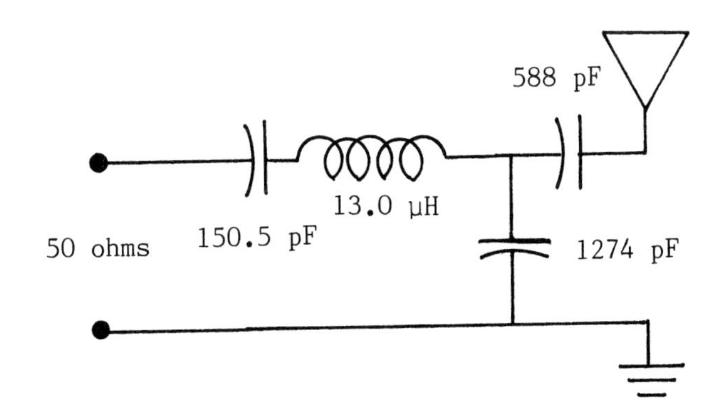

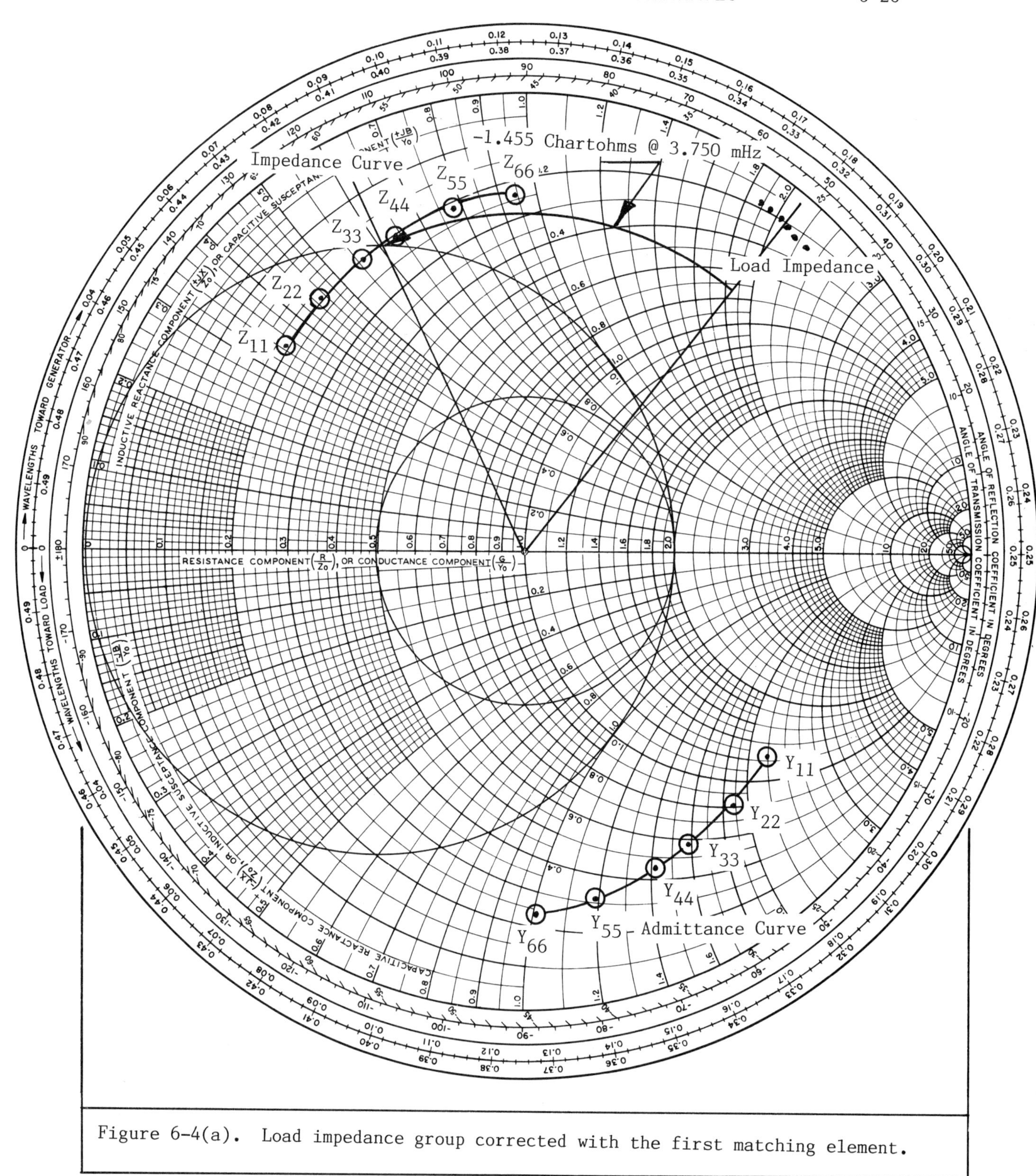

Figure 6-4(a). Load impedance group corrected with the first matching element.

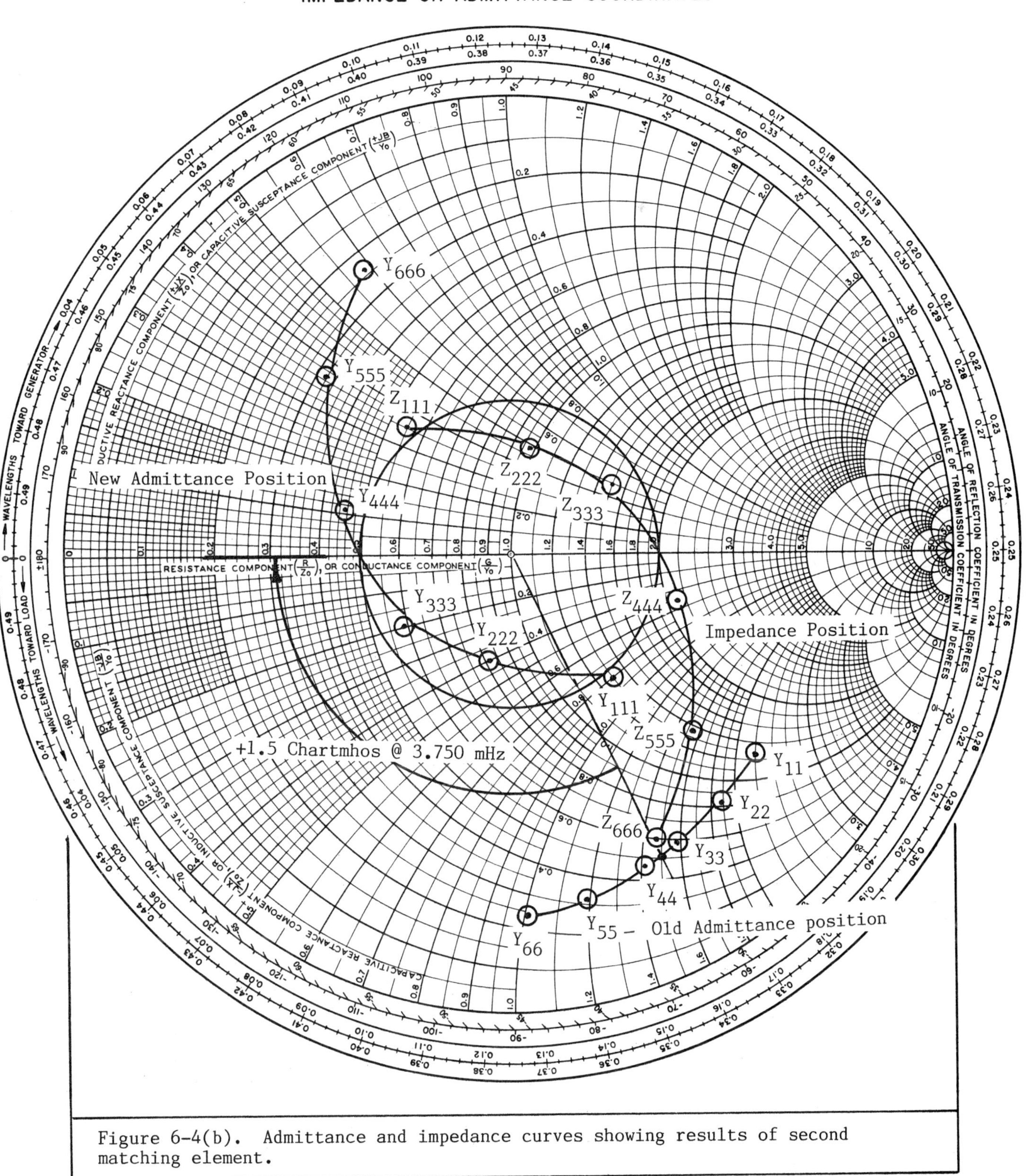

Figure 6-4(b). Admittance and impedance curves showing results of second matching element.

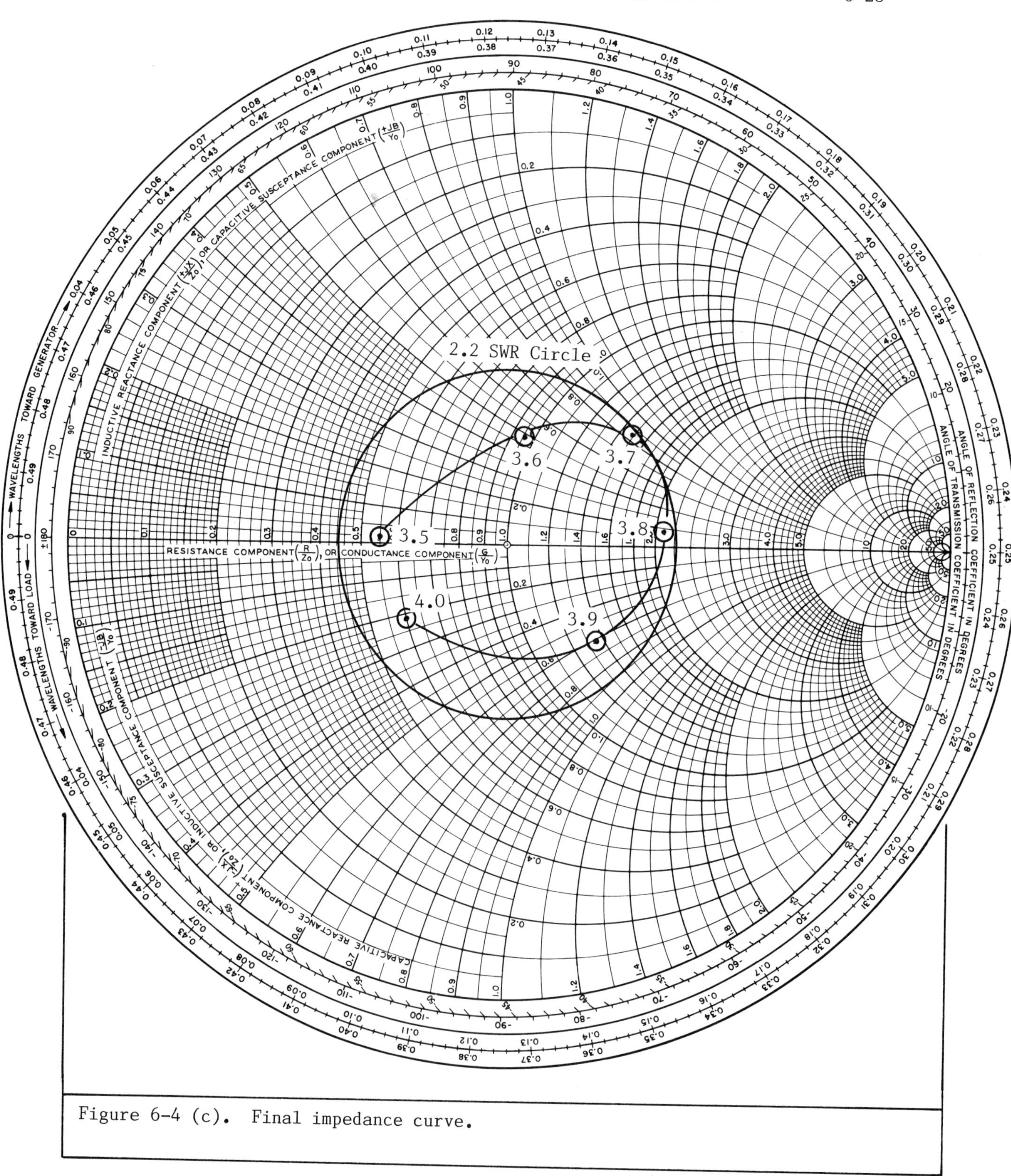

Figure 6-4 (c). Final impedance curve.

Example 5. Problem: A short vertical antenna operating in the 10-meter band has the following impedance. Match this impedance to a SWR of 2.0 to 1 or better.

f_{mHz}	Impedance	Normalized Impedance
28	$Z_1 = 20 - j120$	$Z_1 = 0.400 - j2.400$
29	$Z_2 = 20 - j110$	$Z_1 = 0.40 - j2.200$
30	$Z_3 = 20 - j100$	$Z_3 = 0.400 - j2.000$

Step 1. Plot the normalized impedance on a normalized Smith chart. Draw a SWR circle centered on the Smith chart and passing through 2.0 on the R/Z_o axis. Draw an inner and an outer boundary circle that are tangent to the SWR circle as shown in Figure 6-5(a). An examination of Figures 4-2 and 4-3 shows that the impedance curve is in region 4 and that (h) appears to be the best matching solution. The first move will be to rotate the impedance curve clockwise along lines of constant resistance with a series inductor. This will also cause the curve to become elongated because a series inductor will cause the high frequencies to move faster than the low frequencies.

Step 2. For our first move, the 29 mHz point will be placed on the X = -5.000 chartohm reactance line. A correction of +1.700 is required. To calculate the correction required at other frequencies f_x

$$X_x = +1.700 \times \frac{f_x}{29}$$

f_{mHz}	Old Position	+	Correction	=	New Position
28	$Z_1 = 0.400 - j2.400$		1.641		$Z_{11} = 0.400 - j0.759$
29	$Z_2 = 0.400 - j2.200$		1.700		$Z_{22} = 0.400 - j0.500$
30	$Z_3 = 0.400 - j2.000$		1.759		$Z_{33} = 0.400 - j0.241$

Enter the new impedance position on the Smith chart (see Fig. 6-5(a)). The curve is satisfactorily positioned between the two boundary circles. We can proceed with the next step, the shunt inductor. For shunt elements we must work with admittance.

Step 3. Invert the impedance curve into its equivalent admittance curve. Adding shunt admittance to the curve will cause it to rotate counterclockwise along lines of constant susceptance into the SWR circle.

Step 4. For our next move we are going to move the 29 mHz point to the +0.200 chartmho susceptance line. This requires a correction of -(+1.210 - 0.200) = -1.010 chartmhos. To determine the amount of correction at other frequencies

$$B_x = -1.010 \times \frac{29}{f_x}$$

f_{mHz}	Old Position	+	Correction	=	New Position
28	$Y_{11} = 0.550 + j1.040$		(-1.046)		$Y_{111} = 0.550 - j0.006$
29	$Y_{22} = 0.980 + j1.230$		(-1.010)		$Y_{222} = 0.980 + j0.220$
30	$Y_{33} = 1.800 + j1.150$		(-0.976)		$Y_{333} = 1.800 + j0.174$

Locate the new admittance positions on the Smith chart. The final admittance curve is within the SWR circle as desired. However, it appears that we can further improve the match with additional matching elements. We cannot do much with a vertically oriented curve such as that shown in Figure 6-5(a). If the curve is rotated to a horizontal position we can fold the ends in with a resonant circuit an achieve a much better match.

Figure 5. The final admittance curve of Figure 6-5(a) can be rotated with a short section of 50-ohm line. The first try will be to place the 29 mHz point on the G/Y_o axis. This will make 29 mHz the resonant frequency. Draw a straight line from the center of the Smith chart, through the 29 mHz point, to the Wavelength Toward Generator scale. A scale reading of 0.125 wavelength is obtained. To move the 29 mHz point to the G/Y_o axis (0.250λ on the WTG scale) requires a line length of 0.250λ - 0.125λ = 0.125λ. A section of line will cause the high frequencies to move faster than the low frequencies. To determine the line length at other frequencies

$$\lambda_x = 0.125\lambda \times \frac{f_x}{29}$$

f_{mHz}	λ_x
28	0.121
29	0.125
30	0.129

To determine the amount of rotation at all frequencies

f_{mHz}	Old λ	+	λ_x	=	New λ
28	0.496		0.121		0.617 (0.117)
29	0.125		0.125		0.250
30	0.239		0.129		0.368

Step 6. Without changing the radii of the admittance points, rotate them clockwise to their new positions as shown in Figure 6-5(b). The new admittance points, as a result of this rotation, are

f_{mHz}	Normalized Admittance
28	$Y_{111} = 0.820 + j0.525$
29	$Y_{222} = 1.250 + j0$
30	$Y_{333} = 0.890 - j0.570$

Step 7. It now remains to fold the ends of the curve inward. The frequencies below resonance have positive (+) susceptance whereas the frequencies above resonance have negative (-) susceptance. A short-circuited line, 90 degrees long (0.250λ) at 29 mHz is the choice. It will provide negative susceptance below resonance and positive susceptance above resonance. A very low impedance line is required. By paralleling four 25-ohm lines an impedance of 6.25 ohms can be obtained. (It was determined emperically that higher impedance lines did not provide sufficient shunt susceptance). To determine the reactance and susceptance

$$X = Z_o \tan \theta$$

and

$$B = \frac{1}{Z_o \tan \theta}$$

where Z_o = impedance of the stub line = 6.25 ohms

Since 90 degrees represents one-quarter wavelength at 29 mHz, the electrical length at other frequencies is

$$\theta^o_{f_x} = 90^o \frac{f_x}{29}$$

f_{mHz}	θ^o	$X = Z_o \tan \theta$	$B = 1/Z_o \tan \theta$	B/Y_o
28	86.90	115.4	-0.0087	-0.435
29	90.00	------	0	0
30	93.10	-115.4	+0.0087	+0.435

Step 8. The admittance obtained in Step 8 must now be added to the admittance curve of Figure 6-5(b).

f_{mHz}	Old Position	+	Correction	=	New Position
28	Y = 0.820 + j0.525		(-0.435)		Y = 0.820 + j0.09
29	Y = 1.250 + j0		0		Y = 1.250 + j0
30	Y = 0.890 - j0.570		+0.435		Y = 0.890 - j0.135

Step 9. It now remains to compute the values of the inductors and lengths of the series line and stub line. To determine the value of the series inductor

$$L = \frac{X_L}{2\pi f} \text{ henry}$$

where $X_L = 1.7 \times 50$ ohms (from Step 2)

$f = 29 \times 10^6$ Hz/sec

Substituting

$$L = \frac{85}{6.28 \times 29 \times 10^6} = 0.467 \times 10^{-6} \text{ henry}$$

or

$$L = 0.467\ \mu H$$

Step 10. Determine the value of the shunt inductor

$$L = \frac{1}{2\pi f\ B_L\ Y_o} \text{ henry}$$

where $B_L = 1.010$ (from Step 4)

$Y_o = 0.02$ mho

$f = 29 \times 10^6$ Hz/sec

Substituting

$$L = \frac{1}{6.28 \times 29 \times 10^6 \times 1.010 \times 0.02}$$

$$L = 0.272 \times 10^{-6} \text{ henry or } 0.272\ \mu H$$

Step 11. Determine the length of line required to rotate the admittance curve. From Step 5, the electrical length required is 0.125 wavelength at 29 mHz.

$$\lambda_{29} = \frac{\text{Velocity of Propagation}}{\text{Frequency}}$$

$$= \frac{300 \times 10^6 \text{ meters/sec}}{29 \times 10^6 \text{ Hz/sec}} = 10.34 \text{ meters}$$

Converting meters to feet

$$10.34 \times 3.281 = 33.94 \text{ feet}$$

RG-8 coaxial cable is considered for the series line. It has a velocity factor of 0.66. The physical length required is

$$33.94 \times 0.125 \times 0.66 = 2.8 \text{ feet}$$

Step 12. Determine the length of stub required. From Step 7, a stub length of 90 degrees (0.250λ) at 29 mHz is required.

$$\lambda_{29} = 33.94 \text{ feet} \times 0.250 = 8.49 \text{ feet}$$

The 25-ohm RG-73 coaxial cable which is used as the shunt cable has a velocity factor of 0.655. The physical length required is

$$8.49 \times 0.655 = 5.56 \text{ feet}$$

The illustration shown below shows the arrangement of the matching elements used in this example.

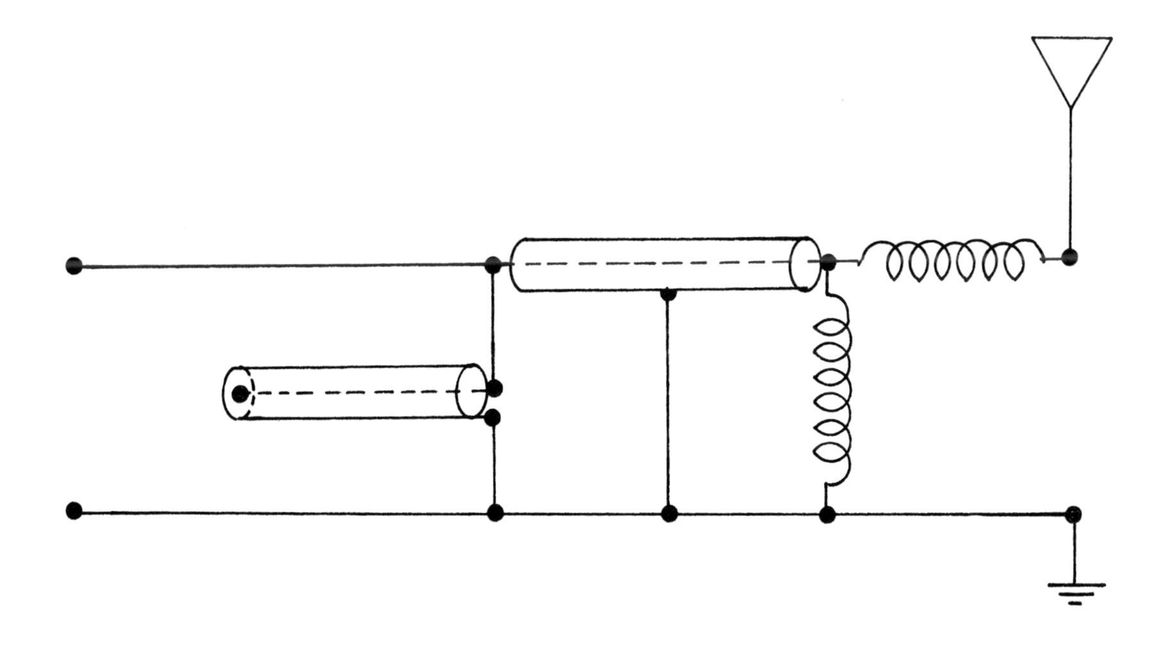

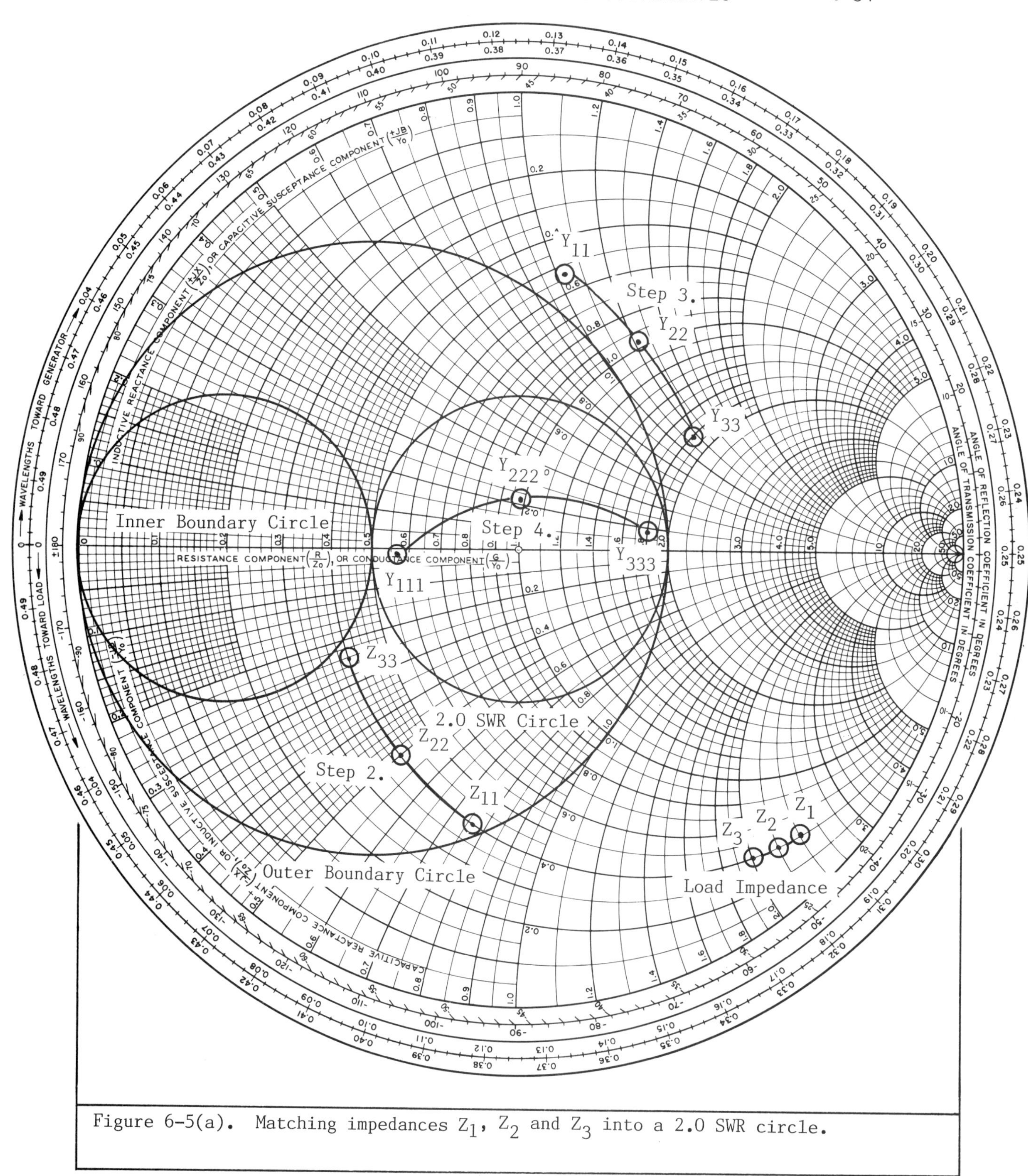

Figure 6-5(a). Matching impedances Z_1, Z_2 and Z_3 into a 2.0 SWR circle.

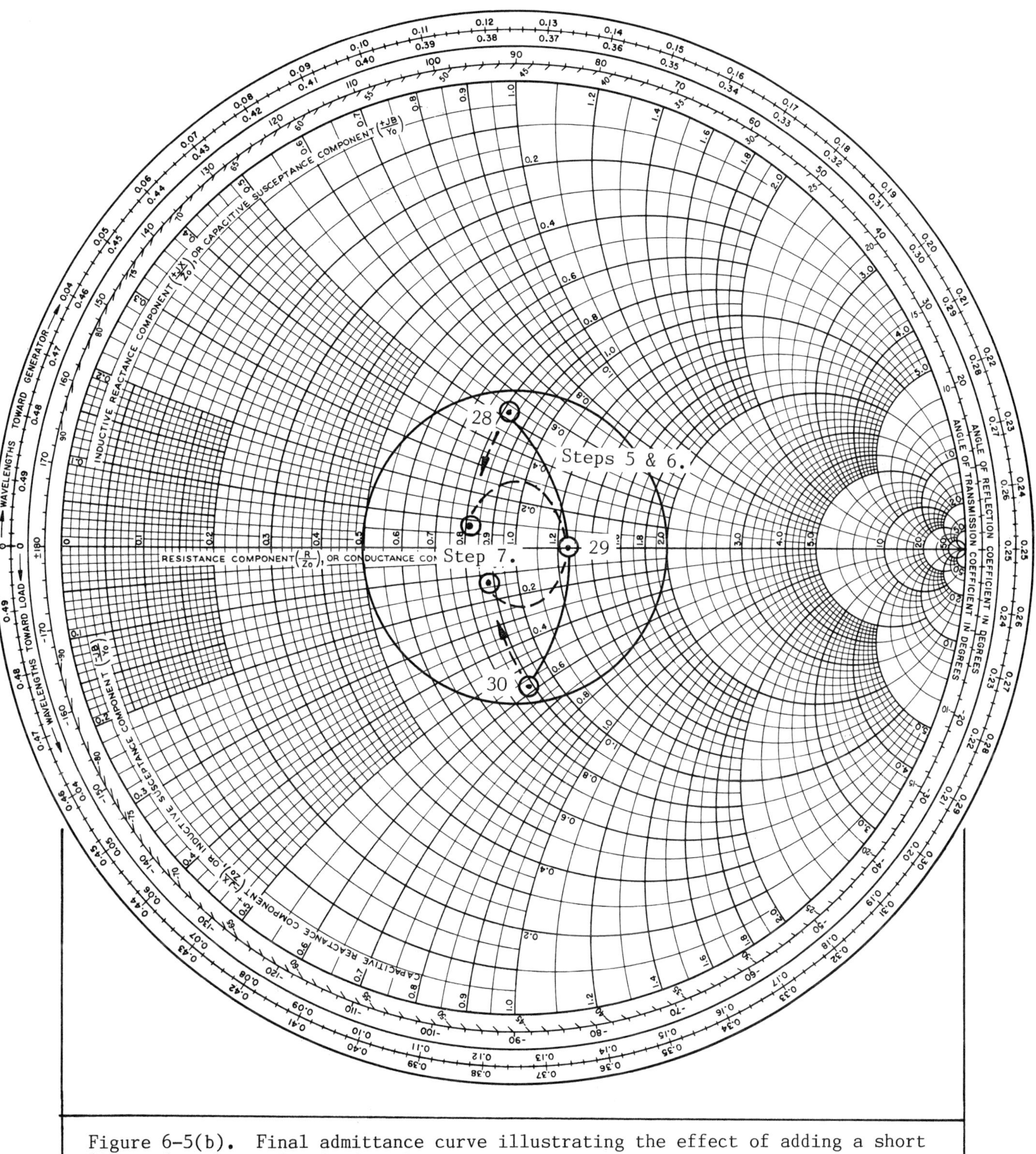

Figure 6-5(b). Final admittance curve illustrating the effect of adding a short line and a short-circuited stub.

Broadband Matching.

Example 6. Problem: A broadband dipole has the following impedance. Match this impedance to a SWR of 3.0 to 1 or better.

f_{mHz}	Impedance	Normalized Impedance
2.0	Z = 92.0 - j90.0	Z = 1.840 - j1.800
2.5	Z = 75.5 - j19.0	Z = 1.510 - j0.380
3.0	Z = 67.0 + j24.0	Z = 1.340 + j0.480
3.5	Z = 82.0 + j62.5	Z = 1.640 + j1.250
4.0	Z = 137.5 + j57.5	Z = 2.750 + j1.150
4.5	Z = 82.5 + j47.5	Z = 1.650 + j0.950
5.0	Z = 77.0 + j92.5	Z = 1.540 + j1.850
5.5	Z = 170.0 + j105	Z = 3.400 + j2.100
6.0	Z = 115.0 - j25.0	Z = 2.300 - j0.500

Step 1. Enter the normalized impedance coordinates on a Smith chart as shown in Figure 6-6(a). Draw a SWR circle centered on the Smith chart with the radius passing through 3.0 on the R/Z_o axis. Draw an inner and an outer boundary circle that are tangent to the SWR circle. The first objective is to move the impedance curve so that it is between the two boundary circles and positioned so that it can be matched with a second matching element. A shunt inductor appears to be the logical choice for the first matching element.

Step 2. A shunt element requires that the impedance curve be inverted into its equivalent admittance position (see Fig. 6-6(a)). The extent of the first move will be -0.430 chartmho at 4.0 mHz. To determine the extent of the move at other frequencies

$$B_x = -0.430 \times \frac{4.0}{f_x}$$

f_{mHz}	Old Position	+	Correction	=	New Position
2.0	Y = 0.275 + j0.275		(-0.860)		Y = 0.275 - j0.585
2.5	Y = 0.620 + j0.160		(-0.688)		Y = 0.620 - j0.528
3.0	Y = 0.675 - j0.240		(-0.573)		Y = 0.675 - j0.813
3.5	Y = 0.380 - j0.290		(-0.491)		Y = 0.380 - j0.781
4.0	Y = 0.280 - j0.160		(-0.430)		Y = 0.280 - j0.590
4.5	Y = 0.460 - j0.260		(-0.382)		Y = 0.460 - j0.642
5.0	Y = 0.260 - j0.320		(-0.344)		Y = 0.260 - j0.664
5.5	Y = 0.200 - j0.140		(-0.313)		Y = 0.200 - j0.453
6.0	Y = 0.400 - j0.090		(-0.287)		Y = 0.400 - j0.377

The new admittance position is shown in Figure 6-6(b). The next step will be a series matching element. This requires that the admittance curve be inverted into its equivalent impedance curve (see Fig. 6-6(b)).

Step 3. From the position of the impedance curve it appears that a series capacitor is required to move the impedance curve counterclockwise along lines of constant resistance into the SWR circle. The 5.5 mHz point is the furthest point from the SWR circle. The extent of the second move will be to place the 5.5 mHz point just inside the SWR circle. Therefore, the extent of the next move will be -(1.850 -1.050) = -0.800. Calculate the extent of the next move for other frequencies from

$$X_x = -0.800 \times \frac{5.5}{f_x}$$

f_{mHz}	Old Position	+	Correction	=	New Position
2.0	Z = 0.625 + j1.370		(-2.200)		Z = 0.625 - j0.830
2.5	Z = 0.925 + j0.800		(-1.760)		Z = 0.925 - j0.960
3.0	Z = 0.590 + j0.780		(-1.467)		Z = 0.590 - j0.687
3.5	Z = 0.500 + j1.040		(-1.257)		Z = 0.500 - j0.217
4.0	Z = 0.675 + j1.400		(-1.100)		Z = 0.675 + j0.300
4.5	Z = 0.740 + j1.050		(-0.978)		Z = 0.740 + j0.072
5.0	Z = 0.510 + j1.300		(-0.880)		Z = 0.510 + j0.420
5.5	Z = 0.850 + j1.850		(-0.800)		Z = 0.850 + j1.050
6.0	Z = 1.300 + j1.240		(-0.733)		Z = 1.300 + j0.507

Plot the impedance data on a Smith chart as shown in Figure 6-6(c). The 5.5 mHz point is inside the SWR circle as expected but the region between 2.5 and 3.0 mHz is outside the circle. The horizontal arrangement of the impedance curve lends itself to stub matching in order to fold the ends of the curve inward.

Step 4. A stub match requires that the impedance curve be inverted into its equivalent admittance curve (see Fig. 6-6(d). A short-circuited stub resonated at about 3.75 mHz and with an impedance of 100 ohms will be tried. To determine the reactance and susceptance of the stub

$$X = Z_o \tan \theta$$

and

$$B = 1/(Z_o \tan \theta)$$

where Z_o = impedance of the stub = 100 ohms

Since 90 degrees represents one-quarter wavelength at 3.75 mHz, the electrical length, reactance and susceptance at other frequencies is

$$\theta^{o}_{f_x} = 90^{o} \times \frac{f_x}{3.75}$$

f_{mHz}	θ^o	$X = Z_o \tan\theta$	$B = 1/(Z_o \tan\theta)$	B/Y_o
2.0	48	111	-0.009	-0.450
2.5	60	173	-0.006	-0.300
3.0	72	308	-0.003	-0.162
3.5	84	951	-0.001	-0.053
3.75	90	---	0	0
4.0	96	-951	+0.001	+0.053
4.5	108	-308	+0.003	+0.162
5.0	120	-173	+0.006	+0.289
5.5	132	-111	+0.009	+0.450
6.0	144	-72.7	+0.014	+0.700

Step 5. Add the susceptance obtained in Step 5 to the admittance curve of Figure 6-6(d) and plot the new admittance position.

f_{mHz}	Old Position	+	Correction	=	New Position
2.0	Y = 0.575 + j0.760		(-0.450)		Y = 0.575 + 0.310
2.5	Y = 0.520 + j0.540		(-0.300)		Y = 0.520 + j0.240
3.0	Y = 0.720 + j0.840		(-0.162)		Y = 0.720 + j0.678
3.5	Y = 1.650 + j0.700		(-0.053)		Y = 1.650 + j0.647
4.0	Y = 1.210 - j0.550		(+0.053)		Y = 1.210 - j0.497
4.5	Y = 1.340 - j0.120		+0.162		Y = 1.340 + j0.042
5.0	Y = 1.170 - j0.950		+0.289		Y = 1.170 - j0.661
5.5	Y = 0.450 - j0.570		+0.450		Y = 0.450 - j0.120
6.0	Y = 0.660 - j0.260		+0.700		Y = 0.660 + j0.440

Summary. The admittance curve of Figure 6-6(e) is well within the 3.0 SWR circle. Three matching elements were required. The final admittance curve is at about 2.5 to 1 SWR.

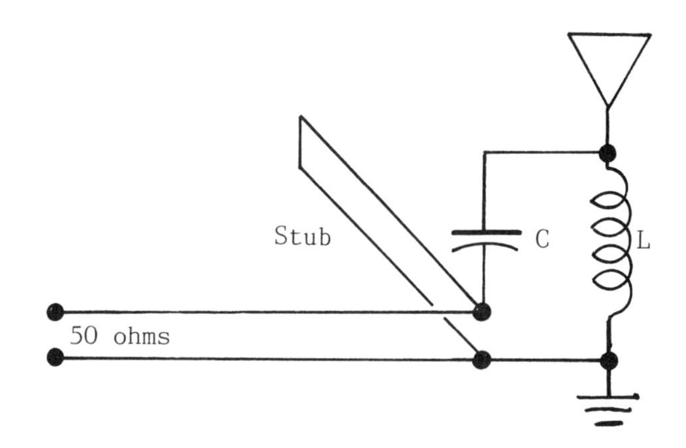

Schematic of matching solution.

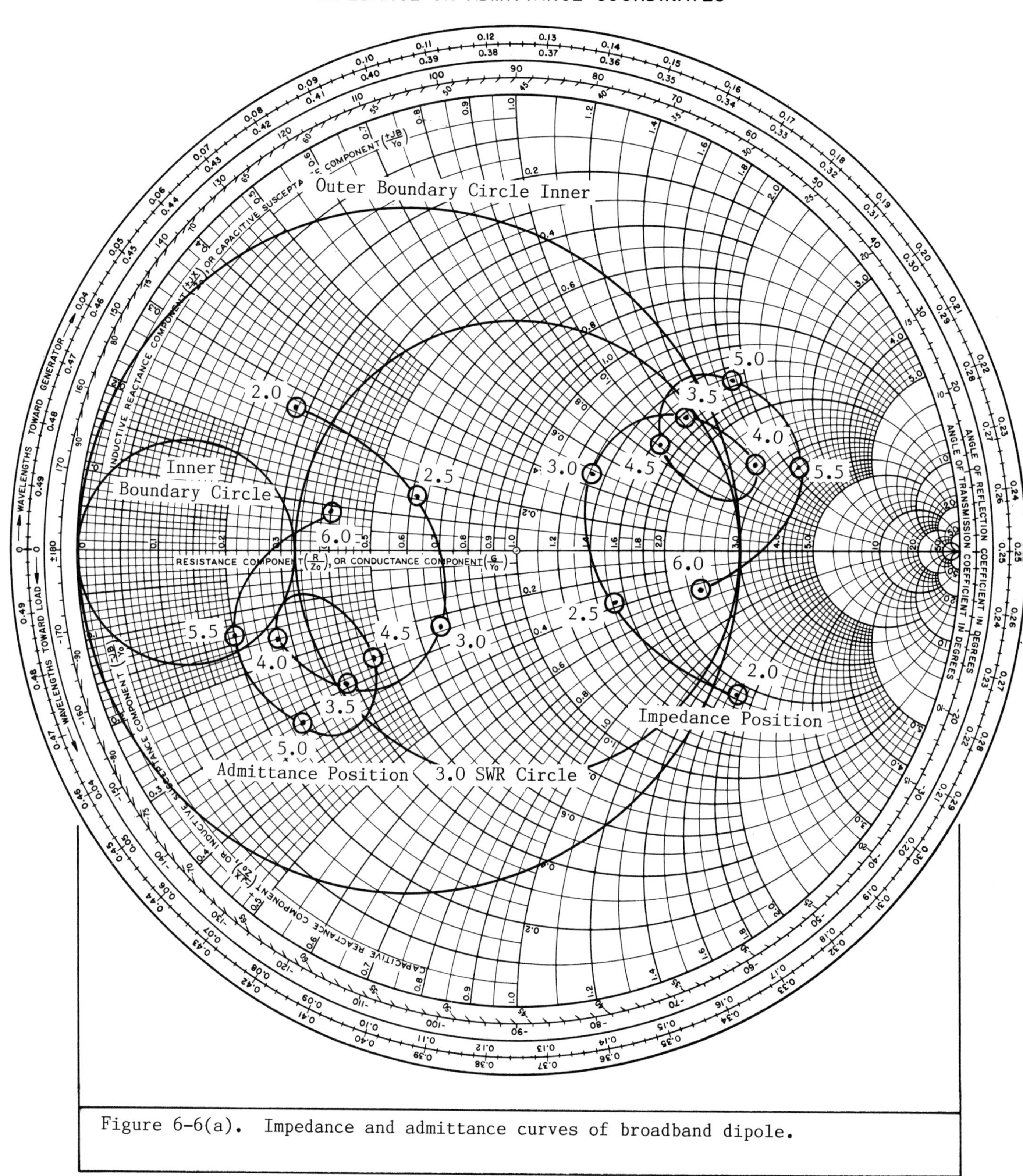

Figure 6-6(a). Impedance and admittance curves of broadband dipole.

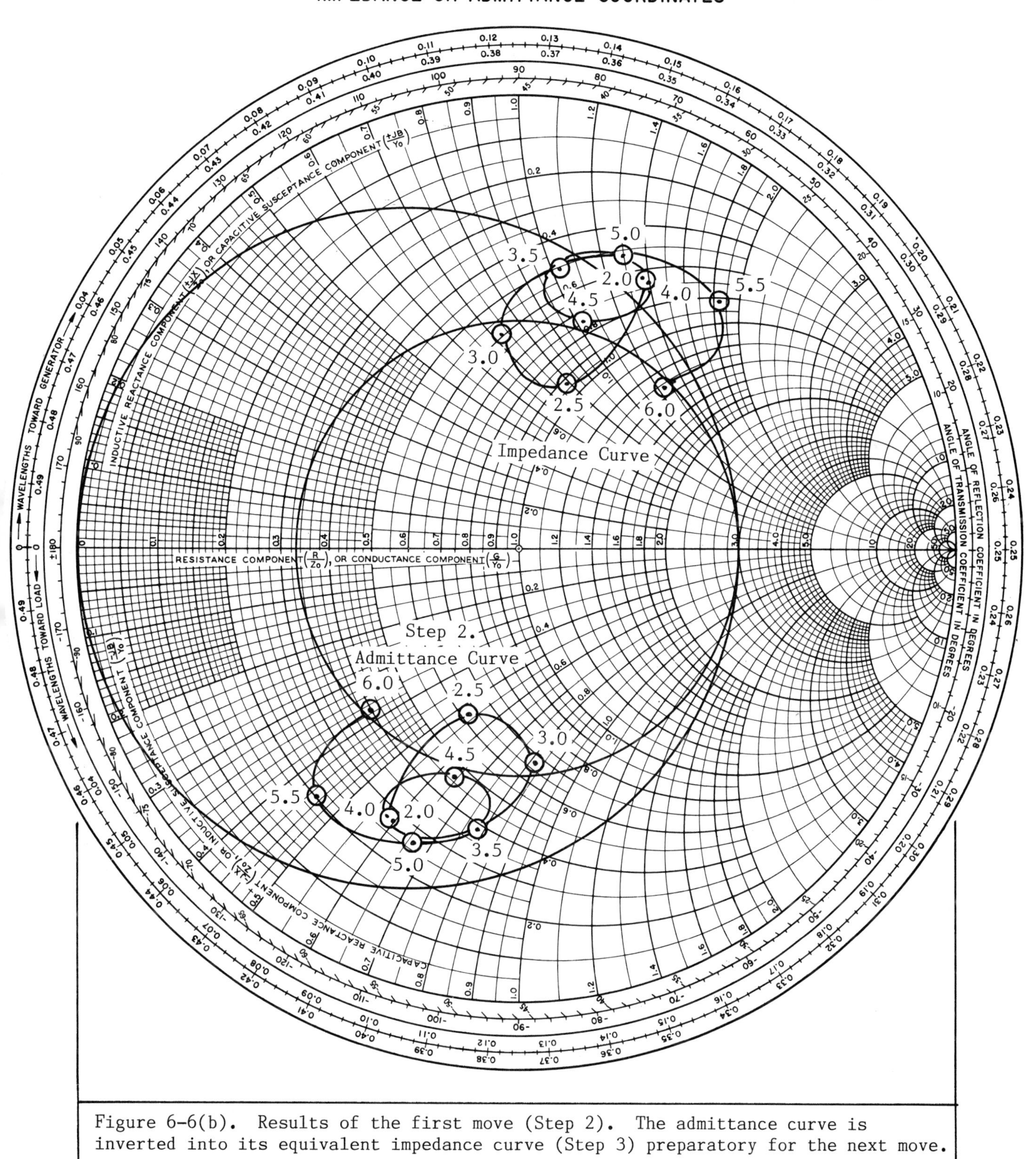

Figure 6-6(b). Results of the first move (Step 2). The admittance curve is inverted into its equivalent impedance curve (Step 3) preparatory for the next move.

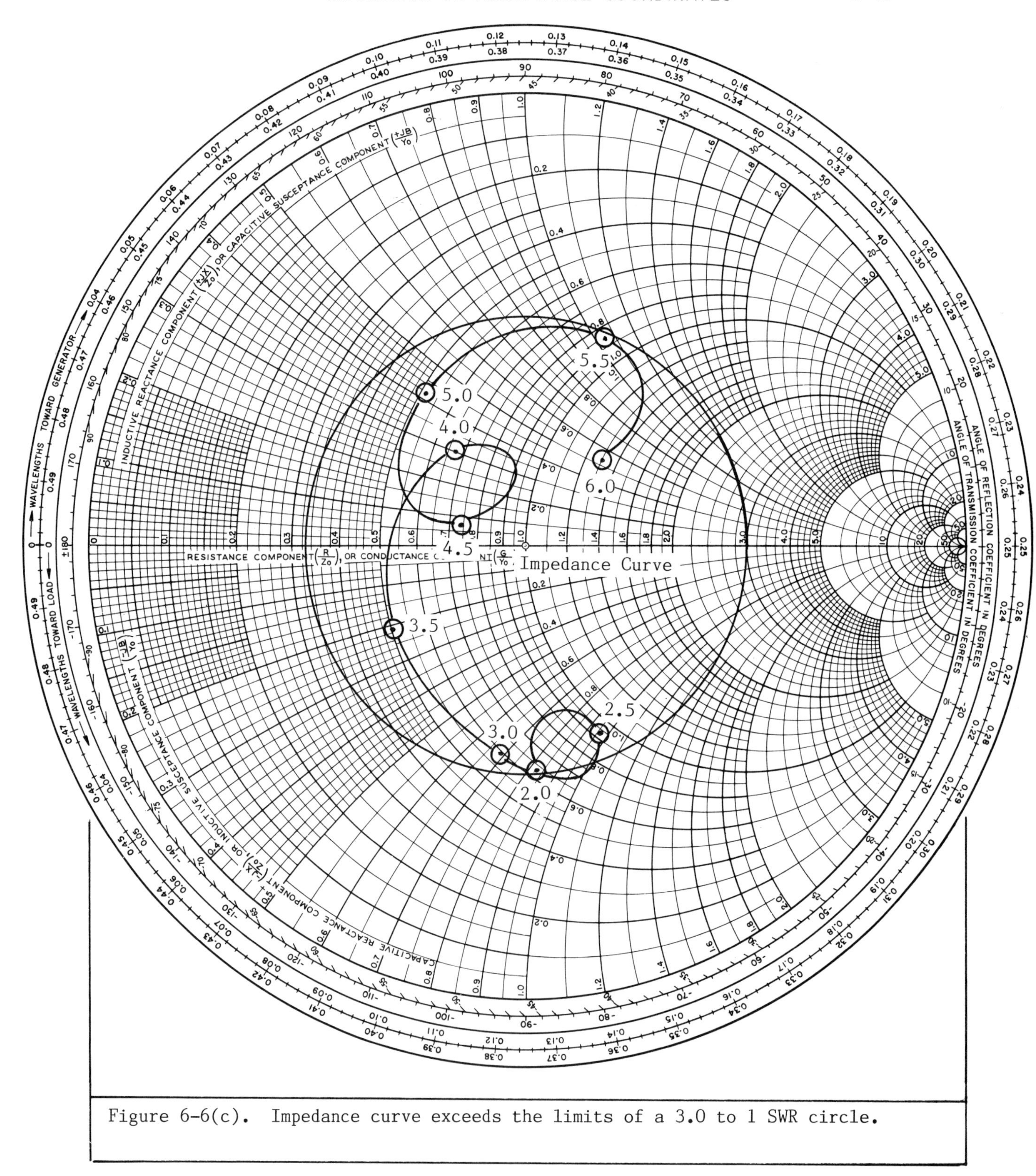

Figure 6-6(c). Impedance curve exceeds the limits of a 3.0 to 1 SWR circle.

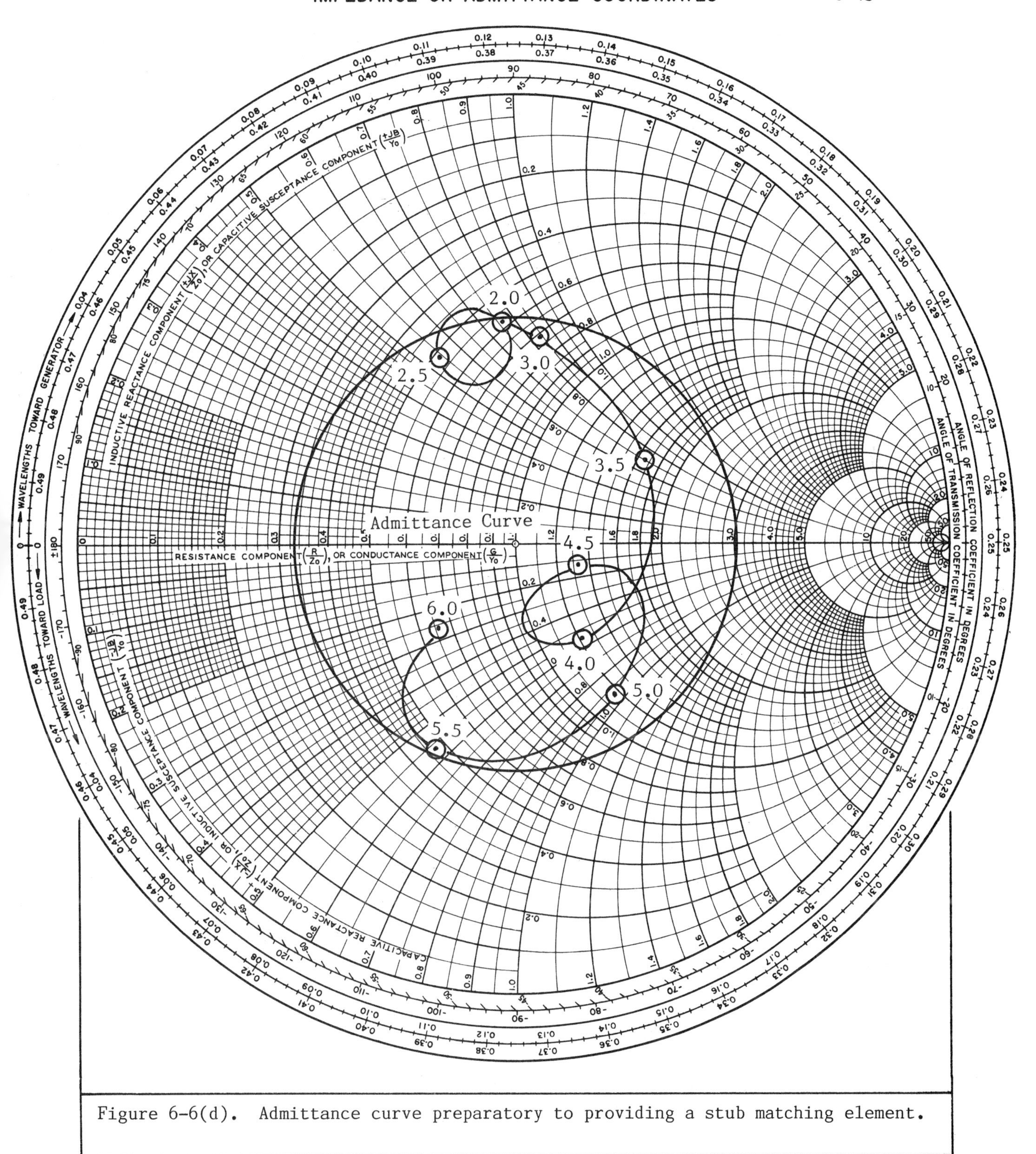

Figure 6-6(d). Admittance curve preparatory to providing a stub matching element.

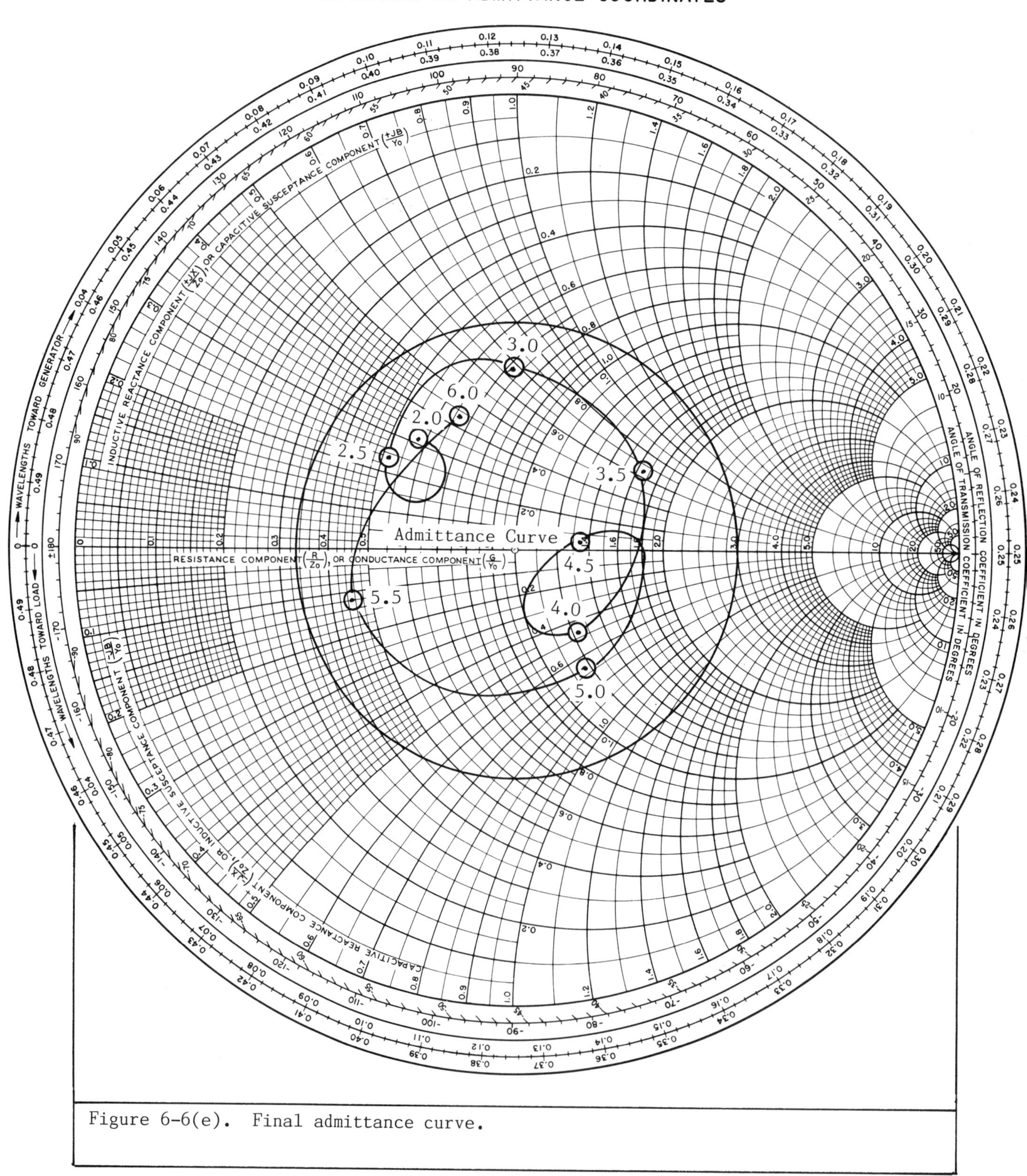

Figure 6-6(e). Final admittance curve.

Example No. 7. Problem: A slot antenna operating in the frequency range from 200 mHz to 350 mHz has the following impedance. Match this impedance to a SWR of 2.0 to 1 or better.

f_{mHz}	Impedance	Normalized Impedance
200	Z = 24.5 - j31.5	Z = 0.490 - j0.630
225	Z = 33.5 - j12.5	Z = 0.670 - j0.250
250	Z = 47.0 + j8.50	Z = 0.940 + j0.170
275	Z = 70.0 - j4.50	Z = 1.400 - j0.090
300	Z = 45.5 - j5.50	Z = 0.910 - j0.110
325	Z = 37.0 + 18.5	Z = 0.740 + j0.370
350	Z = 28.5 + j36.5	Z = 0.570 + j0.730

Step 1. Enter the normalized impedance on a normalized Smith chart as shown in Figure 6-7(a).

Step 2. The impedance curve has a natural loop which simplifies the matching procedure. It appears that the ends of the curve can be folded inward with a shunt stub. A shunt stub element requires that we work with admittance instead of impedance. Invert the impedance curve into its equivalent admittance (see Fig. 6-7(b)).

f_{mHz}	Normalized Admittance
200	Y = 0.760 + j0.980
225	Y = 1.300 + j0.500
250	Y = 1.100 - j0.190
275	Y = 0.710 + j0.050
300	Y = 1.090 + j0.120
325	Y = 1.100 - j0.550
350	Y = 0.670 - j0.850

Step 3. At VHF and above, half-wave shunt stubs become practical due to their short physical lengths. Two shunt stubs will be chosen for this example, a short-circuited line 90 degrees long and an open-circuited line 180 degrees long at the mid frequency. These stubs have the effect of moving all the frequency points lower than mid frequency in a counterclockwise direction along lines of constant conductance and all

frequency points higher than mid frequency is a clockwise direction. The size of the loop, in this case, is expected to blossom with this arrangement. A short-circuited 25-ohm line 90 degrees long and a 180 degrees long line at 275 mHz will be used for comparison purposes. Compute for the line length, reactance and susceptance at other frequencies from

$$\theta^o_{f_x} = 90^o \times \frac{f_x}{275}$$

f_{mHz}	θ^o	X = 25 tan θ	B = 1/(25tanθ)	B/Y_o
200	65.5	54.9	-0.018	-0.911
225	73.6	84.9	-0.012	-0.589
250	81.8	173.5	-0.006	-0.288
275	90.0	---	0	0
300	98.2	-173.5	+0.006	+0.288
325	106.4	-84.9	+0.012	+0.589
350	114.5	-54.9	+0.018	+0.911

Step 4. Add the susceptance obtained in Step 3 to the admittance curve of Figure 6-7(b) and plot the new admittance positions (see Fig. 6-7(d)).

f_{mHz}	Old Position	+	Correction	=	New Position
200	Y = 0.760 + j0.980		(-0.911)		Y = 0.760 + j0.069
225	Y = 1.300 + j0.500		(-0.589		Y = 1.300 - j0.089
250	Y = 1.100 - j0.190		(-0.288)		Y = 1.100 - j0.478
275	Y = 0.710 + j0.050		0		Y = 0.710 + j0.050
300	Y = 1.090 + j0.120		+0.288		Y = 1.090 + j0.408
325	Y = 1.100 - j0.550		+0.589		Y = 1.100 + j0.039
350	Y = 0.670 - j0.850		+0.911		Y = 0.670 + j0.061

Step 5. Compute for the line length, reactance and susceptance for the open-circuited 180-degree long line at other frequencies from

$$\theta^o_{f_x} = 180^o \times \frac{f_x}{275}$$

f_{mHz}	θ^o	X = -75 cot θ	B = 1/(75cot θ)	B/Y_o
200	130.9	65.0	-0.015	-0.750
225	147.3	116.8	-0.009	-0.428
250	163.6	254.8	-0.004	-0.196
275	180.0	---	0	0
300	196.4	-254.8	+0.004	+0.196
325	212.7	-116.8	+0.009	+0.428
350	229.1	-65.0	+0.015	+0.750

Step 6. Add the susceptance obtained in Step 5 to the admittance curve of Figure 6-7(b) and plot the new admittance position (see Fig. 6-7(d)).

f_{mHz}	Old Position	+	Correction	=	New Position
200	Y = 0.760 + j0.980		(-0.750)		Y = 0.760 + j0.230
225	Y = 1.300 + j0.500		(-0.428)		Y = 1.300 + j0.072
250	Y = 1.100 - j0.190		(-0.196)		Y = 1.100 - j0.386
275	Y = 0.710 + j0.050		0		Y = 0.170 + j0.050
300	Y = 1.090 + j0.120		+0.196		Y = 1.090 + j0.316
325	Y = 1.100 - j0.550		+0.428		Y = 1.100 - j0.122
350	Y = 0.670 - j0.850		+0.750		Y = 0.670 - j0.100

Summary. Both the low impedance 90-degree shunt line and the high impedance 180-degree shunt line are effective matching devices. As shown, both the final admittance curves are matched to a SWR circle that is better than 1.6 to 1. The noted difference between the stub lines is that a stub line between 90 degrees and 180 degrees long has a more rapid reactance variation vs. frequency.

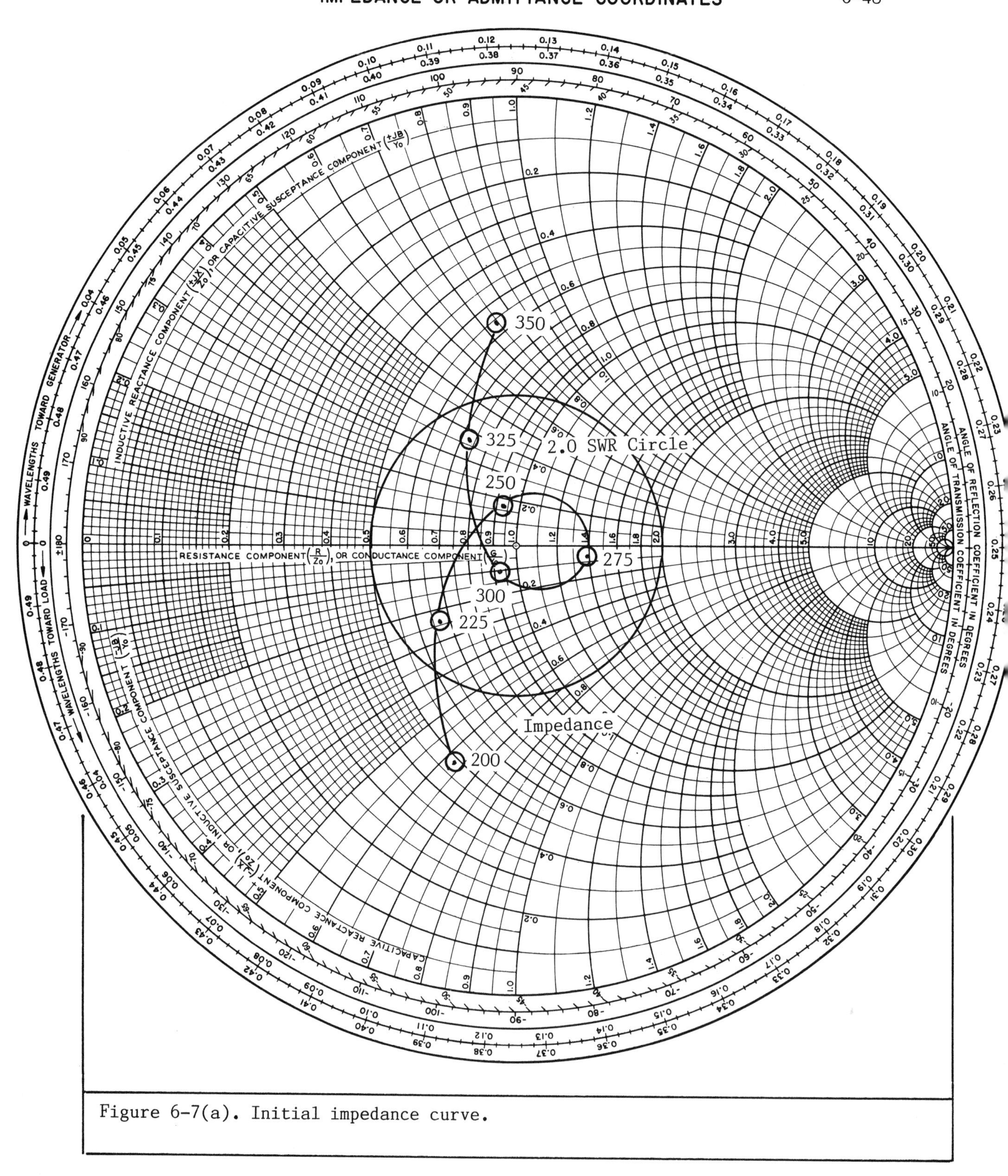

Figure 6-7(a). Initial impedance curve.

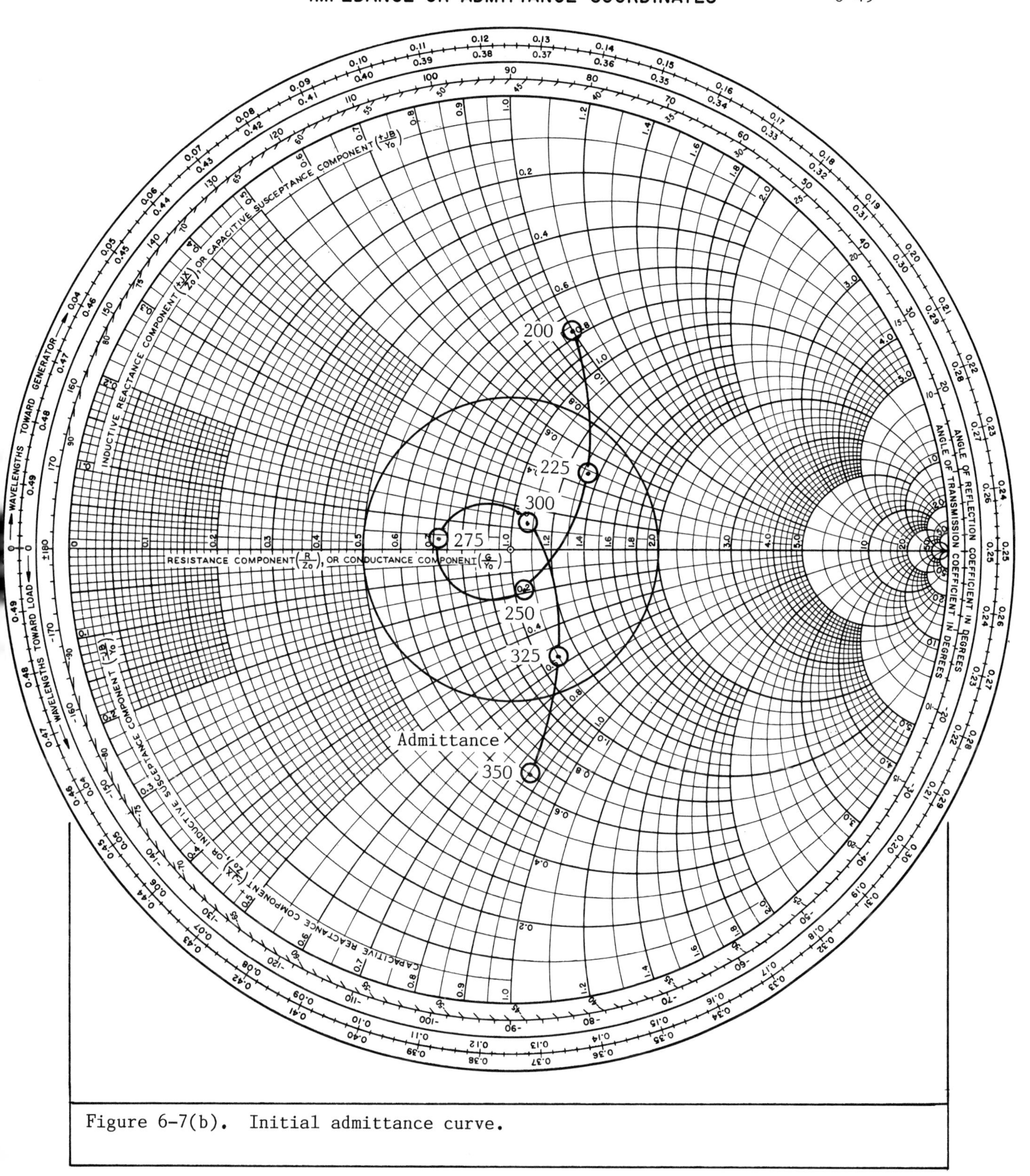

Figure 6-7(b). Initial admittance curve.

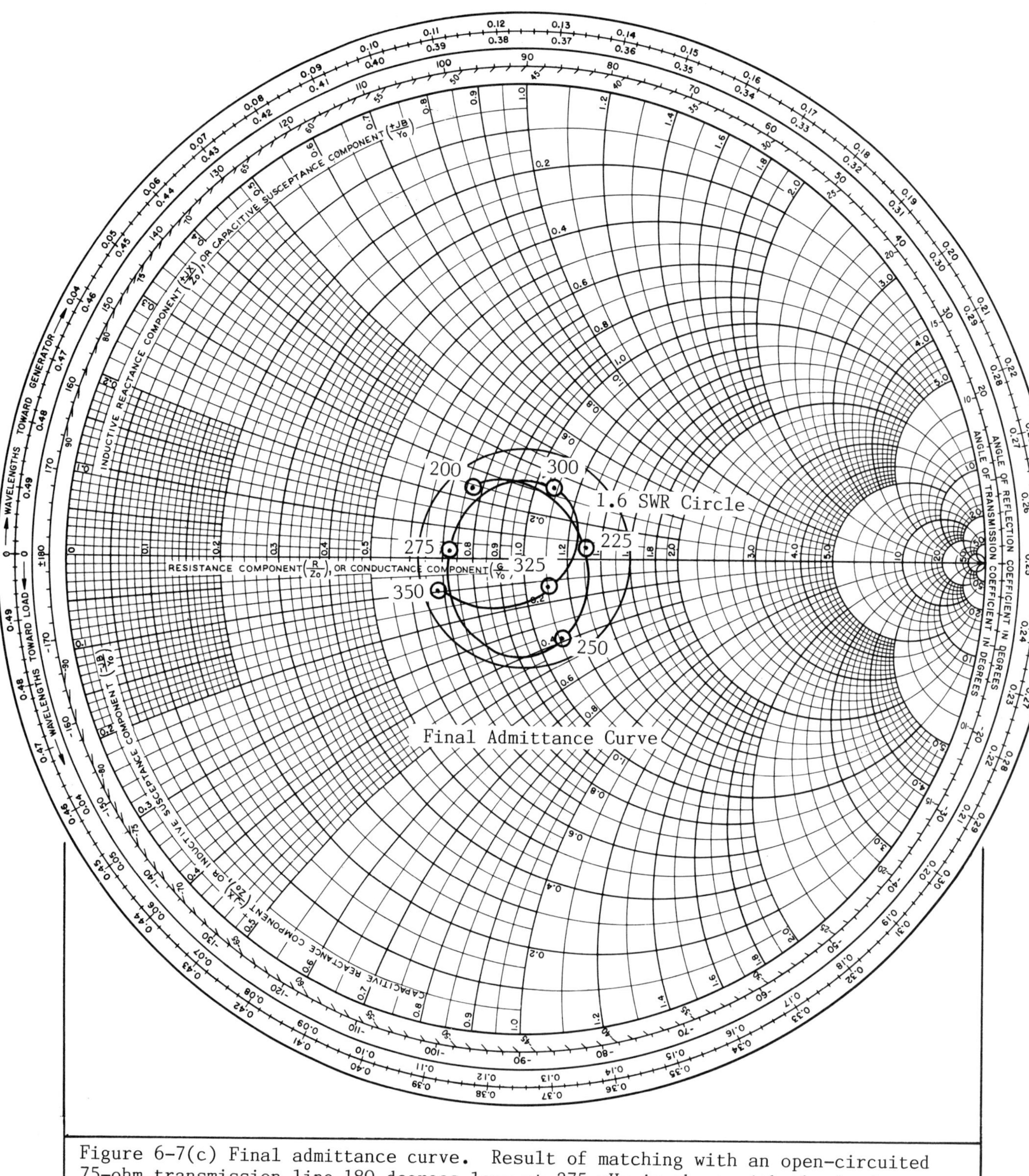

Figure 6-7(c) Final admittance curve. Result of matching with an open-circuited 75-ohm transmission line 180 degrees long at 275 mHz in shunt with the load.

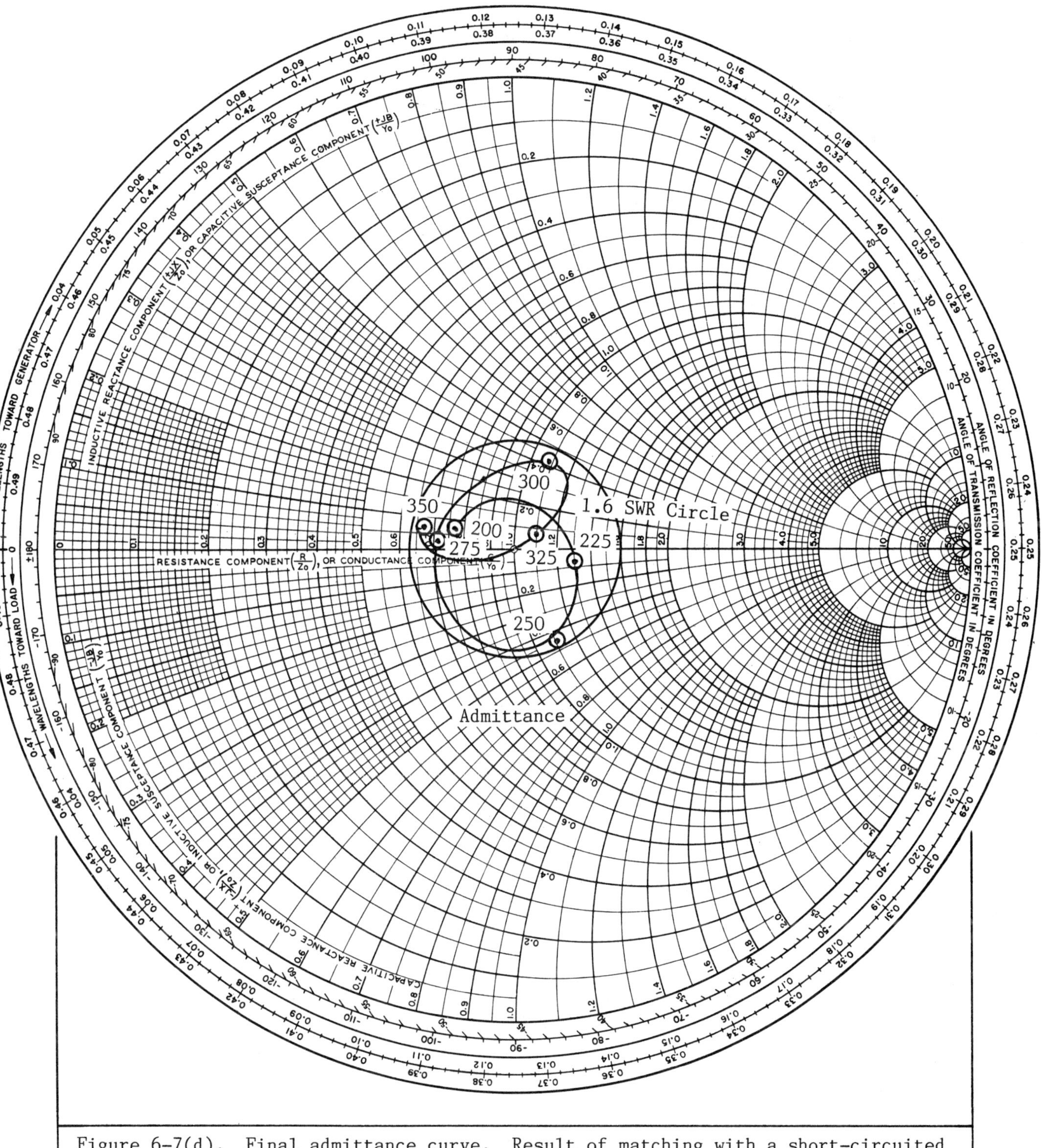

Figure 6-7(d). Final admittance curve. Result of matching with a short-circuited 25-ohm transmission line 90 degrees long at 275 mHz in shunt with the load.

Example 8. Problem: A long wire antenna of low length-to-diameter ratio has the following impedance. Match this impedance to a SWR of 2.0 to 1 or better.

fmHz	Impedance	Normalized Impedance
10	Z = 250 - j50.0	Z = 5.000 - j1.000
12	Z = 200 - j80.0	Z = 4.000 - j1.600
14	Z = 150 - j82.5	Z = 3.000 - j1.650
16	Z = 100 - j62.5	Z = 2.000 - j1.250
18	Z = 69.5 - j25.0	Z = 1.390 - j0.500
19	Z = 65 + j2.50	Z = 1.300 + j0.05
20	Z = 67.5 + j31.5	Z = 1.350 + j0.63
22	Z = 112.5 + j67.5	Z = 2.250 + j1.350
24	Z = 145 + j23.0	Z = 2.900 + j0.460
25	Z = 170 + j10.5	Z = 3.400 + j0.210

Step 1. Inter the normalized impedance on a normalized Smith chart as shown in Figure 6-8(a).

Step 2. Draw the desired SWR circle (SWR = 2.0 to 1).

Step 3. A study of the impedance curve indicates that a line transformer is required to move the impedance curve towards the center of the Smith chart. We must first determine the impedance Z_o' of the line transformer. Draw an outer boundary circle that is tangent to the SWR circle and drawn in such a way as to include the desired portion of the impedance curve (see Figure 6-8(a)).

Step 4. The line transformer impedance is determined from the minimum and maximum of the boundary circle as follows

$$\text{Min.} = 0.5 \times 50 = 25 \text{ ohms}$$

$$\text{Max.} = 5.0 \times 50 = 250 \text{ ohms}$$

$$Z_o' = \sqrt{\text{Max.} \times \text{Min.}} = \sqrt{25 \times 250} = 79 \text{ ohms}$$

Step 5. Normalize the impedance curve and SWR circle to the line transformer impedance (see Fig. 6-8(b)).

f_{mHz}	Impedance Normalized to 79 ohms
10	Z = 3.160 - j0.630
12	Z = 2.530 - j1.010
14	Z = 1.900 - j1.040
16	Z = 1.270 - j0.790
18	Z = 0.880 - j0.320
19	Z = 0.820 + j0.030
20	Z = 0.850 + j0.400
22	Z = 1.420 + j0.850
24	Z = 1.840 + j0.290
25	Z = 2.150 + j0.130

SWR Min. = 0.32

SWR Max. = 1.27

Step 6. A center frequency of 19 mHz will be used to establish the electrical length of the transformer. Draw a straight line from the center of the Smith chart, through the 19 mHz point, to the Wavelength Toward Generator scale. A wavelength of 0.012 is located on this scale. The 19 mHz point must now be rotated clockwise to the 0.0250λ on the WTG scale. The extent of this rotation is

$$0.250\lambda - 0.012\lambda = 0.238\lambda$$

Step 7. Determine the extent of the rotation required for the other frequencies f_x from

$$\lambda_{f_x} = 0.238\lambda \times \frac{f_x}{19}$$

f_{mHz}	Rotation (λ)
10	0.125
12	0.150
14	0.175
16	0.200
18	0.225
19	0.238
20	0.251
22	0.276
24	0.301
25	0.313

Step 8. Starting at 10 mHz, draw a line from the center of the Smith chart, through the 10 mHz point, to the Wavelength Toward Generator scale. A wavelength of 0.261 is located on this scale. The 10 mHz point must now be rotated in a clockwise direction so that a line drawn through it coincides with the 0.386λ on the scale

$$0.261\lambda + 0.125\lambda = 0.386\lambda$$

Repeat the procedure for the other frequencies

f_{mHz}	Old Position (λ)	+	Correction (λ)	=	New Position (λ)
10	0.261		0.125		0.386
12	0.275		0.150		0.425
14	0.290		0.175		0.465
16	0.322		0.200		0.522 (0.022)
18	0.390		0.225		0.615 (0.115)
19	0.012		0.238		0.250
20	0.113		0.251		0.364
22	0.190		0.276		0.466
24	0.232		0.301		0.533 (0.033)
25	0.243		0.313		0.556 (0.056)

Figure 6-8(c) represents the new impedance curve.

Step 9. Normalize the new impedance group obtained in Step 8 to 50 ohms.

f_{mHz}	Impedance
10	Z = 0.790 - j1.170
12	Z = 0.650 - j0.700
14	Z = 0.630 - j0.300
16	Z = 0.770 + j0.170
18	Z = 1.420 + j0.540
19	Z = 1.910 + j0
20	Z = 1.530 - j0.710
22	Z = 0.770 - j0.270
24	Z = 0.870 + j0.240
25	Z = 0.820 + j0.440

Step 10. We can see from Figure 6-8(d) that the 10 mHz point is outside the outer boundary circle thus making it impossible to match with the next matching element. To overcome this difficulty the impedance curve must be rotated in a clockwise direction so as to bring the 10 mHz point inside the outer boundary circle. The extent of the move will be a cautious one, 0.055λ at 10 mHz. To determine the amount of rotation at other frequencies

$$\lambda_{f_x} = 0.055\lambda \times \frac{f_x}{10}$$

f_{mHz}	Rotation (λ)
10	0.055
12	0.066
14	0.077
16	0.088
18	0.099
19	0.105
20	0.110
22	0.121
24	0.132
25	0.138

Step 11. Add the amount of rotation obtained in Step 10 to the old position to obtain the new position.

f_{mHz}	Old Position (λ)	+	Correction (λ)	=	New Position (λ)
10	0.344		0.055		0.399
12	0.380		0.066		0.446
14	0.431		0.077		0.508 (0.008)
16	0.058		0.088		0.146
18	0.195		0.099		0.294
19	0.250		0.105		0.355
20	0.302		0.110		0.412
22	0.418		0.121		0.539 (0.039)
24	0.095		0.132		0.227
25	0.112		0.138		0.250

Step 12. Without changing the radius of each frequency, rotate the curve to its new position. Figure 6-8(e) illustrates the rotated curve. Note that the low frequency end of the curve is now between the inner and outer boundary circles thus permitting matching with a shunt inductor. A shunt element requires that we work with admittance, therefore, invert the impedance curve of Figure 6-8(e) into its equivalent admittance curve (see Fig. 6-8(f)).

Step 13. The extent of the next move will be a cautious one. A susceptance of -0.6 chartmho at 10 mHz will be added to the admittance curve of Figure 6-8(f). To determine the amount of susceptance at other frequencies

$$G_{f_x} = -0.6 \times \frac{10}{f_x}$$

f_{mHz}	Old Position	+	Correction	=	New Position
10	Y = 0.720 + j1.090		(-0.600)		Y = 0.720 + j0.490
12	Y = 1.595 + j1.010		(-0.500)		Y = 1.595 + 0.510
14	Y = 1.780 - j0.150		(-0.429)		Y = 1.780 - j0.579
16	Y = 0.860 - j0.280		(-0.375)		Y = 0.860 - j0.655
18	Y = 0.600 + j0.180		(-0.333)		Y = 0.600 - j0.153
19	Y = 0.725 + j0.470		(-0.316)		Y = 0.725 + j0.154
20	Y = 1.100 + j0.750		(-0.300		Y = 1.100 + j0.450
22	Y = 1.400 - j0.280		(-0.273)		Y = 1.400 - j0.553
24	Y = 0.760 - j0.060		(-0.250)		Y = 0.760 - j0.310
25	Y = 0.600 - j0.020		(-0.240)		Y = 0.600 - j0.260

Figure 6-8(g) is that of the final admittance curve. All points of the curve are matched to 2.0 to 1 SWR or better.

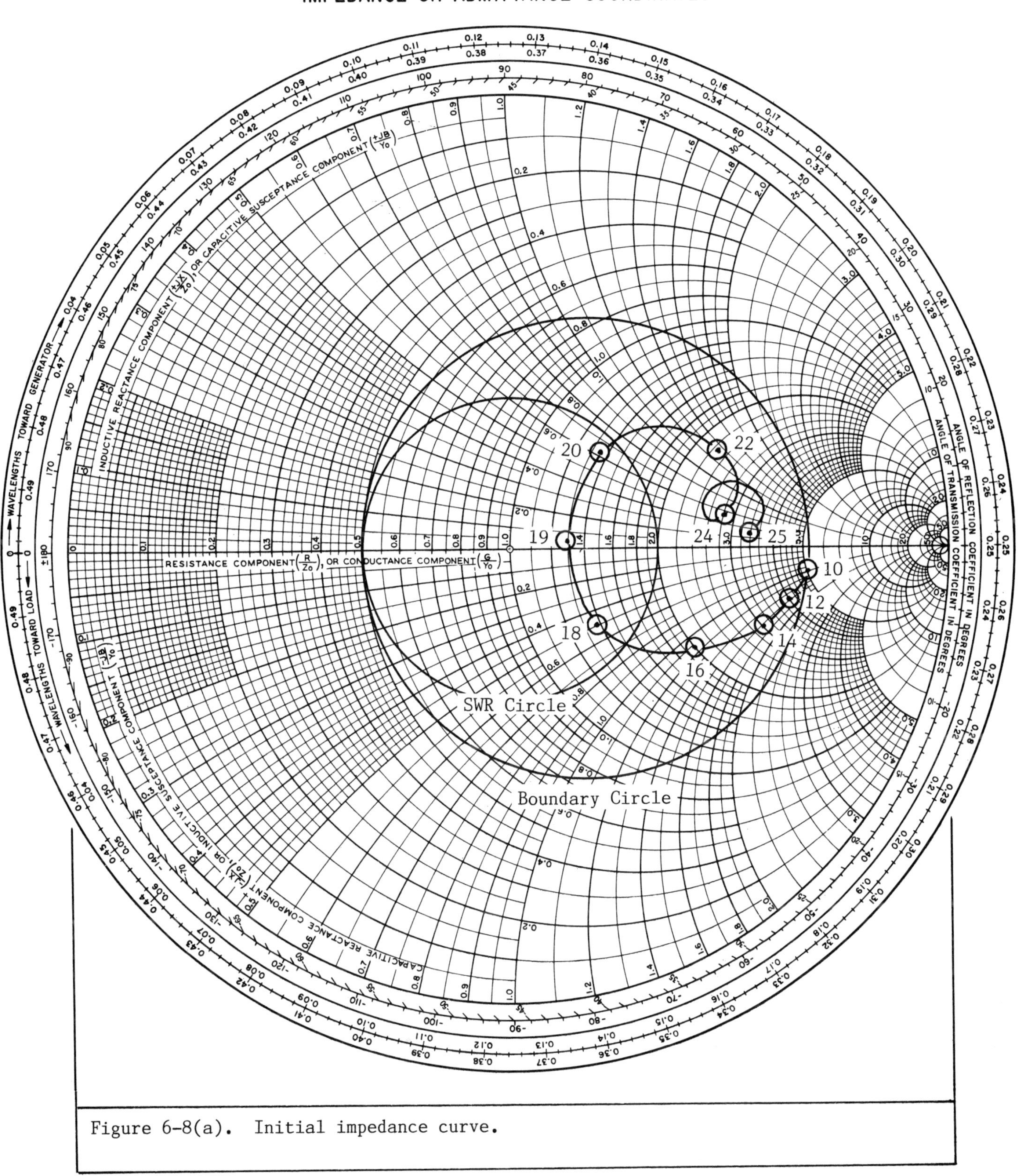

Figure 6-8(a). Initial impedance curve.

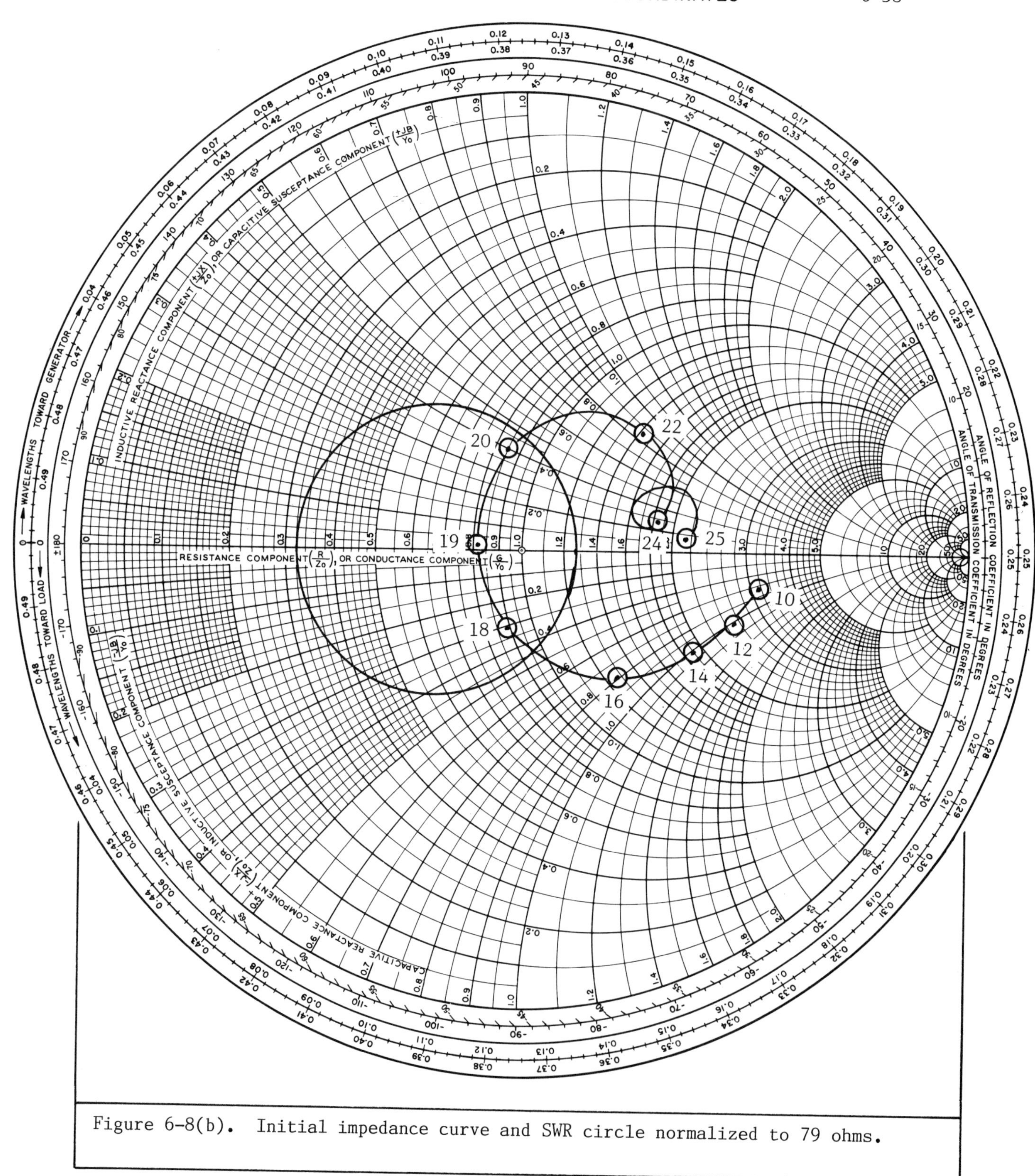

Figure 6-8(b). Initial impedance curve and SWR circle normalized to 79 ohms.

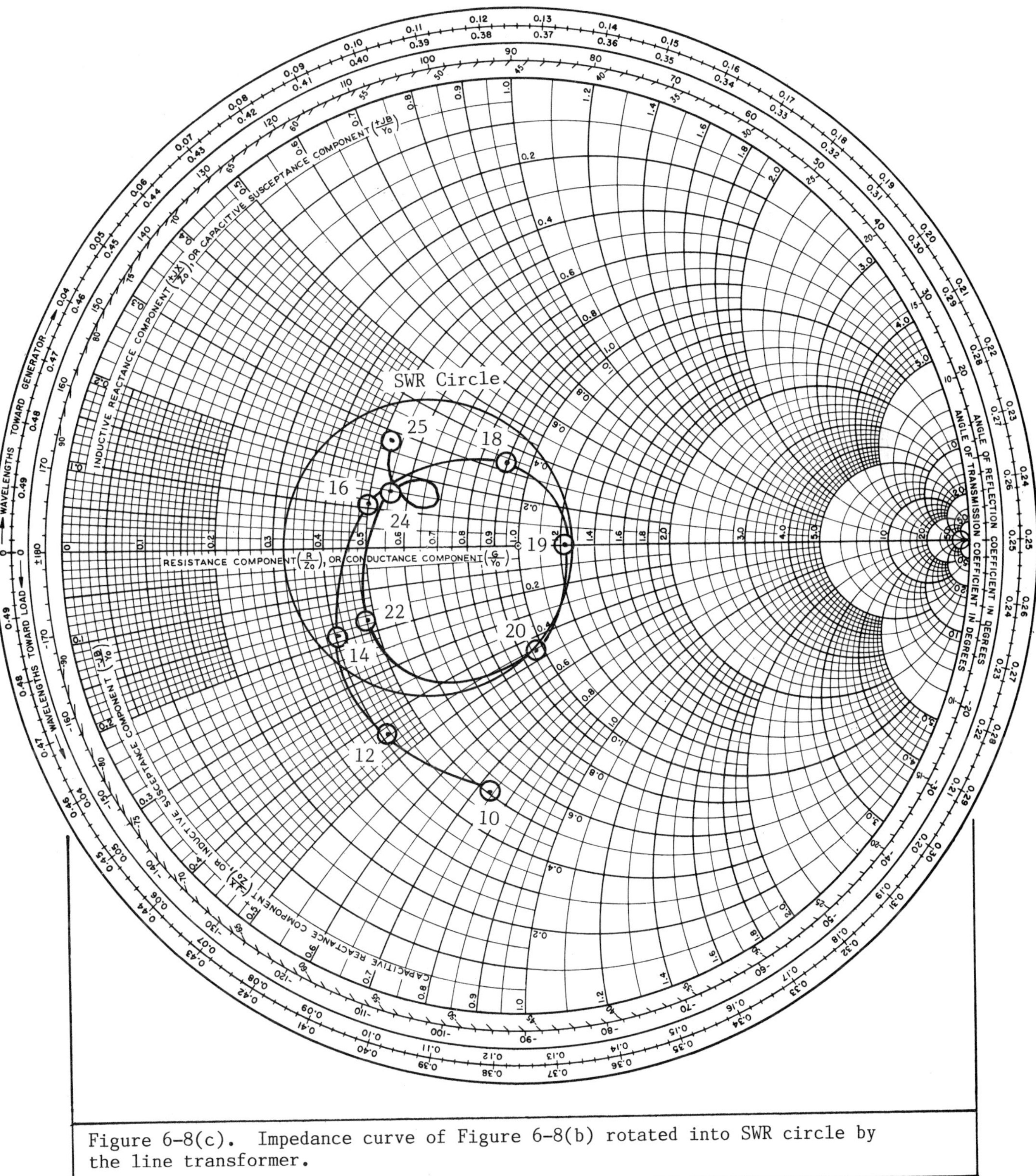

Figure 6-8(c). Impedance curve of Figure 6-8(b) rotated into SWR circle by the line transformer.

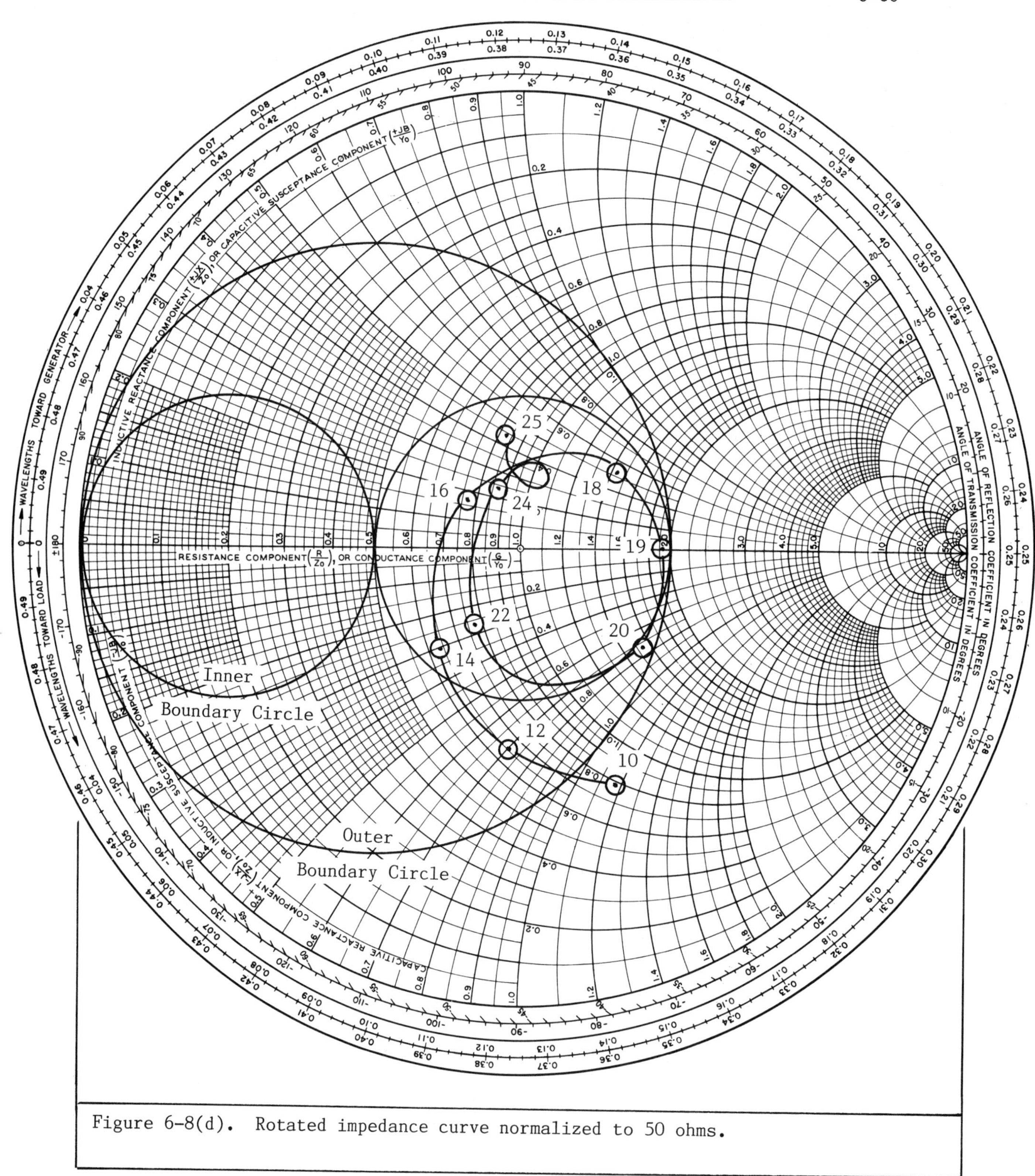

Figure 6-8(d). Rotated impedance curve normalized to 50 ohms.

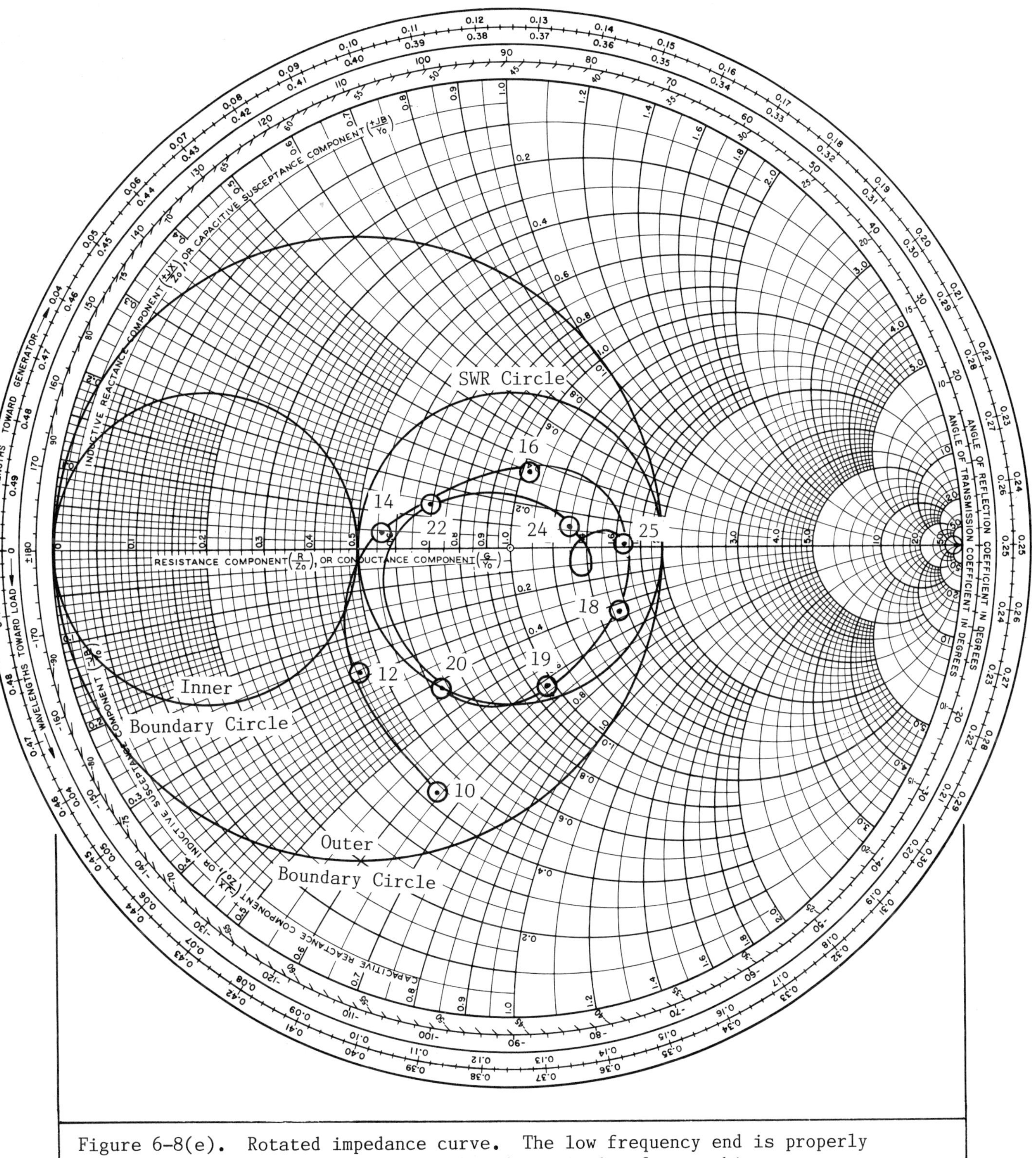

Figure 6-8(e). Rotated impedance curve. The low frequency end is properly located between the inner and outer boundary circles for matching.

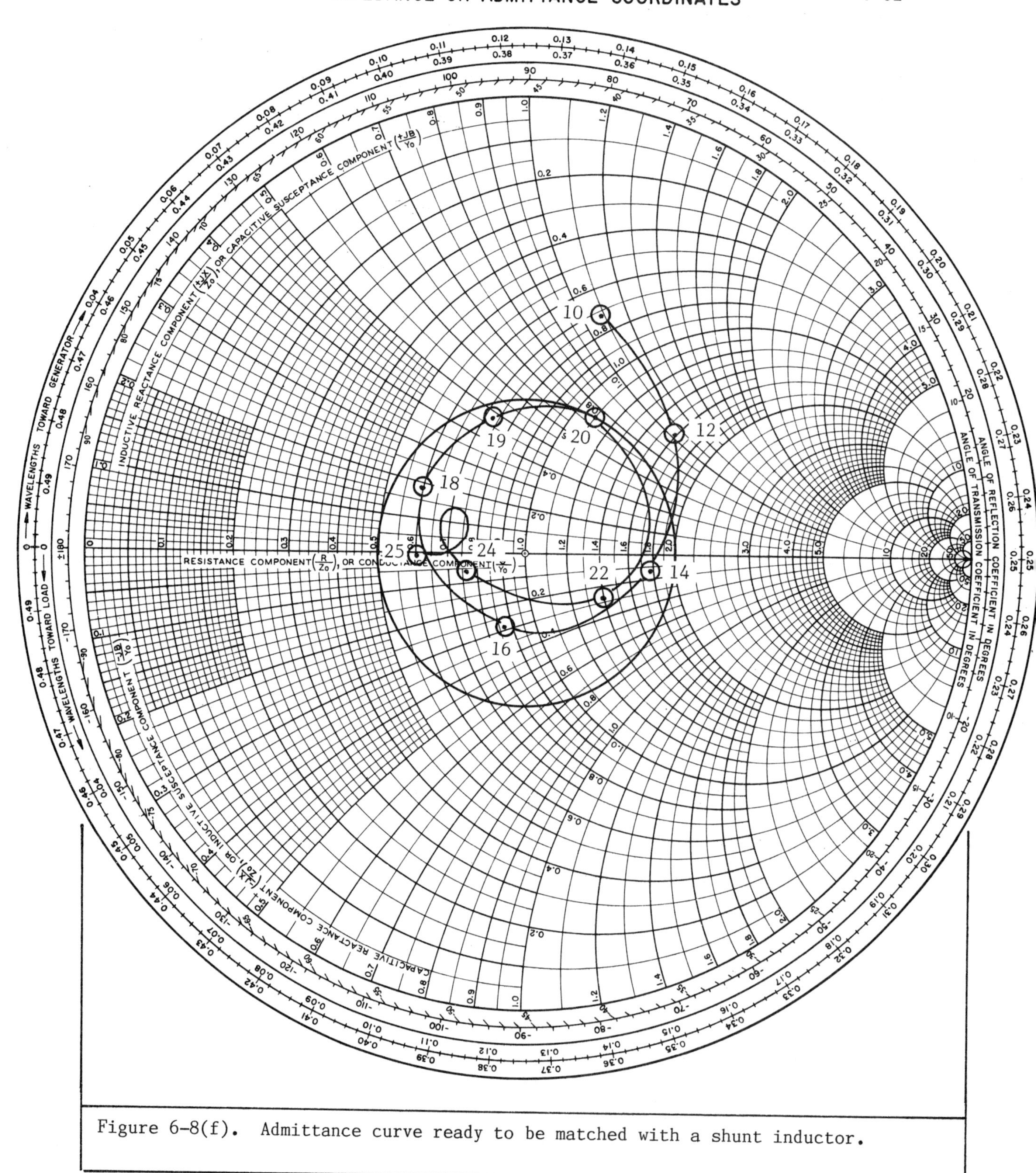

Figure 6-8(f). Admittance curve ready to be matched with a shunt inductor.

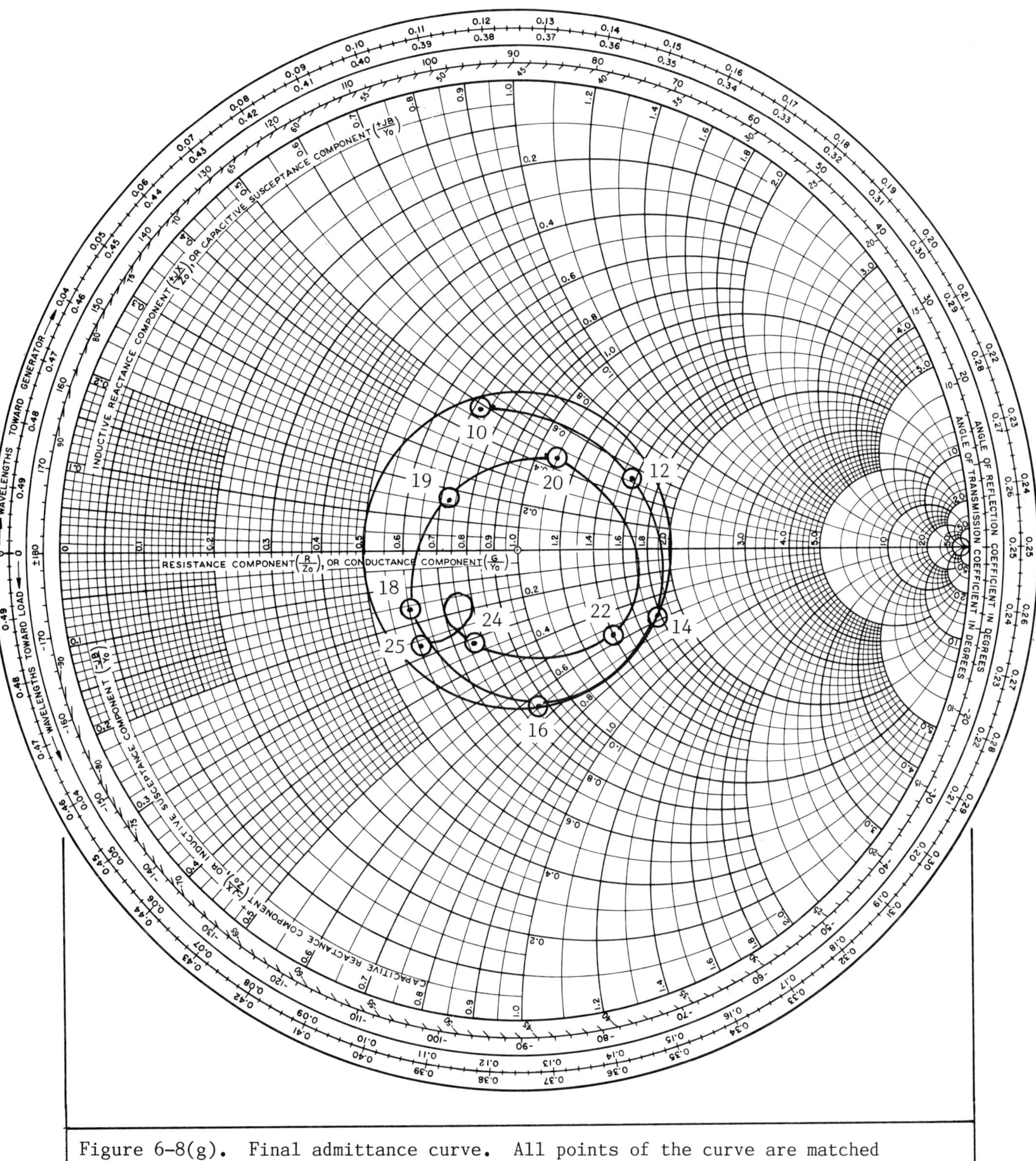

Figure 6-8(g). Final admittance curve. All points of the curve are matched within a 2.0 to 1 SWR circle.

Example No. 9. Problem: The objective of this example is to match the low impedance of a notched blade antenna to a 50-ohm line with a SWR of 1.5 to 1 or better.

f_{mHz}	Impedance	Normalized Impedance
26	Z = 11.0 - j5.00	Z = 0.220 - j0.100
27	Z = 10.0 - j4.00	Z = 0.200 - j0.080
28	Z = 9.0 - j2.00	Z = 0.180 - j0.040
29	Z = 9.0 - j0.50	Z = 0.180 - j0.010
30	Z = 10.0 + j1.00	Z = 0.200 + j0.020
31	Z = 13.0 + j0.50	Z = 0.260 + j0.010
32	Z = 12.5 - j5.00	Z = 0.250 - j0.100

Step 1. Plot the normalized impedance on a normalized Smith chart. Draw a 1.5 SWR circle centered on the Smith chart.

Step 2. From the data presented, it appears that a line transformer can transform the low impedance curve to the center of the Smith chart. Draw an outer boundary circle that is tangent to the SWR circle and drawn in such a way as to include the impedance curve (see Fig. 6-9(a)),

Step 3. Determine the line transformer impedance Z'_o from the minimum and maximum of the boundary circle

$$\text{Min} = 0.17 \times 50 = 8.5 \text{ ohms}$$

$$\text{Max} = 1.5 \times 50 = 75 \text{ ohms}$$

$$Z'_o = \sqrt{\text{Min. x Max.}} = \sqrt{8.5 \times 75} = 25.25 \text{ ohms}$$

Step 4. Normalize the impedance curve and SWR circle of Figure 6-9(a) to the line transformer impedance, Z'_o = 25.25 (see Fig. 6-9(b)).

f_{mHz}	R50/25.25 ± jX50/25.25
26	Z = 0.44 - j0.200
27	Z = 0.39 - j0.160
28	Z = 0.36 - j0.080
29	Z = 0.35 - j0.020
30	Z = 0.40 + j0.040
31	Z = 0.51 + j0.020
32	Z = 0.50 - j0.200

SWR Min. = 1.33

SWR Max. = 2.97

Step 5. Determine the length of the line transformer. As an initial approach, the center frequency, 30 mHz, will be used to establish the length. Draw a line from the center of the Smith chart, through the 30 mHz point, to the Wavelength Toward Generator scale. A wavelength of 0.008 is located on this scale. Rotate the 30 mHz point clockwise to the zero reactance axis (0.250λ). The amount of rotation required is

$$0.250\lambda - 0.008\lambda = 0.242\lambda$$

Step 6. Determine the amount of rotation required at the other frequencies

$$\lambda_{f_x} = 0.242\lambda \times \frac{f_x}{30}$$

f_{mHz}	Old Position (λ)	+	Correction (λ)	=	New Position (λ)
26	0.461		0.210		0.671 (0.171)
27	0.471		0.218		0.689 (0.189)
28	0.485		0.226		0.711 (0.211)
29	0.495		0.234		0.729 (0.229)
30	0.008		0.242		0.250
31	0.003		0.250		0.253
32	0.459		0.258		0.717 (0.217)

The new impedance curve is shown as a solid line in Figure 6-9(c). It appears that the line is too short. Another try is required; a lower frequency, 28 mHz will be chosen to establish a longer line transformer length. The amount of rotation required at 28 mHz is

$$0.250\lambda + 0.015\lambda = 0.265\lambda$$

Step 7. Determine the amount of rotation required at the other frequencies from

$$\lambda_{f_x} = 0.265\lambda \times \frac{f_x}{28}$$

f_{mHz}	Old Position (λ)	+	Correction (λ)	=	New Position (λ)
26	0.461		0.246		0.707 (0.207)
27	0.471		0.256		0.727 (0.227)
28	0.485		0.265		0.750 (0.250)
29	0.495		0.274		0.769 (0.269)
30	0.008		0.284		0.292
31	0.003		0.293		0.296
32	0.459		0.303		0.762 (0.262)

The new impedance curve is shown as a dash line in Figure 6-9(c). We have found the proper length for the line transformer. We can now proceed with the next matching element.

Step 8. Normalize the new impedance curve of Figure 6-9(c) to 50 ohms (see Fig. 6-9(d)).

f_{mHz}	R25.25/50 ± jX25.25/50
26	Z = 0.91 + j0.450
27	Z = 1.16 + j0.370
28	Z = 1.41 + j0
29	Z = 1.31 - j0.350
30	Z = 0.93 - j0.480
31	Z = 0.81 - j0.310
32	Z = 1.04 - j0.130

Step 9. The shape and placement of curve normalized in Step 8 calls for an open-circuited 90 degree series line of about 75 ohms. Determine the electrical length of the series line at other frequencies from

$$\theta f_x = 90^o \times \frac{f_x}{28}$$

f_{mHz}	Degrees
26	83.57
27	86.79
28	90.00
29	93.21
30	96.43
31	99.64
32	102.85

Step 10. Determine the reactance of the series line for all frequencies from

$$X_{f_x} = -75 \cot \theta$$

f_{mHz}	θ	$X = -75 \cot \theta$	X/50
26	83.57	− 8.45	−0.17
27	86.79	− 4.20	−0.08
28	90.00	0	0
29	93.21	+ 4.20	+0.08
30	96.43	+ 8.45	+0.17
31	99.64	+12.74	+0.25
32	102.85	+17.00	+0.34

Step 11. Add the series line reactance to the curve of Figure 6-9(c) to obtain the final impedance curve.

f_{mHz}	Old Position	+	Correction	=	New Position
26	Z = 0.920 + j0.450		(−0.170)		Z = 0.920 + j0.280
27	Z = 1.130 + j0.360		(−0.080)		Z = 1.130 + j0.280
28	Z = 1.450 + j0		0		Z = 1.450 + j0
29	Z = 1.320 − j0.360		+0.080		Z = 1.320 − j0.280
30	Z = 0.930 − j0.480		+0.170		Z = 0.930 − j0.310
31	Z = 0.820 − j0.320		+0.250		Z = 0.820 − j0.070
32	Z = 1.040 − j0.140		+0.340		Z = 1.040 + j0.200

The result of adding the series inductance to the impedance curve of Figure 6-9(d) is shown in Figure 6-9(e).

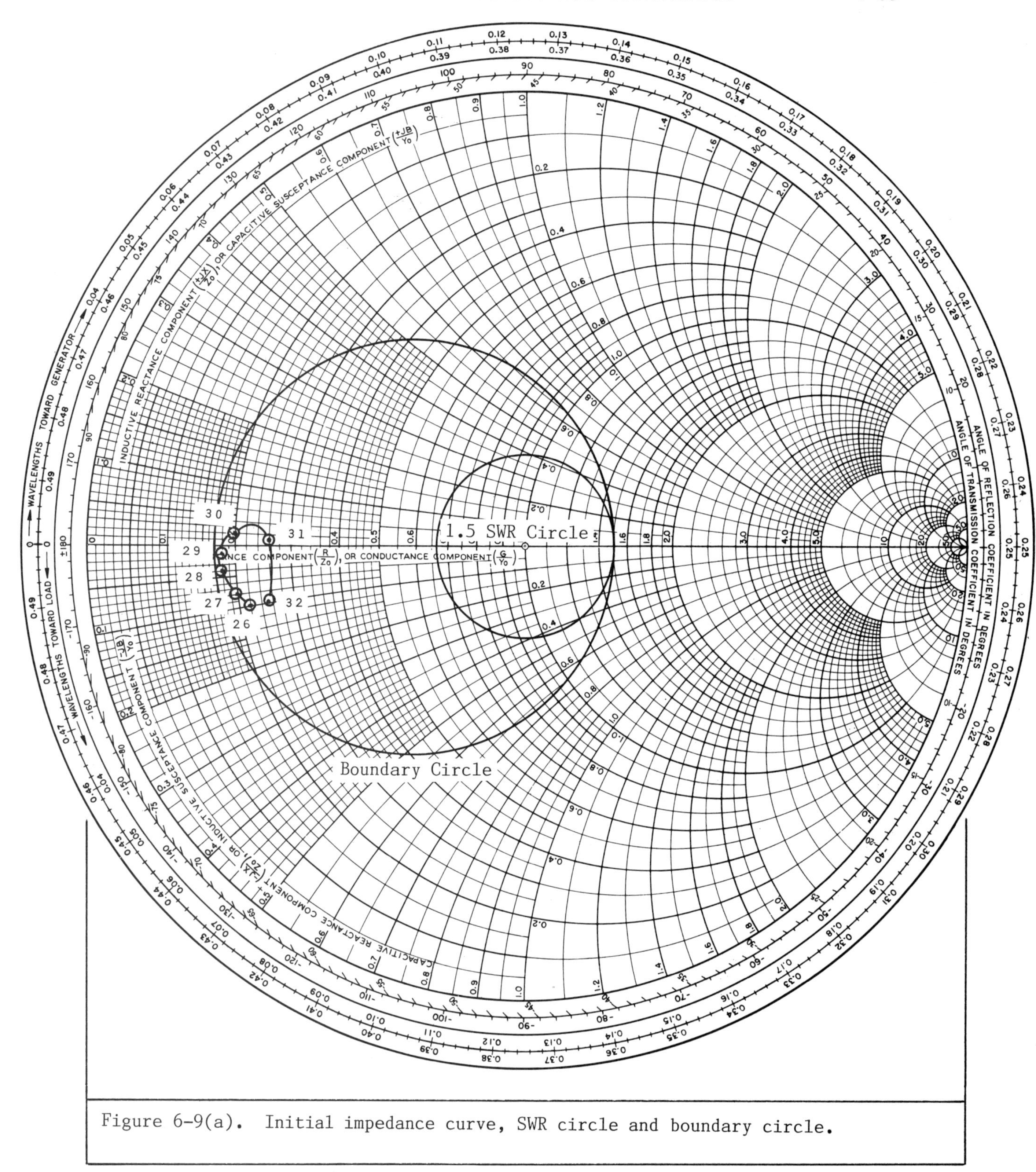

Figure 6-9(a). Initial impedance curve, SWR circle and boundary circle.

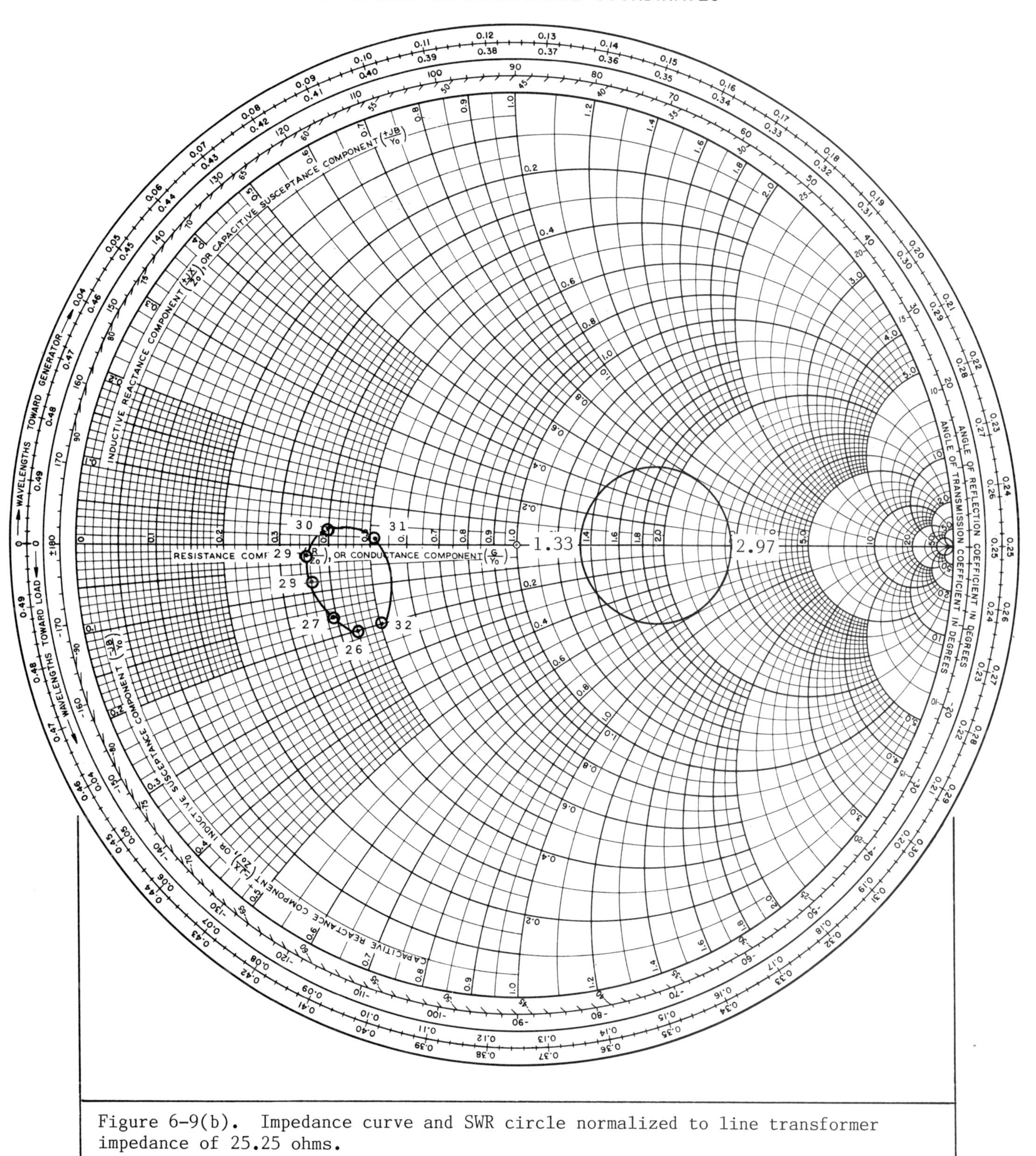

Figure 6-9(b). Impedance curve and SWR circle normalized to line transformer impedance of 25.25 ohms.

IMPEDANCE OR ADMITTANCE COORDINATES

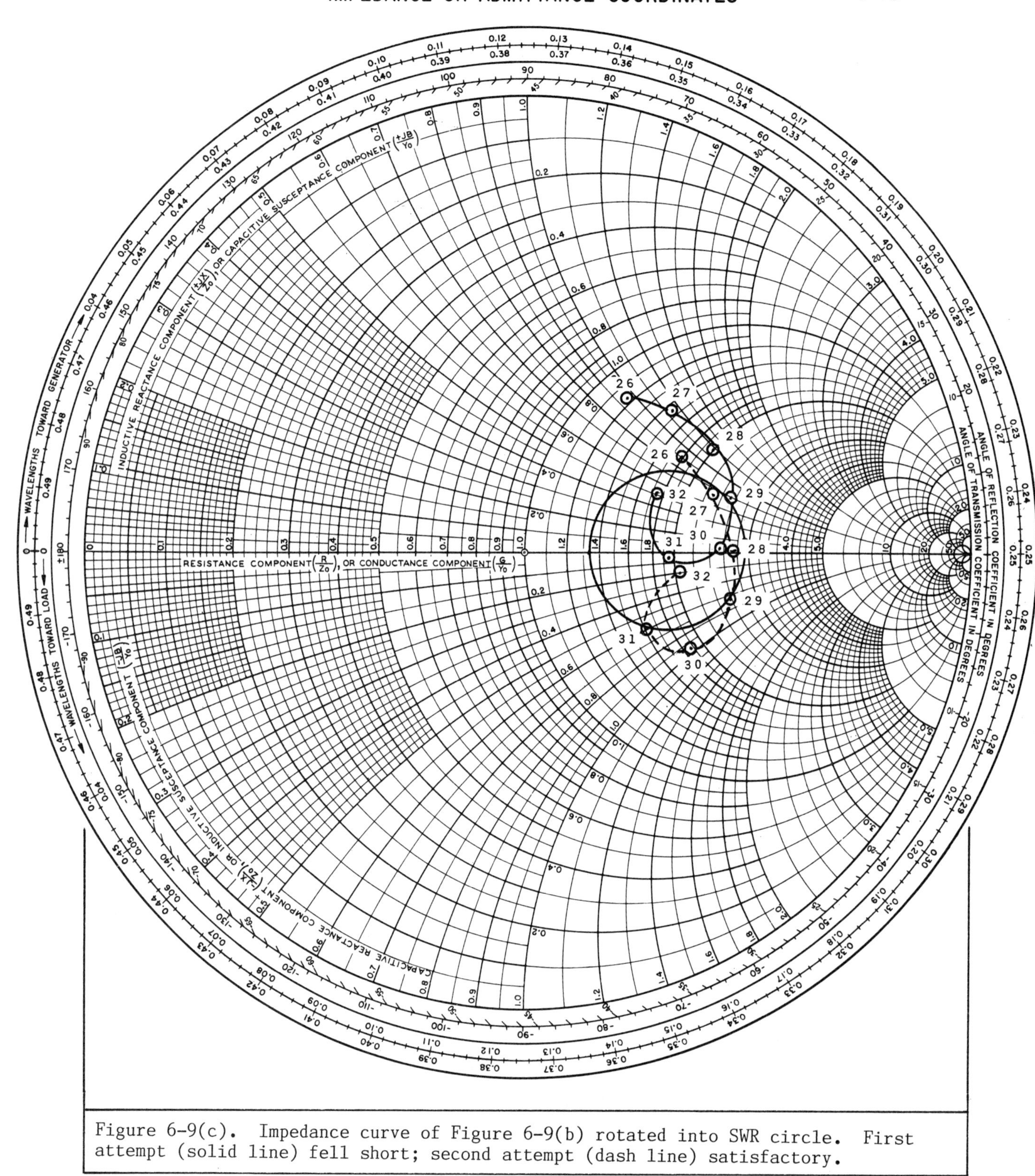

Figure 6-9(c). Impedance curve of Figure 6-9(b) rotated into SWR circle. First attempt (solid line) fell short; second attempt (dash line) satisfactory.

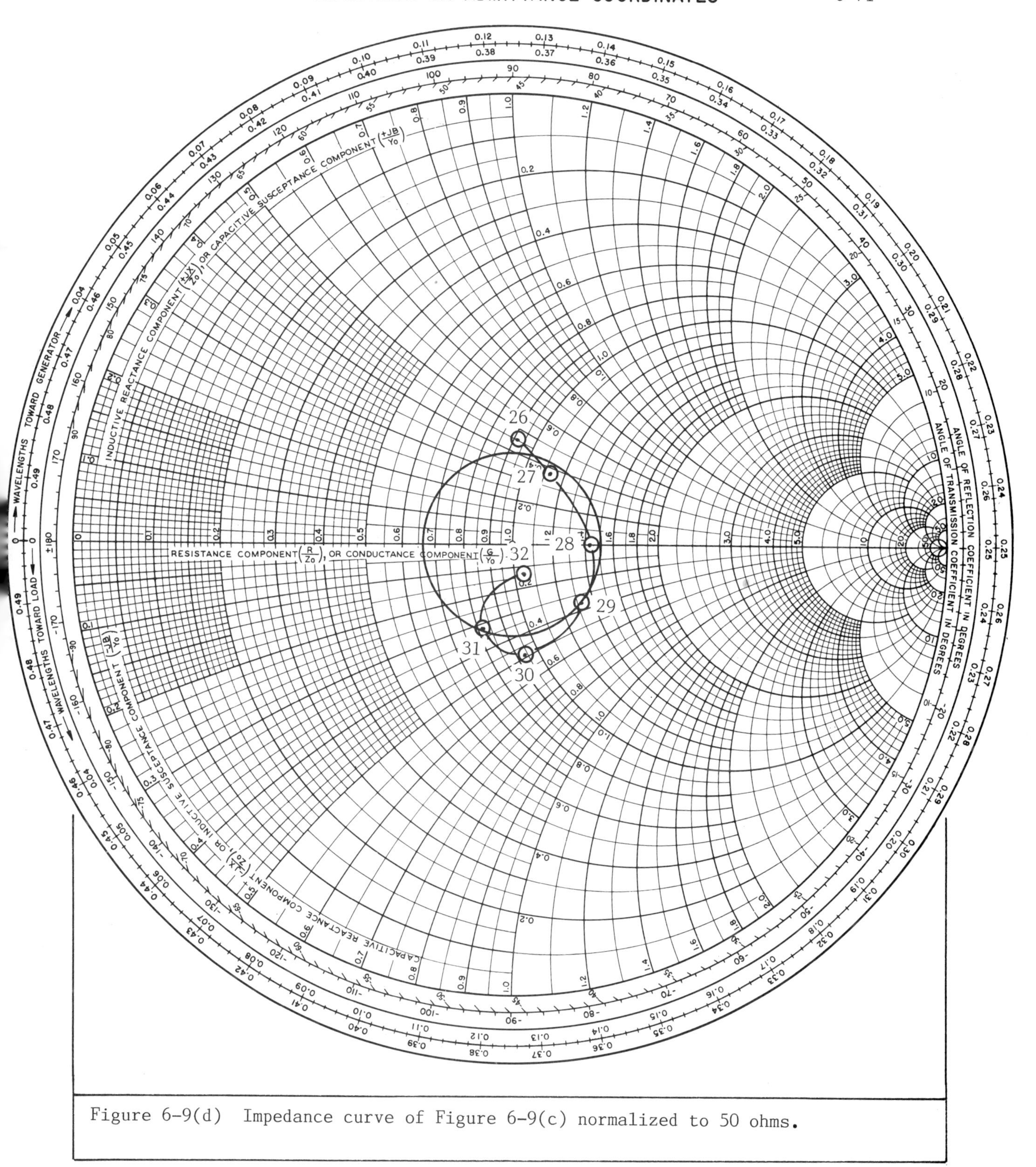

Figure 6-9(d) Impedance curve of Figure 6-9(c) normalized to 50 ohms.

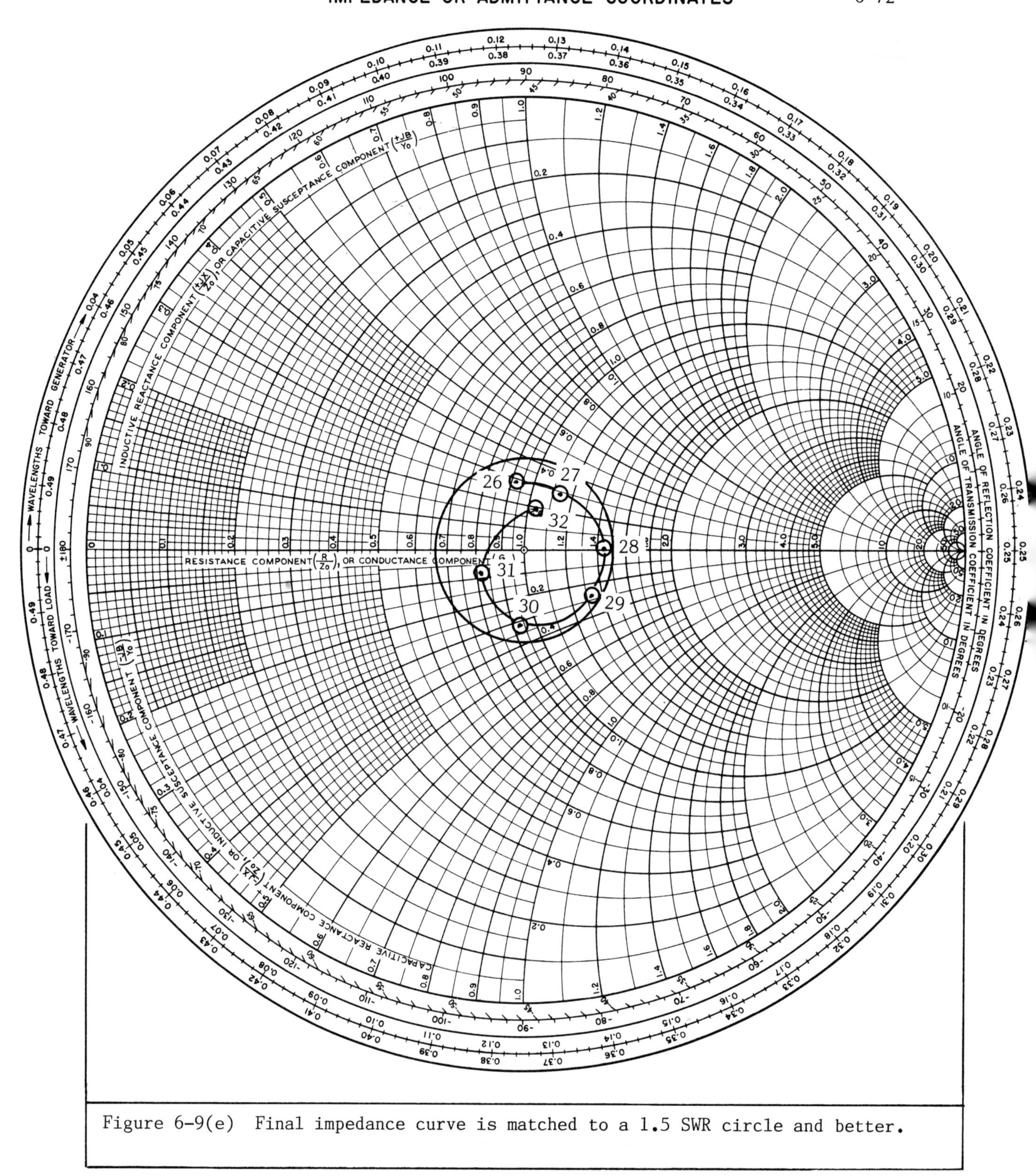

Figure 6-9(e) Final impedance curve is matched to a 1.5 SWR circle and better.

Example No. 10. Problem: A folded blade antenna has the following impedance. Match this impedance to a SWR of 2.0 to 1 or better.

f_{mHz}	Impedance	Normalized Impedance
100	Z = 32 - j55.0	Z = 0.64 - j1.100
105	Z = 45 - j63.0	Z = 0.90 - j1.260
110	Z = 28 - j60.0	Z = 0.56 - j1.200
120	Z = 29 - j50.0	Z = 0.58 - j1.000
130	Z = 30 - j38.5	Z = 0.60 - j0.770
140	Z = 33 - j28.0	Z = 0.66 - j0.560
150	Z = 36 - j20.0	Z = 0.72 - j0.400
160	Z = 40 - j12.5	Z = 0.80 - j0.250

Step 1. Enter the normalized impedance on a normalized Smith chart as shown in Figure 6-10(a). Draw a 2.0 to 1 SWR circle.

Step 2. The first move will be to move the impedance curve to the right along lines of constant resistance. The center frequency, 130 mHz, will be placed on the R/Z_o axis. This move calls for a short-circuited series line that provides a reactance of +0.770 chartohm at 130 mHz. Determine the extent of the move at other frequencies from

$$X_{f_x} = 0.770 \times \frac{f_x}{130}$$

f_{mHz}	X_{f_x}
100	0.592
105	0.622
110	0.652
120	0.711
130	0.770
140	0.829
150	0.888
160	0.948

Step 3. Add the reactance obtained in Step 2 to the impedance curve to obtain the new position.

f_{mHz}	Old Position	+	Correction	=	New Position
100	Z = 0.640 - j1.100		+0.592		Z = 0.640 - j0.508
105	Z = 0.900 - j1.260		+0.622		Z = 0.900 - j0.638
110	Z = 0.560 - j1.200		+0.652		Z = 0.560 - j0.548
120	Z = 0.580 - j1.000		+0.711		Z = 0.580 - j0.289
130	Z = 0.600 - j0.770		+0.770		Z = 0.600 + j0
140	Z = 0.660 - j0.560		+0.829		Z = 0.660 + j0.269
150	Z = 0.720 - j0.400		+0.888		Z = 0.720 + j0.488
160	Z = 0.800 - j0.250		+0.948		Z = 0.800 + j0.698

The result of this move is shown in Figure 6-10(b).

Step 4. The characteristic of the new impedance curve calls for a shunt stub to fold the curve into the SWR circle. Shunt elements require that we work with admittance instead of impedance. Invert the impedance curve into its equivalent admittance curve.(see Fig. 6-10(c)).

Step 5. A short-circuited 50-ohm shunt stub 90 degrees long at 130 mHz will be the initial approach. To determine the stub length at other frequencies

$$\theta^{o}_{f_x} = 90^{o} \times \frac{f_x}{130}$$

f_{mHz}	θ_{f_x}
100	69.2
105	72.7
110	76.2
120	83.1
130	90.0
140	96.9
150	103.8
160	110.8

Step 6. Determine the susceptance at other frequencies.

f_{mHz}	θ^o	X = 50 tan θ	B = 1/(50 tan θ)	B/Y_0
100	69.2	131.6	-0.0076	-0.380
105	72.7	160.5	-0.0062	-0.312
110	76.2	203.6	-0.0049	-0.246
120	83.1	413.2	-0.0024	-0.121
130	90.0	-----	0	0
140	96.9	-413.2	+0.0024	+0.121
150	103.8	-203.6	+0.0049	+0.246
160	110.8	-131.6	+0.0076	+0.380

Step 7. Add the susceptance obtained in Step 6 to the admittance curve of Figure 6-10(c).

fmHz	Old Position	+	Correction	=	New Position
100	Y = 0.850 + j0.770		(-0.380)		Y = 0.850 + j0.390
105	Y = 0.745 + j0.510		(-0.312)		Y = 0.745 + j0.198
110	Y = 0.940 + j0.875		(-0.246)		Y = 0.940 + j0.629
120	Y = 1.380 + j0.650		(-0.121)		Y = 1.380 + j0.529
130	Y = 1.650 + j0		0		Y = 1.650 + j0
140	Y = 1.290 - j0.525		+0.121		Y = 1.290 - j0.404
150	Y = 0.950 - j0.650		+0.246		Y = 0.950 - j0.404
160	Y = 0.720 - j0.620		+0.380		Y = 0.720 - j0.240

The new admittance position is shown in Figure 6-10(d). The curve has not folded a sufficient amount. Another attempt will be made using a 25-ohm shunt stub line. Reducing the shunt stub line impedance from 50 ohms to 25 ohms will double the amount of susceptance. Compute for the susceptance using 25 ohms as the line impedance.

f_{mHz}	Old Position	+	Correction	=	New Position
100	Y = 0.850 + j0.770		(-0.760)		Y = 0.850 + j0.010
105	Y = 0.745 + j0.510		(-0.624)		Y = 0.745 - j0.114
110	Y = 0.940 + j0.875		(-0.492)		Y = 0.940 + j0.383
120	Y = 1.380 + j0.650		(-0.242		Y = 1.380 + j0.408
130	Y = 1.650 + j0		0		Y = 1.650 + j0
140	Y = 1.290 - j0.525		+0.242		Y = 1.290 - j0.283
150	Y = 0.950 - j0.650		+0.492		Y = 0.950 - 0.158
160	Y = 0.720 - j0.620		+0.760		Y = 0.720 + j0.140

Summary. This has been a relatively successful matching exercise. The requirement of placing the impedance curve within a SWR circle of 2.0 to 1 was achieved with a 50-ohm shunt stub resonant at 130 mHz. It was felt that the final impedance curve could be improved with a 25-ohm shunt stub. The results obtained with the 25-ohm stub are shown in Figure 6-10(e). Note that the worse case SWR is at 130 mHz which is 1.65 to 1.

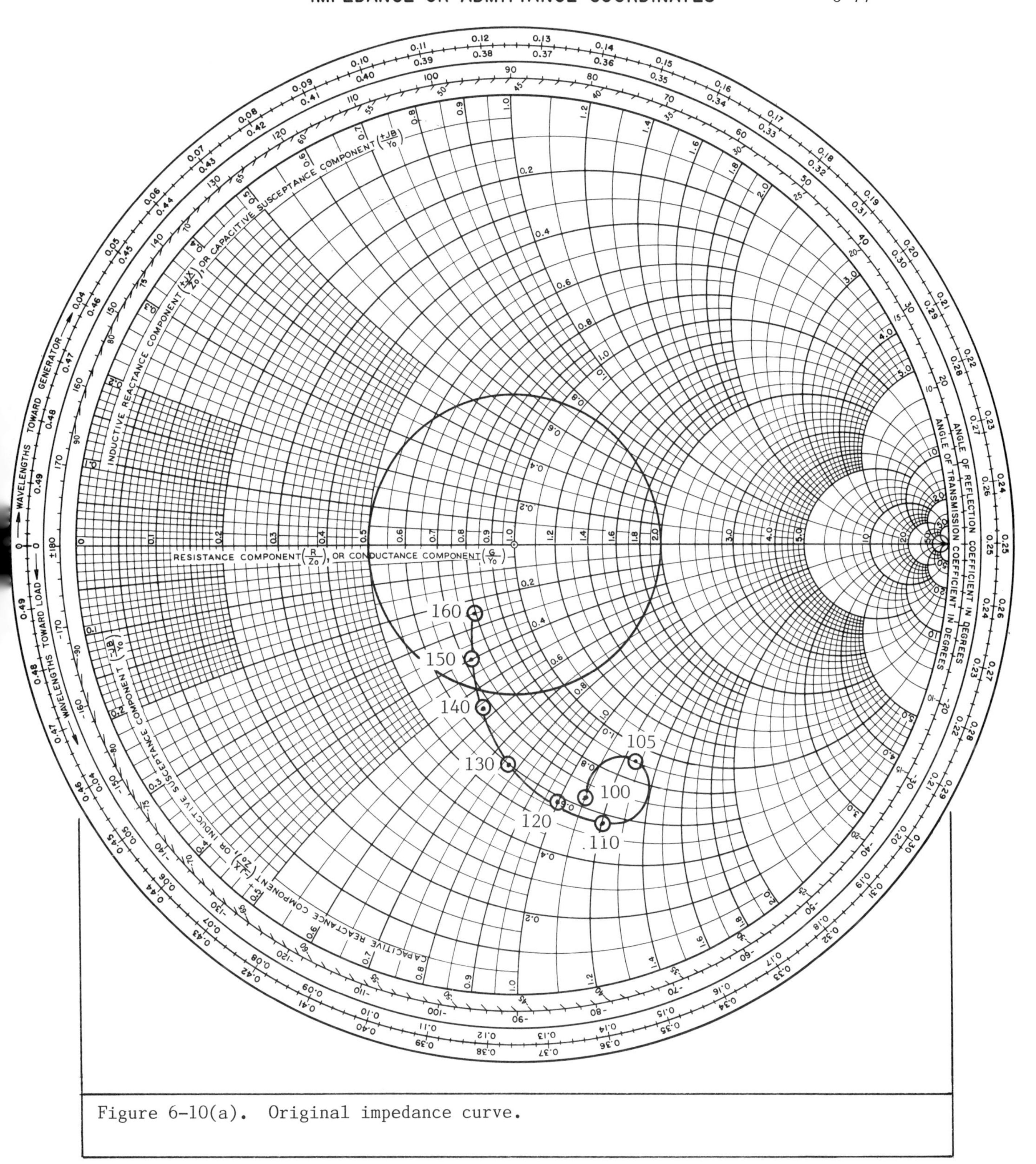

Figure 6-10(a). Original impedance curve.

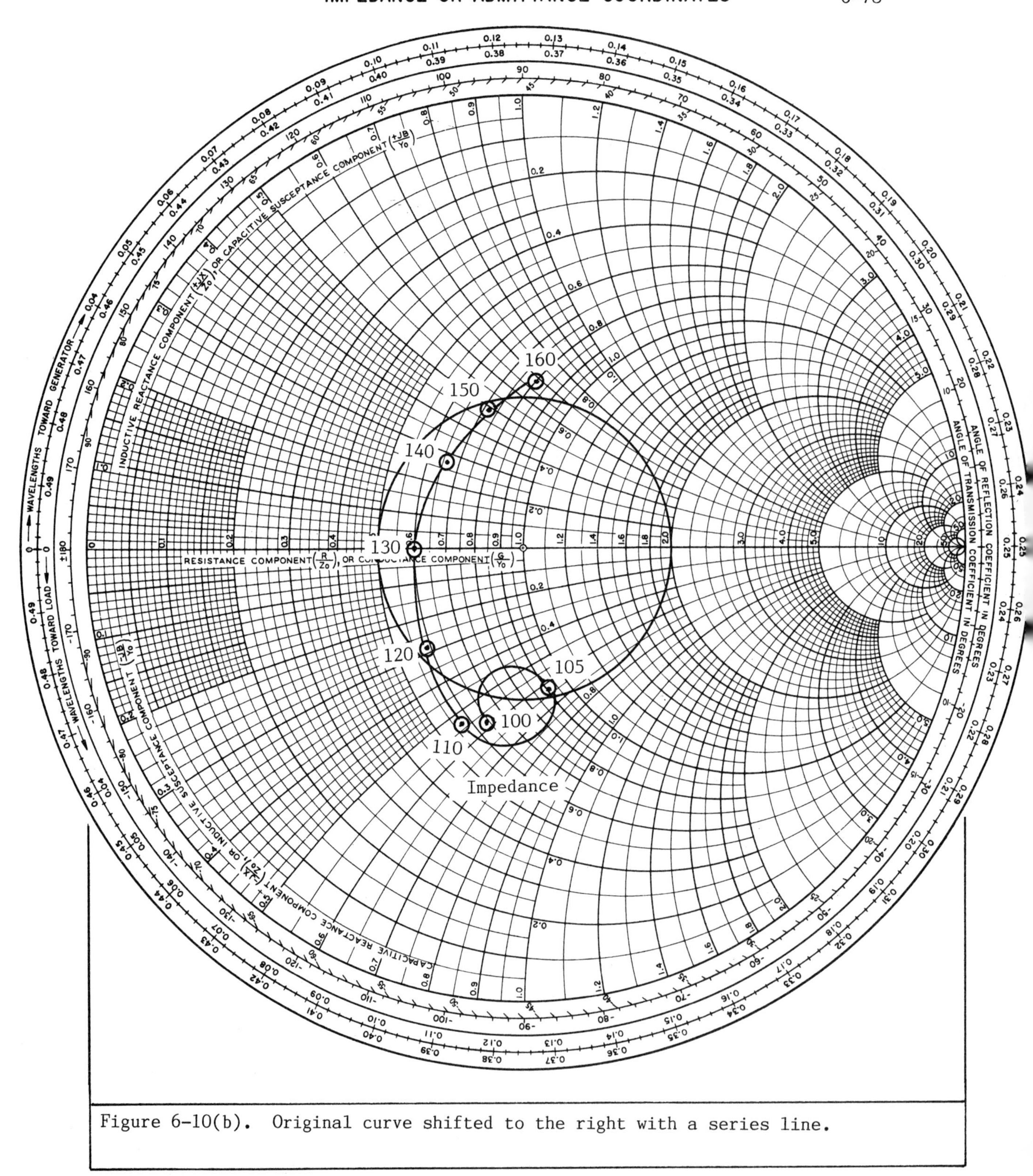

Figure 6-10(b). Original curve shifted to the right with a series line.

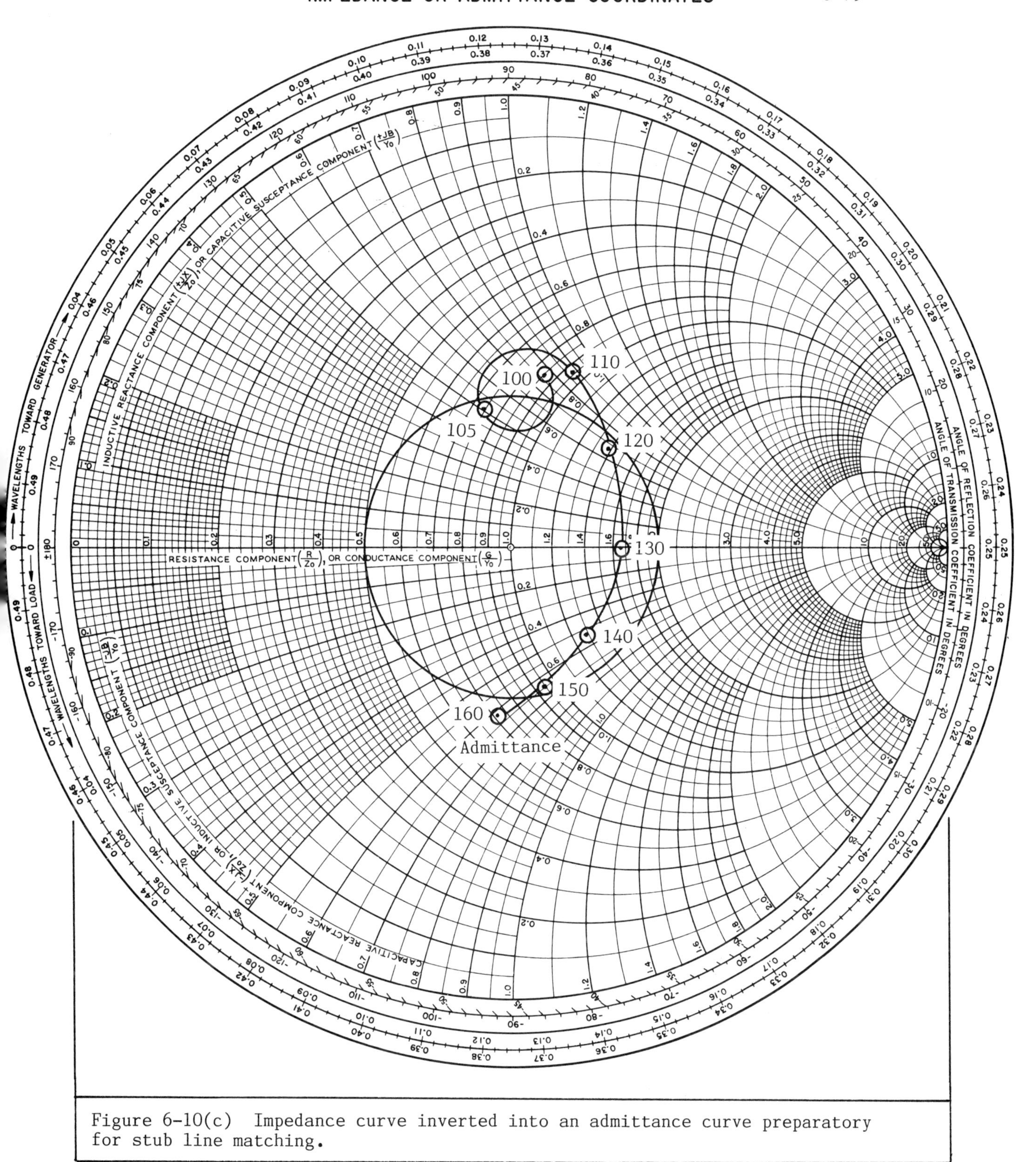

Figure 6-10(c) Impedance curve inverted into an admittance curve preparatory for stub line matching.

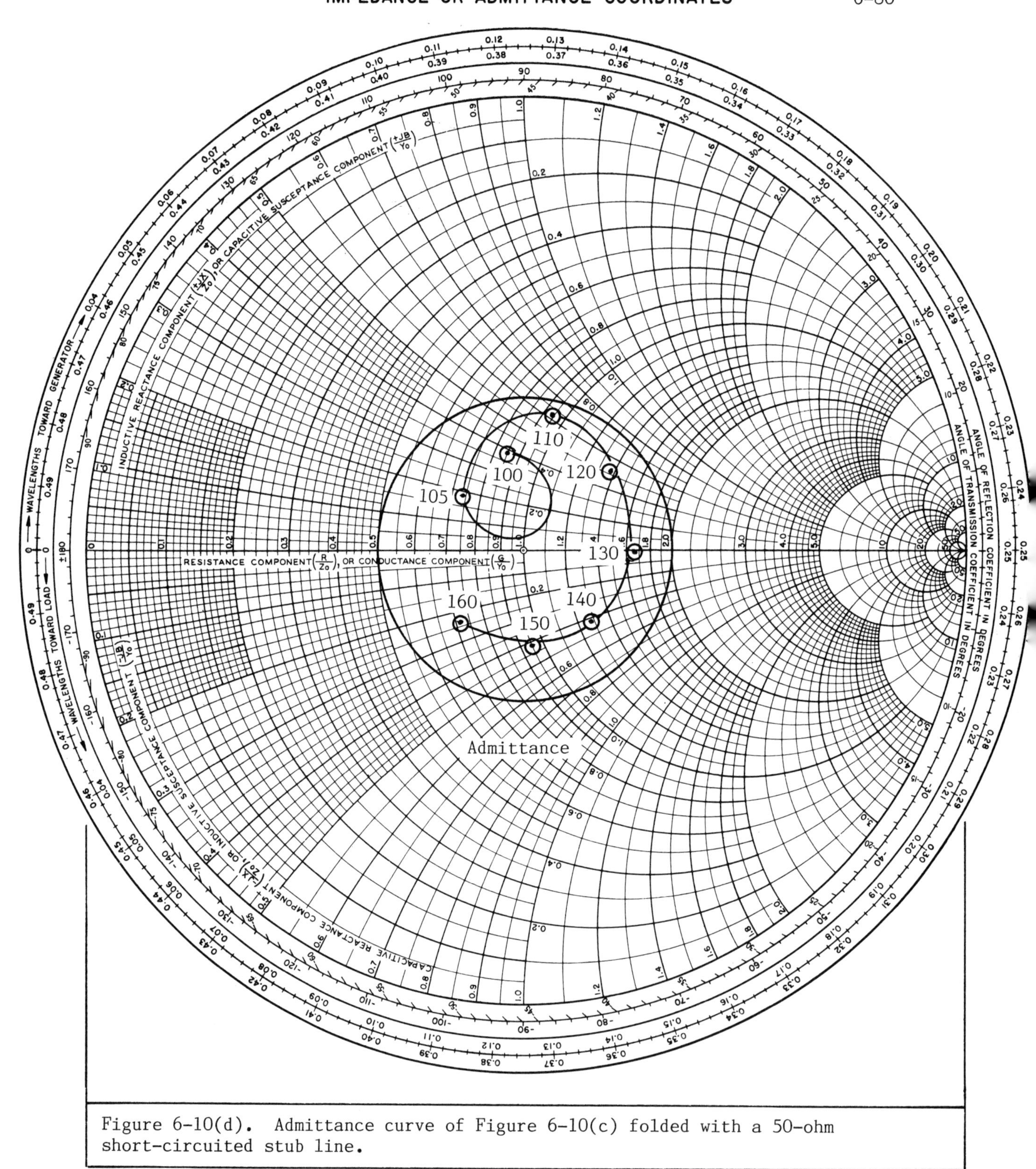

Figure 6-10(d). Admittance curve of Figure 6-10(c) folded with a 50-ohm short-circuited stub line.

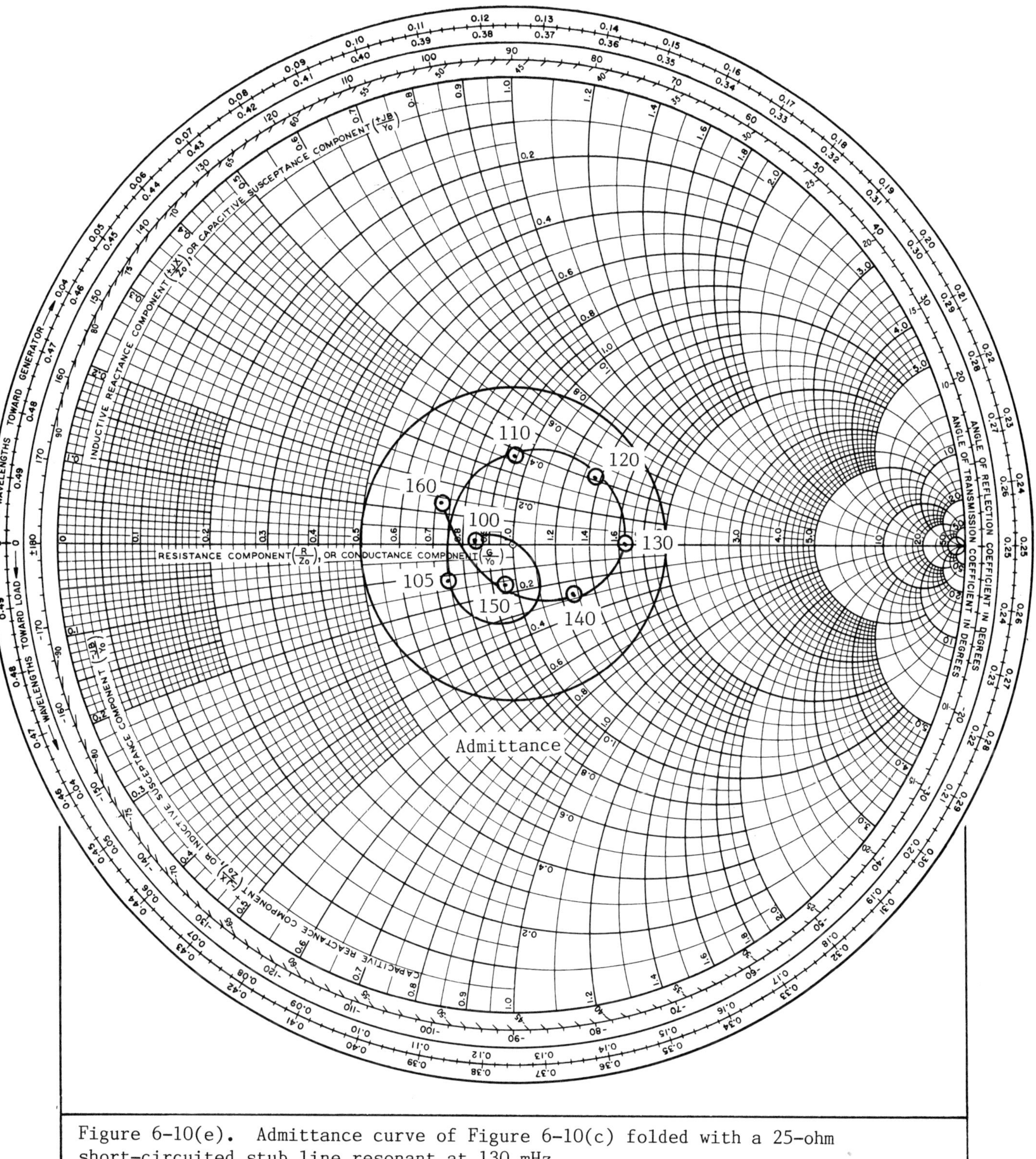

Figure 6-10(e). Admittance curve of Figure 6-10(c) folded with a 25-ohm short-circuited stub line resonant at 130 mHz.

Example No. 11. Problem: The following is the impedance of a long wire receiving antenna. Match this antenna to a SWR of 5.0 to 1 or better. This is a particularly difficult and tedious exercise because of the extreme bandwidth and the number of frequency points that must be plotted.

f_{mHz}	Impedance	Normalized Impedance
2.0	Z = 450 - j150	Z = 9.00 - j3.00
2.2	Z = 100 - j150	Z = 2.00 - j3.00
2.4	Z = 40 - j92.5	Z = 0.80 - j1.85
2.6	Z = 45 - j45.0	Z = 0.90 - j0.90
2.8	Z = 59 + j25.0	Z = 1.18 + j0.50
3.0	Z = 73 + j65.0	Z = 1.46 + j1.30
3.2	Z = 50 + j85.0	Z = 1.00 + j1.70
3.4	Z = 80 + j147.5	Z = 1.60 + j2.95
3.6	Z = 145 + j85.0	Z = 2.90 + j1.70
3.8	Z = 107.5 + j90	Z = 2.15 + j1.80
4.0	Z = 215 + j170	Z = 4.30 + j3.40
4.2	Z = 215 + j110	Z = 4.30 + j2.20
4.4	Z = 375 + j190	Z = 7.50 + j3.80
4.6	Z = 375 + j50.0	Z = 7.50 + j1.00
4.8	Z = 600 - j200	Z = 12.0 - j4.00
5.0	Z = 450 - j75.0	Z = 9.00 - j1.50
5.2	Z = 300 - j135	Z = 6.00 - j2.70
5.4	Z = 400 - j225	Z = 8.00 - j4.50
5.6	Z = 300 - j325	Z = 6.00 - j6.50
5.8	Z = 210 - j250	Z = 4.20 - j5.00
6.0	Z = 150 - j300	Z = 3.00 - j6.00

The impedance curve is presented in Figure 6-11(a).

Step 1. The first move will be to rotate the impedance curve out of the critical boundary circle "B". A shunt capacitor will be used. The advantage is that the shunt capacitor will cause the high frequencies to move faster than the low frequencies thus reducing the size of the impedance curve. The direction of rotation will be clockwise. Since the first move is with a shunt capacitor, the impedance curve must be inverted into its equivalent admittance curve (see Fig. 6-11(b)). A susceptance of +0.360 chartmho at 5.4 mHz will be tried. The extent of the move at other frequencies is determined by

$$B_{f_x} = +0.360 \times \frac{f_x}{5.4} \text{ chartmho}$$

f_{mHz}	Old Position	+	Correction	=	New Position
2.0	Y = 0.100 + j0.035		0.133		Y = 0.100 + j0.168
2.2	Y = 0.150 + j0.230		0.147		Y = 0.150 + j0.377
2.4	Y = 0.200 + j0.460		0.160		Y = 0.200 + j0.620
2.6	Y = 0.550 + j0.560		0.173		Y = 0.550 + j0.733
2.8	Y = 0.720 - j0.300		0.187		Y = 0.720 - j0.113
3.0	Y = 0.381 - j0.340		0.200		Y = 0.381 - j0.140
3.2	Y = 0.240 - j0.430		0.213		Y = 0.240 - j0.217
3.4	Y = 0.140 - j0.260		0.227		Y = 0.140 - j0.033
3.6	Y = 0.250 - j0.150		0.240		Y = 0.250 + j0.090
3.8	Y = 0.270 - j0.210		0.253		Y = 0.270 + j0.043
4.0	Y = 0.140 - j0.115		0.267		Y = 0.140 + j0.152
4.2	Y = 0.180 - j0.095		0.280		Y = 0.180 + j0.185
4.4	Y = 0.100 - j0.051		0.293		Y = 0.100 + j0.242
4.6	Y = 0.125 - j0.015		0.307		Y = 0.125 + j0.292
4.8	Y = 0.070 + j0.025		0.320		Y = 0.070 + j0.345
5.0	Y = 0.105 + j0.020		0.333		Y = 0.105 + j0.353
5.2	Y = 0.135 + j0.065		0.347		Y = 0.135 + j0.412
5.4	Y = 0.095 + j0.055		0.360		Y = 0.095 + j0.415
5.6	Y = 0.075 + j0.085		0.373		Y = 0.075 + j0.458
5.8	Y = 0.095 + j0.125		0.387		Y = 0.095 + j0.512
6.0	Y = 0.060 + j0.135		0.400		Y = 0.060 + j0.535

The new admittance curve is plotted in Figure 6-11(c).

Step 2. This step will be made with a series inductor. The inductor will move the curve along lines of constant resistance in a clockwise manner. Before incorporating the series inductor the admittance curve must be inverted into its equivalent impedance curve (see Fig. 6-11(d)) and the reactance added to it. A reactance of +1.360 chartohms at 6.0 mHz will be tried. To compute for the reactance at other frequencies

$$X_{f_x} = 1.360 \times \frac{f_x}{6.0} \quad \text{chartohms}$$

f_{mHz}	Old Position	+	Correction	=	New Position
2.0	Z = 2.700 - j4.500		0.453		Z = 2.700 - j4.047
2.2	Z = 0.900 - j2.300		0.499		Z = 0.900 - j1.801
2.4	Z = 0.480 - j1.450		0.544		Z = 0.480 - j0.906
2.6	Z = 0.650 - j0.875		0.589		Z = 0.650 - j0.286
2.8	Z = 1.340 + j0.220		0.635		Z = 1.340 + j0.855
3.0	Z = 2.300 + j0.800		0.680		Z = 2.300 + j1.480
3.2	Z = 2.300 + j2.000		0.725		Z = 2.300 + j2.725
3.4	Z = 7.700 + j1.950		0.771		Z = 7.700 + j2.721
3.6	Z = 3.500 - j1.200		0.816		Z = 3.500 - j0.384
3.8	Z = 3.500 - j0.550		0.861		Z = 3.500 + j0.311
4.0	Z = 3.300 - j3.500		0.907		Z = 3.300 - j2.593
4.2	Z = 2.750 - j2.800		0.952		Z = 2.750 - j1.848
4.4	Z = 1.400 - j3.500		0.997		Z = 1.400 - j2.503
4.6	Z = 1.200 - j2.900		1.043		Z = 1.200 - j1.857
4.8	Z = 0.550 - j2.750		1.088		Z = 0.550 - j1.662
5.0	Z = 0.750 - j2.750		1.133		Z = 0.750 - j1.617
5.2	Z = 0.710 - j2.210		1.179		Z = 0.710 - j1.031
5.4	Z = 0.500 - j2.300		1.224		Z = 0.500 - j1.076
5.6	Z = 0.370 - j2.150		1.269		Z = 0.370 - j0.881
5.8	Z = 0.340 - j1.880		1.315		Z = 0.340 - j0.565
6.0	Z = 0.210 - j1.820		1.360		Z = 0.210 - j0.460

The new impedance curve is plotted in Figure 6-11(e).

Step 3. This step involves a shunt inductor. This inductor will cause the impedance curve to rotate in a counterclockwise direction along lines of constant conductance. Hopefully, this should place the impedance curve more central in the SWR circle and out of the boundary circle. A shunt element requires that the impedance curve be inverted into its equivalent admittance curve (see Fig. 6-11(f)). A susceptance of -0.850 chartmho at 2.0 will be tried. Determine the susceptance for other frequencies and add to the admittance.

$$B_{f_x} = -0.850 \times \frac{2.0}{f_x} \text{ chartmho}$$

f_{mHz}	Old Position	+	Correction	=	New Position
2.0	Y = 0.115 + j0.170		(-0.850)		Y = 0.115 - j0.680
2.2	Y = 0.220 + j0.435		(-0.773)		Y = 0.220 - j0.338
2.4	Y = 0.450 + j0.850		(-0.708)		Y = 0.450 + j0.142
2.6	Y = 1.300 + j0.570		(-0.654)		Y = 1.300 - j0.084
2.8	Y = 0.525 - j0.340		(-0.607)		Y = 0.525 - j0.947
3.0	Y = 0.300 - j0.200		(-0.567)		Y = 0.300 - j0.767
3.2	Y = 0.180 - j0.220		(-0.531)		Y = 0.180 - j0.751
3.4	Y = 0.120 - j0.045		(-0.500)		Y = 0.120 - j0.545
3.6	Y = 0.275 + j0.030		(-0.472)		Y = 0.275 - j0.442
3.8	Y = 0.280 - j0.030		(-0.447)		Y = 0.280 - j0.477
4.0	Y = 0.185 + j0.145		(-0.425)		Y = 0.185 - j0.280
4.2	Y = 0.245 + j0.170		(-0.405)		Y = 0.245 - j0.235
4.4	Y = 0.170 + j0.300		(-0.386)		Y = 0.170 - j0.086
4.6	Y = 0.250 + j0.380		(-0.370)		Y = 0.250 + j0.010
4.8	Y = 0.190 + j0.540		(-0.354)		Y = 0.190 + j0.186
5.0	Y = 0.230 + j0.500		(-0.340)		Y = 0.230 + j0.160
5.2	Y = 0.470 + j0.650		(-0.327)		Y = 0.470 + j0.323
5.4	Y = 0.380 + j0.770		(-0.315)		Y = 0.380 + j0.455
5.6	Y = 0.400 + j0.960		(-0.304)		Y = 0.400 + j0.656
5.8	Y = 0.790 + j1.310		(-0.293)		Y = 0.790 + j1.017
6.0	Y = 0.840 + j1.770		(-0.283)		Y = 0.840 + j1.487

The new admittance curve is plotted in Figure 6-11(g).

Step 4. A series capacitor will be added to further improve the impedance curve. The capacitor should pull into the SWR circle the low frequency end and have negligible effect on the high frequencies. In order to add reactance to the curve the admittance curve must be inverted into its equivalent impedance curve (see Fig. 6-11(h)). A capacitive reactance of +0.800 chartohm at 3.4 mHz will be added. Determine the reactance at other frequencies from

$$X_{f_x} = -0.800 \times \frac{3.4}{f_x} \text{ chartohm}$$

f_{mHz}	Old Position	+	Correction	=	New Position
2.0	Z = 0.270 + j1.500		(-1.360)		Z = 0.270 + j0.140
2.2	Z = 1.350 + j2.070		(-1.236)		Z = 1.350 + j0.834
2.4	Z = 2.000 + j0.650		(-1.133)		Z = 2.000 - j0.483
2.6	Z = 0.775 + j0.050		(-1.046)		Z = 0.775 - j0.996
2.8	Z = 0.450 + j0.800		(-0.971)		Z = 0.450 - j0.171
3.0	Z = 0.440 + j1.130		(-0.907)		Z = 0.440 + j0.223
3.2	Z = 0.300 + j1.250		(-0.850)		Z = 0.300 + j0.400
3.4	Z = 0.400 + j1.750		(-0.800)		Z = 0.400 + j0.950
3.6	Z = 0.750 + j1.470		(-0.756)		Z = 0.750 + j0.714
3.8	Z = 0.950 + j1.600		(-0.716)		Z = 0.950 + j0.884
4.0	Z = 1.700 + j2.500		(-0.680)		Z = 1.700 + j1.820
4.2	Z = 2.150 + j2.070		(-0.648)		Z = 2.150 + j1.422
4.4	Z = 4.800 + j2.200		(-0.618)		Z = 4.800 + j1.582
4.6	Z = 4.000 - j0.300		(-0.591)		Z = 4.000 - j0.891
4.8	Z = 2.700 - j2.400		(-0.567)		Z = 2.700 - j2.967
5.0	Z = 2.800 - j1.900		(-0.544)		Z = 2.800 - j2.444
5.2	Z = 1.480 - j1.100		(-0.523)		Z = 1.480 - j1.623
5.4	Z = 1.100 - j1.300		(-0.504)		Z = 1.100 - j1.804
5.6	Z = 0.675 - j1.100		(-0.486)		Z = 0.675 - j1.586
5.8	Z = 0.460 - j0.630		(-0.467)		Z = 0.460 - j1.097
6.0	Z = 0.310 - j0.500		(-0.453)		Z = 0.310 - j0.953

<u>Summary.</u> This has been a particularly difficult exercise, not only because of the extreme bandwidth but also because the impedance curve had to be moved out of the limiting boundary circle. Most of the objective of this exercise have been met, namely, a SWR not to exceed 5.0 to 1. This limit is exceeded at relatively few frequencies (see Fig. 6-11(j)). It now remains to compute the values of each matching element.

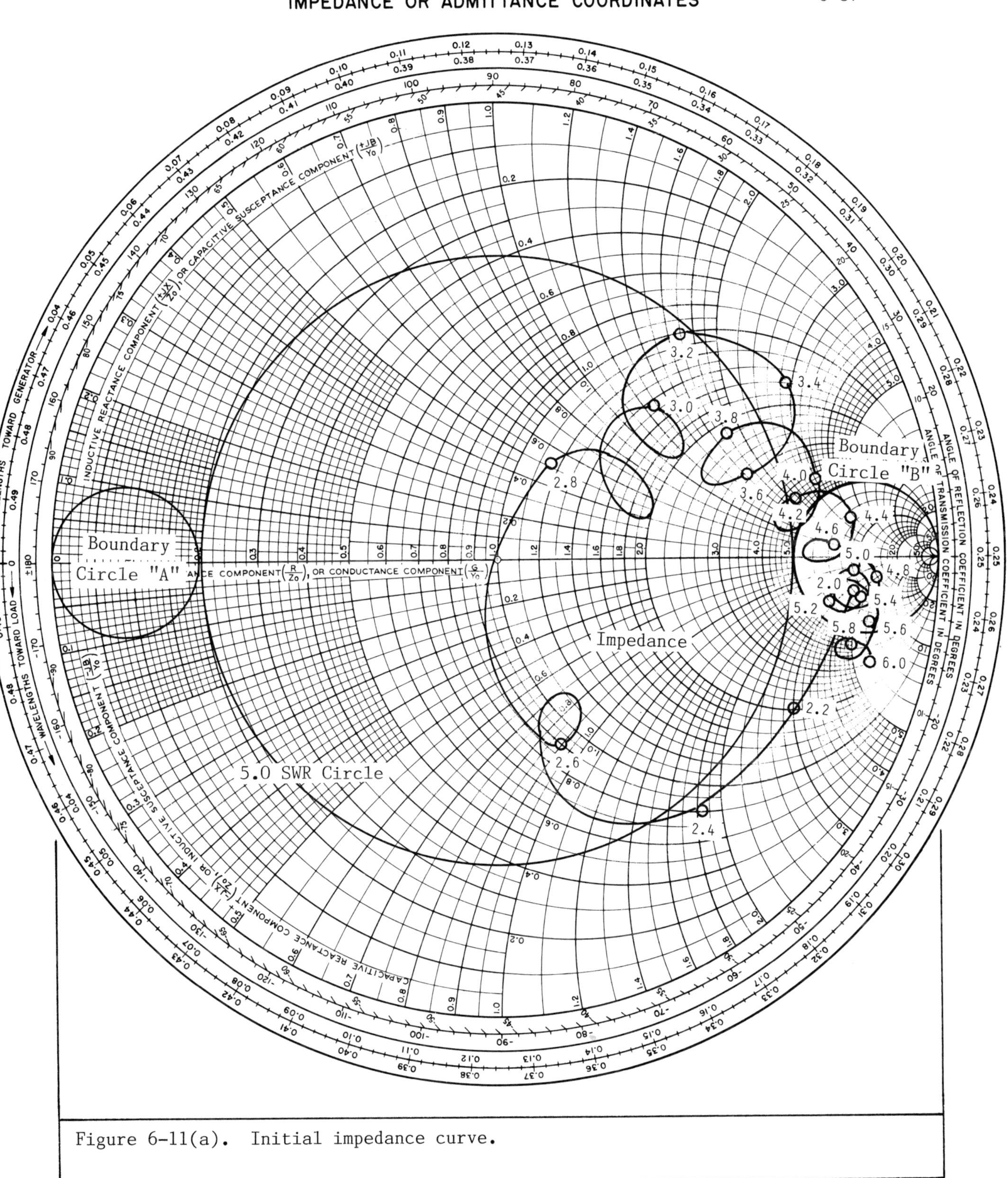

Figure 6-11(a). Initial impedance curve.

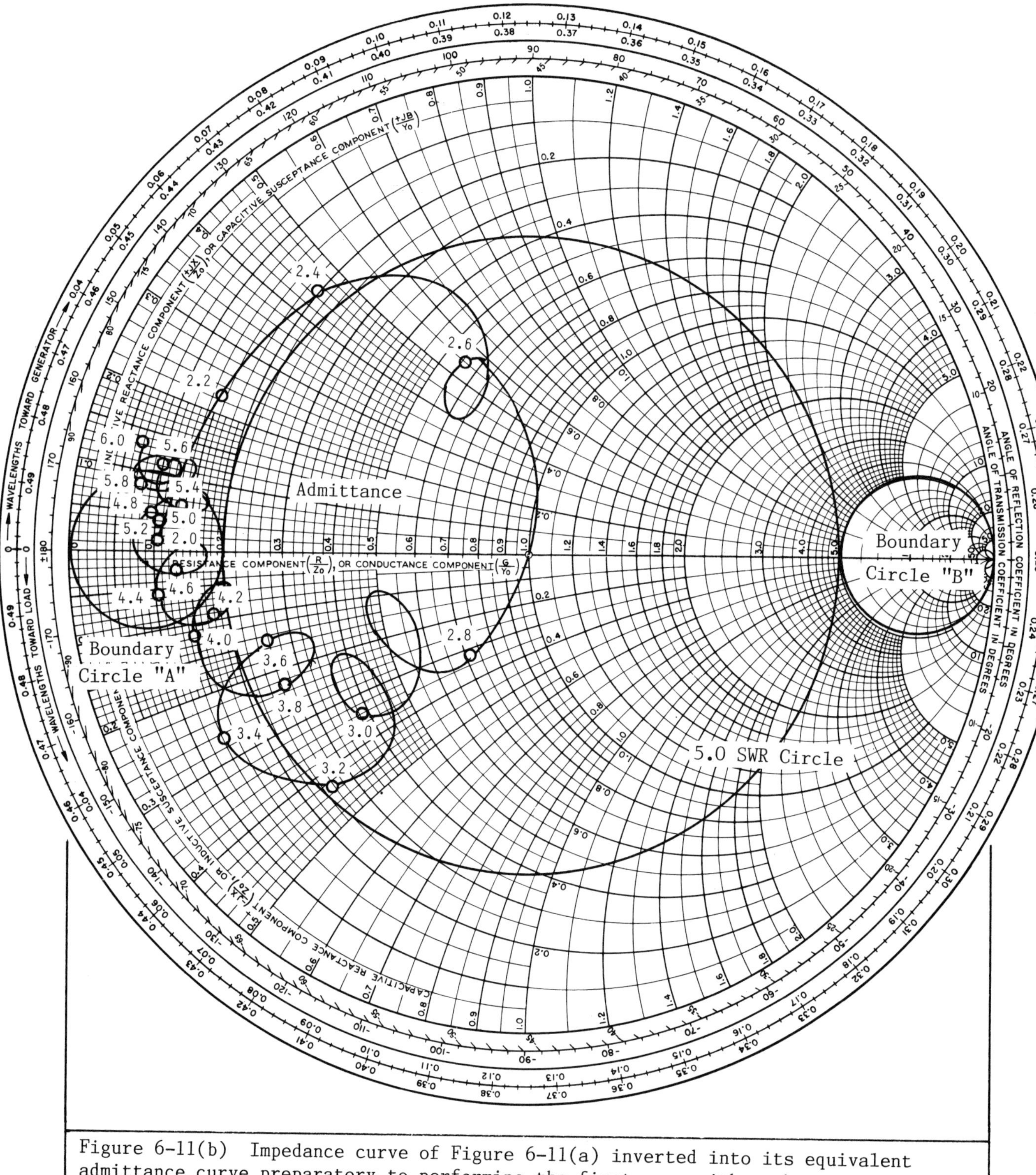

Figure 6-11(b) Impedance curve of Figure 6-11(a) inverted into its equivalent admittance curve preparatory to performing the first move with a shunt capacitor.

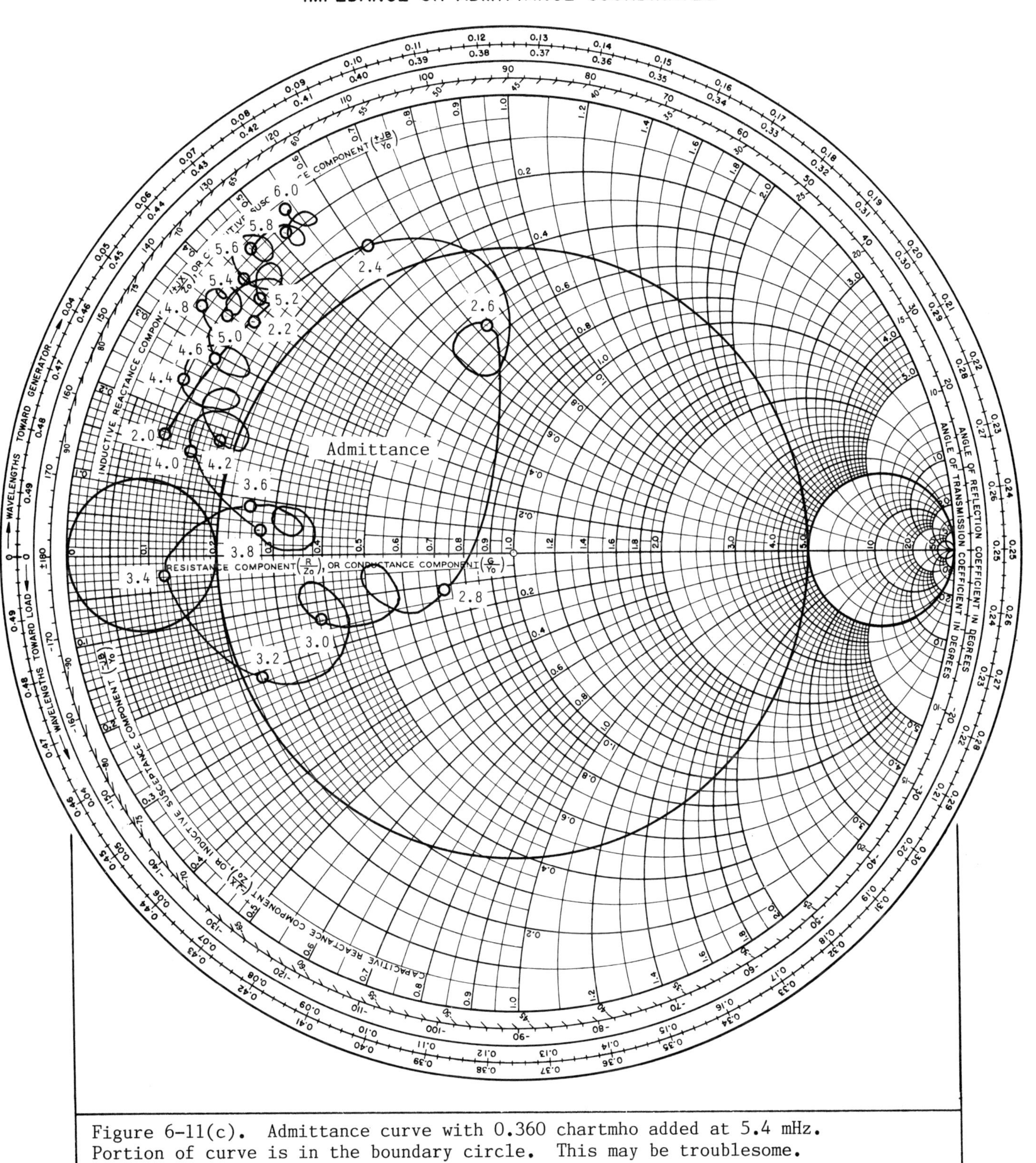

Figure 6-11(c). Admittance curve with 0.360 chartmho added at 5.4 mHz. Portion of curve is in the boundary circle. This may be troublesome.

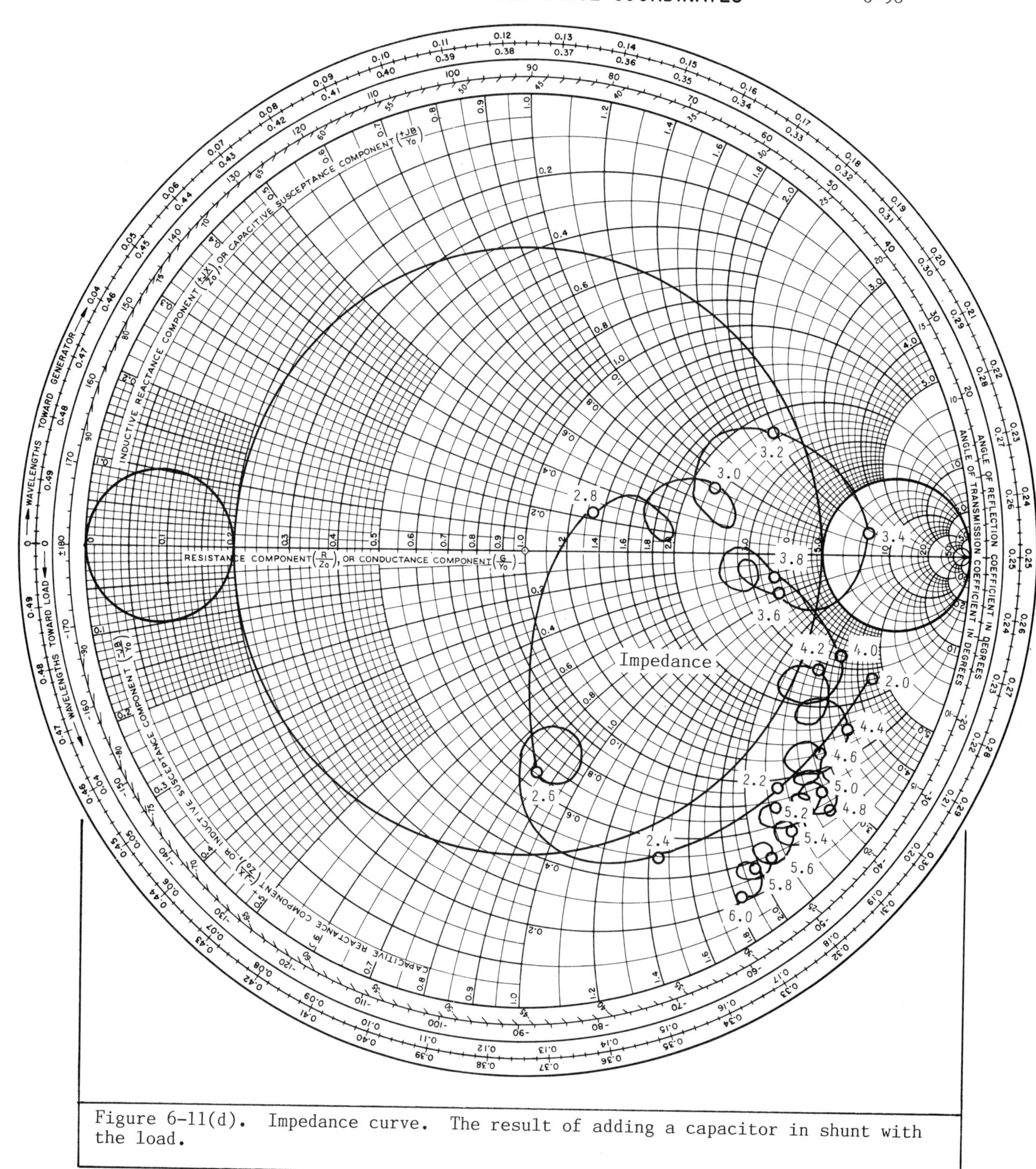

Figure 6-11(d). Impedance curve. The result of adding a capacitor in shunt with the load.

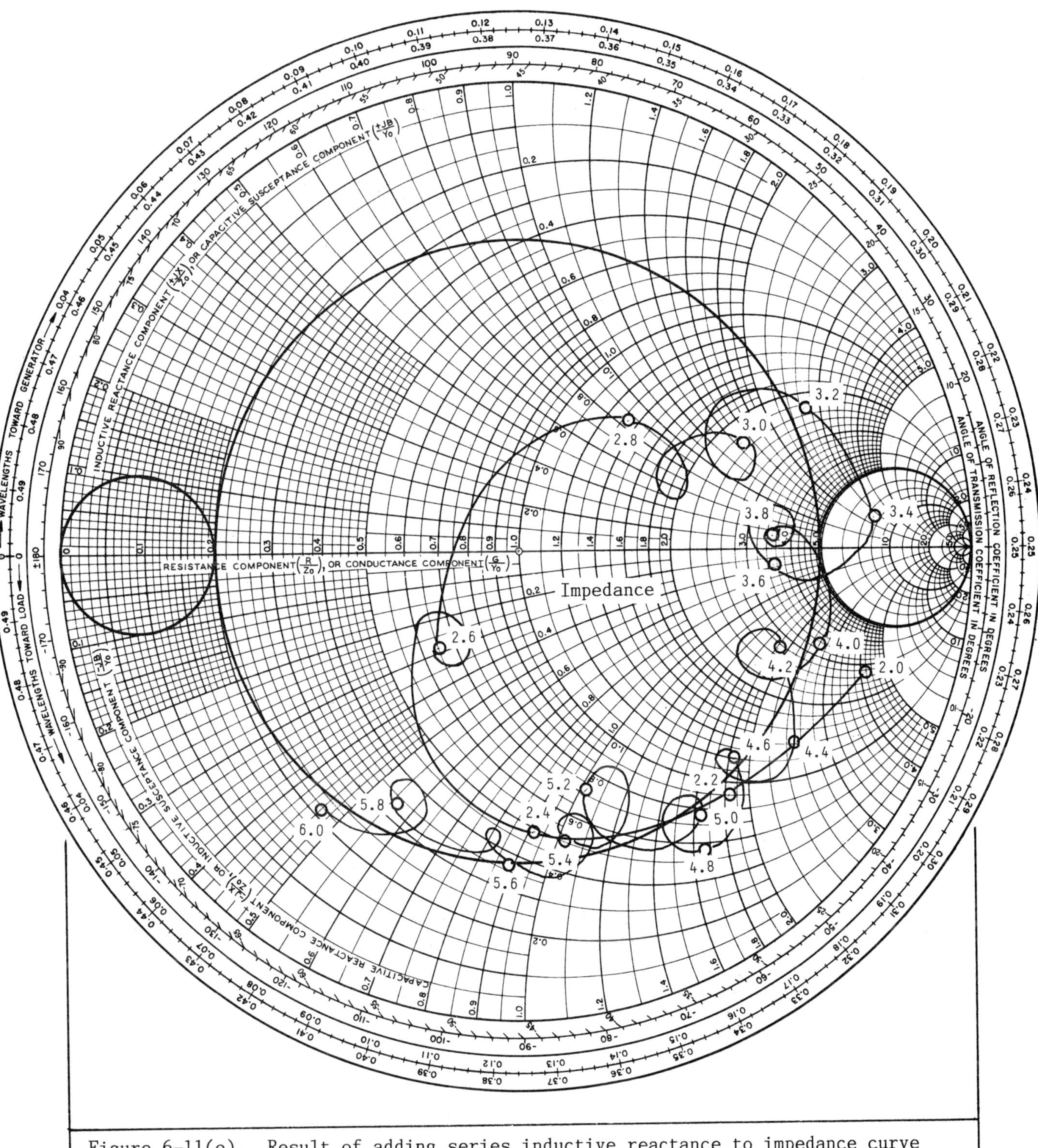

Figure 6-11(e). Result of adding series inductive reactance to impedance curve of Figure 6-11(d). Part of the curve is caught in the boundary circle.

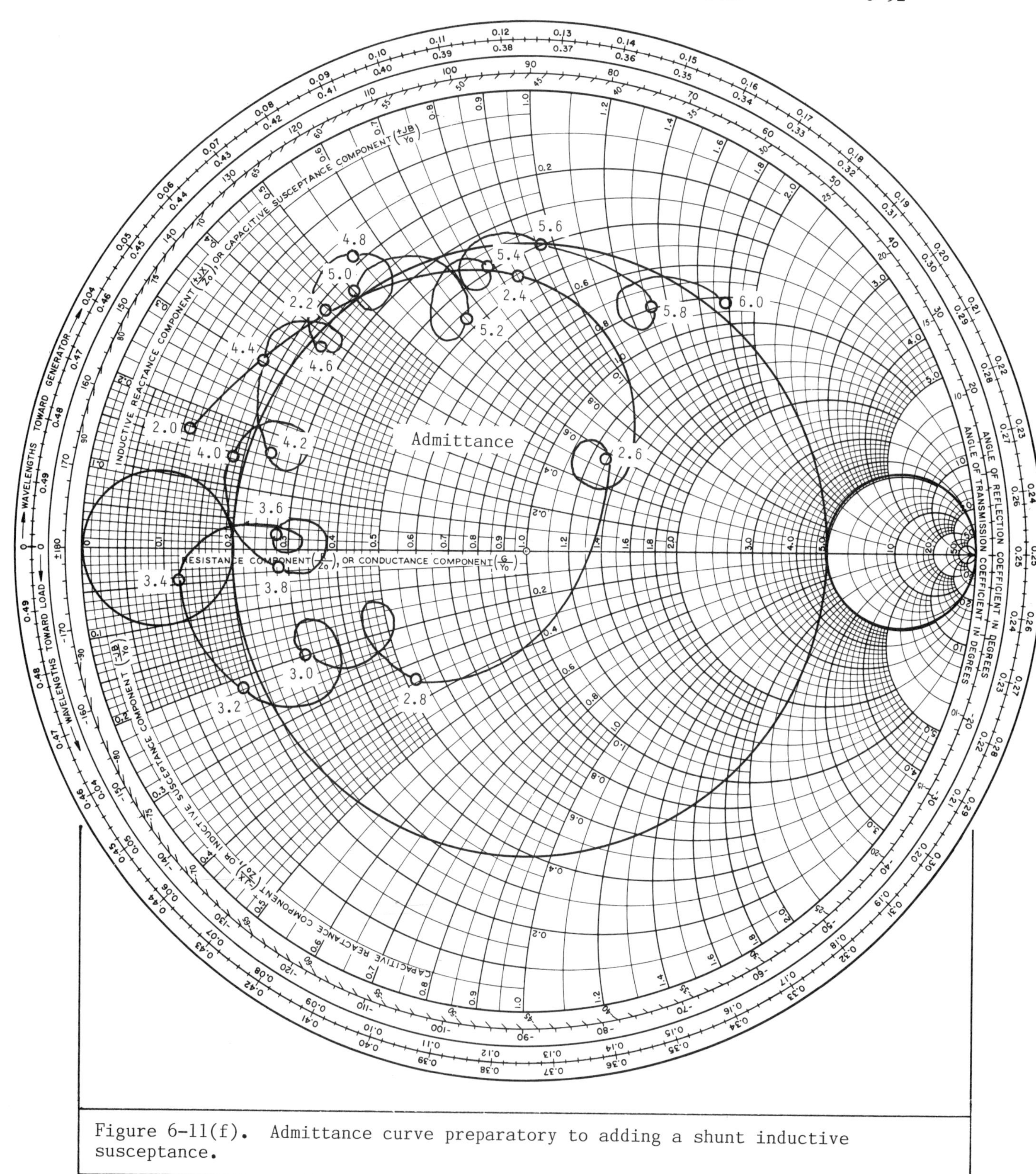

Figure 6-11(f). Admittance curve preparatory to adding a shunt inductive susceptance.

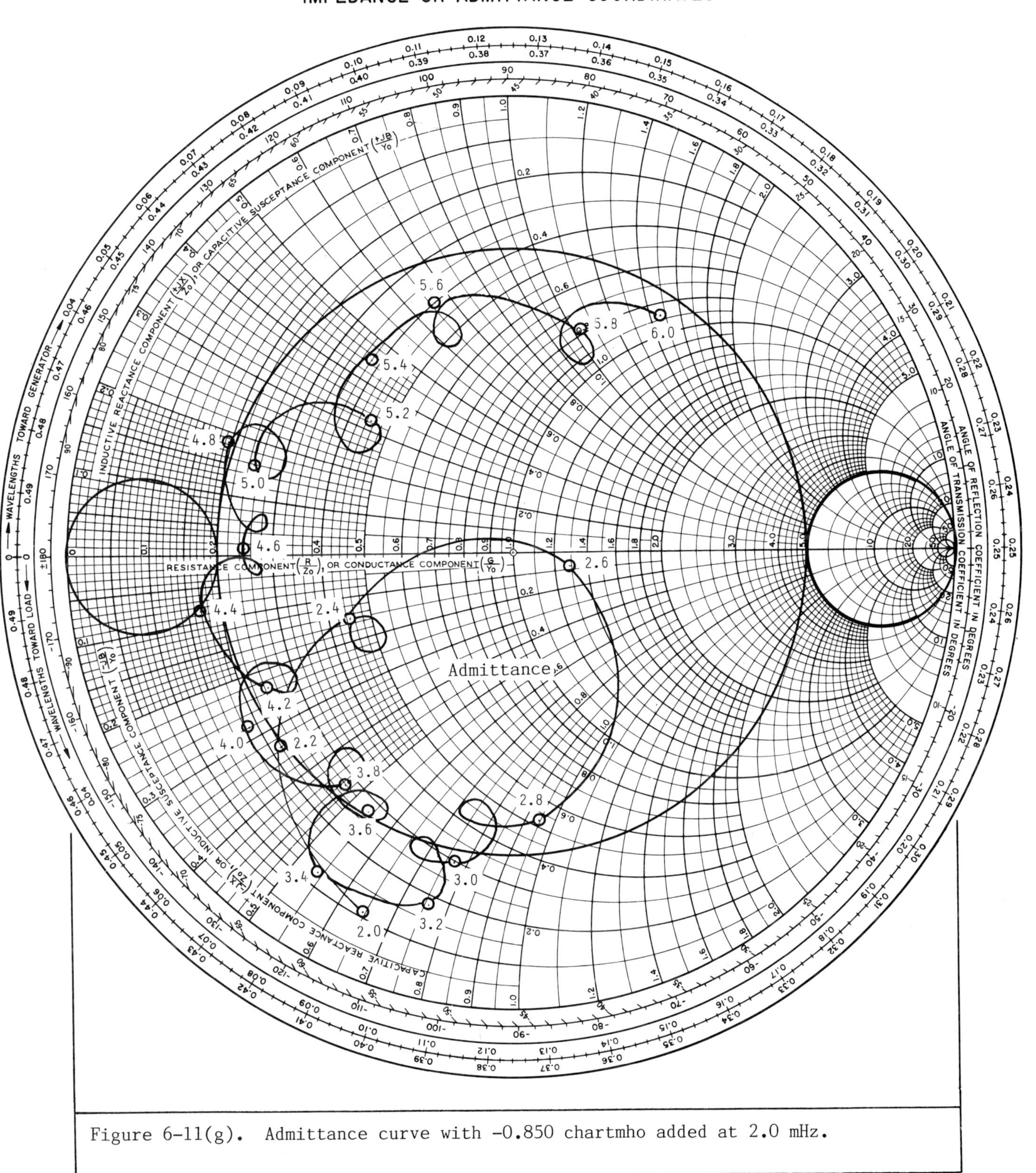

Figure 6-11(g). Admittance curve with -0.850 chartmho added at 2.0 mHz.

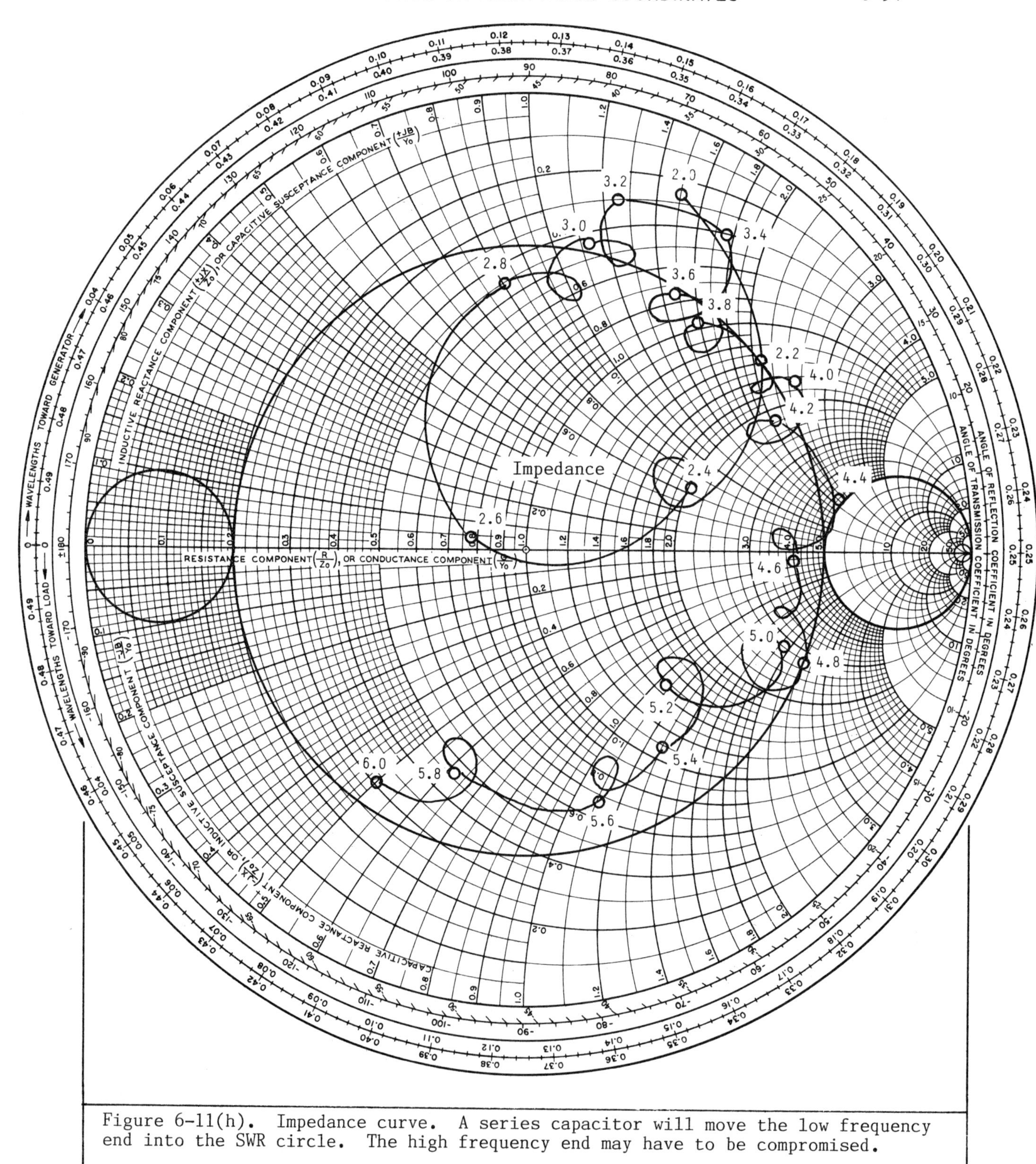

Figure 6-11(h). Impedance curve. A series capacitor will move the low frequency end into the SWR circle. The high frequency end may have to be compromised.

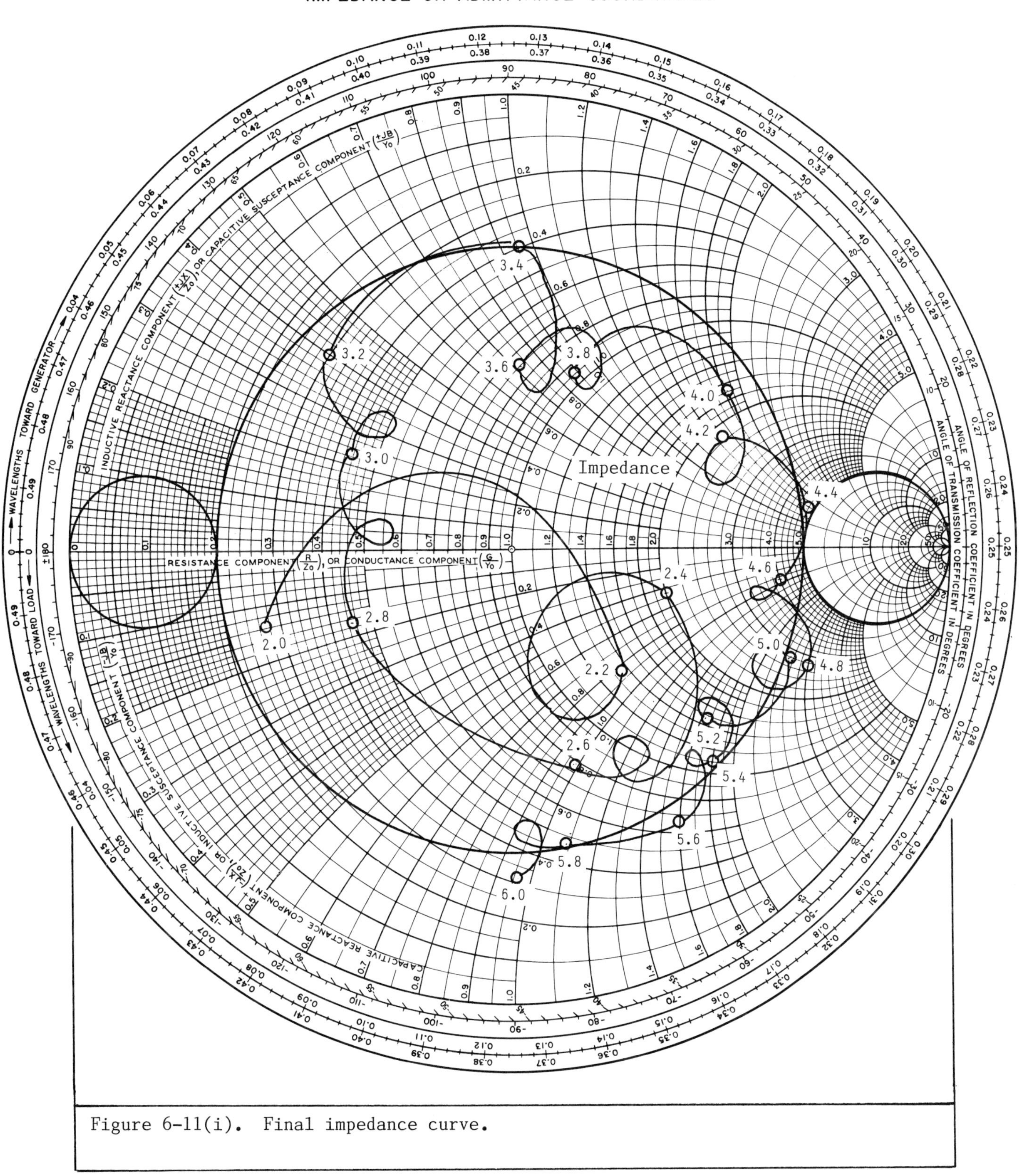

Figure 6-11(i). Final impedance curve.

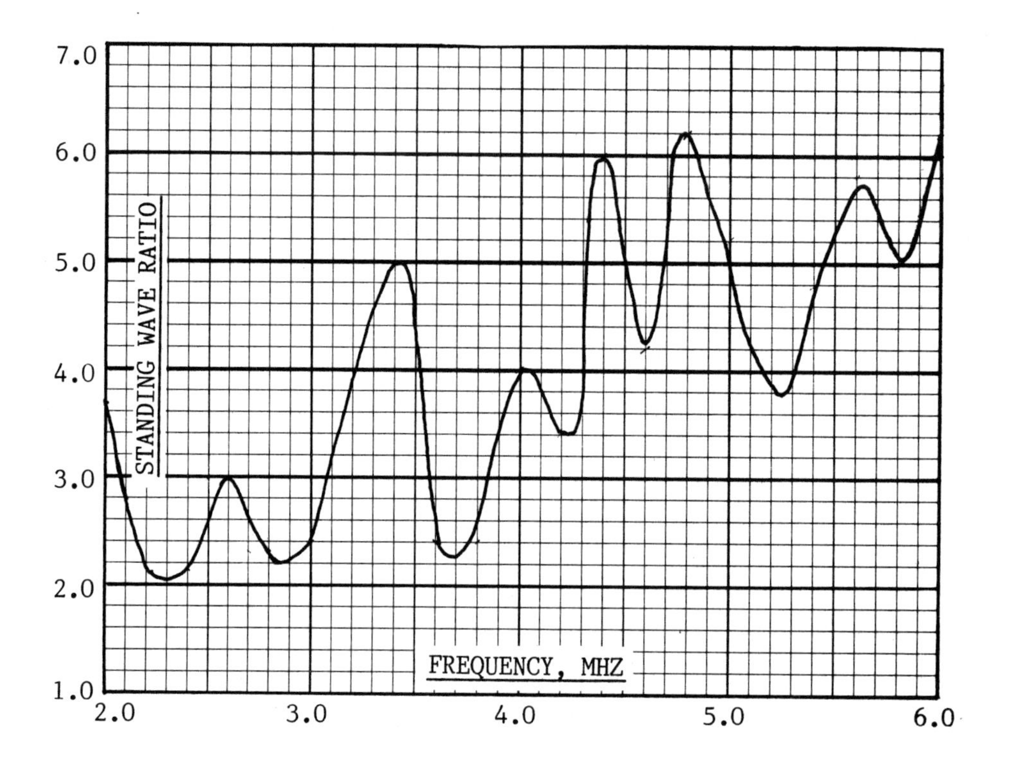

Figure 6-11(j). Standing wave ratio vs. frequency.

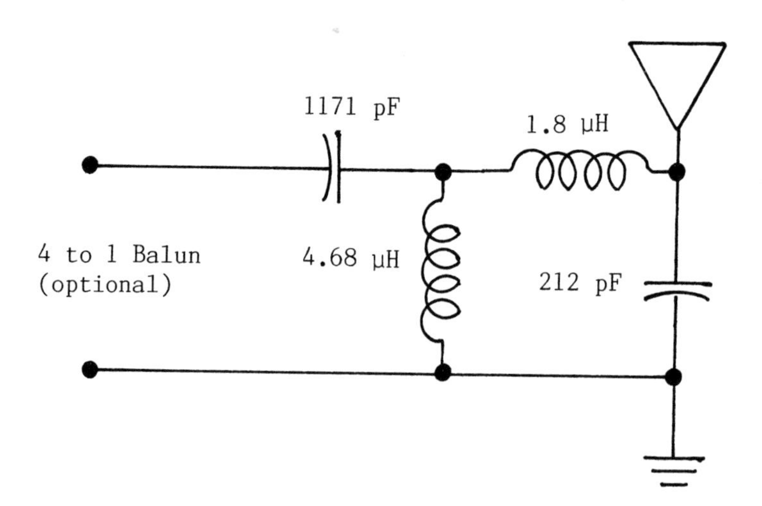

Figure 6-11(k). Schematic of matching solution.

Step 5. Determine the capacitance of the shunting capacitor:

$$C = \frac{BY_o}{2\pi f}$$

where B = 0.360 chartmho at 5.4 mHz
$Y_o = 1/Z_o$ 1/50 = 0.02 mho
f = 5.4 mHz

Substituting

$$C = \frac{0.360 \times 0.02}{6.28 \times 5.4 \times 10^6} = 212 \text{ pF}$$

Step 6. Determine the inductance of the series inductor:

$$L = \frac{XZ_o}{2\pi f}$$

where X = 1.360 chartohm at 6.0 mHz
Z_o = 50 ohms
f = 6.0 mHz

Substituting

$$L = \frac{1.360 \times 50}{6.28 \times 6.0 \times 10^6} = 1.8 \ \mu\text{H}$$

Step 7. Determine the inductance of the shunt inductor:

$$L = \frac{1}{2\pi f BY_o}$$

where B = 0.850 chartmho at 2.0 mHz
$Y_o = 1/Z_o$ = 1/50 = 0.02 mho
f = 2.0 mHz

Substituting

$$L = \frac{10^{-6}}{6.28 \times 2.0 \times 0.850 \times 0.02} = \frac{10^{-6}}{0.2135}$$

$$L = 4.68 \ \mu\text{H}$$

Step 8. Determine the capacitance of the series capacitor:

$$C = \frac{1}{2\pi fXZ_o}$$

where X = 0.80 chartohm at 3.4 mHz
Z_o = 50 ohms
f = 3.4 mHz

Substituting

$$C = \frac{10^{-6}}{6.28 \times 3.4 \times 0.80 \times 50} = \frac{10^{-6}}{854} = 1171 \text{ pF}$$

CHAPTER VII

CONSTRUCTION OF OVERLAY TRACING BOX

General.

Admittedly, using the overlay technique when inverting from impedance to admittance or vice versa saves a great deal of labor and time. For this reason the overlay tracing box was developed. There is nothing critical about the construction of this box. It can be built of readily available materials. Although construction details are provided, any convenient arrangement can be employed. This is a must project for the serious antenna designer.

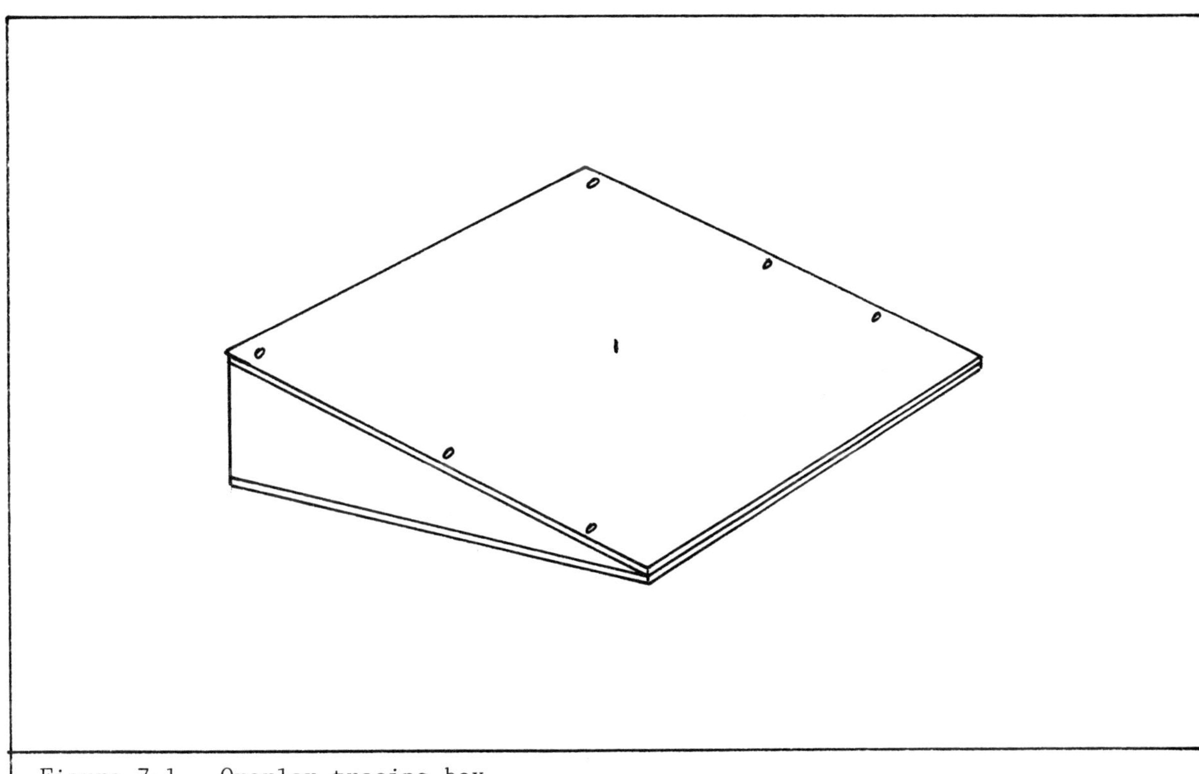

Figure 7-1. Overlay tracing box.

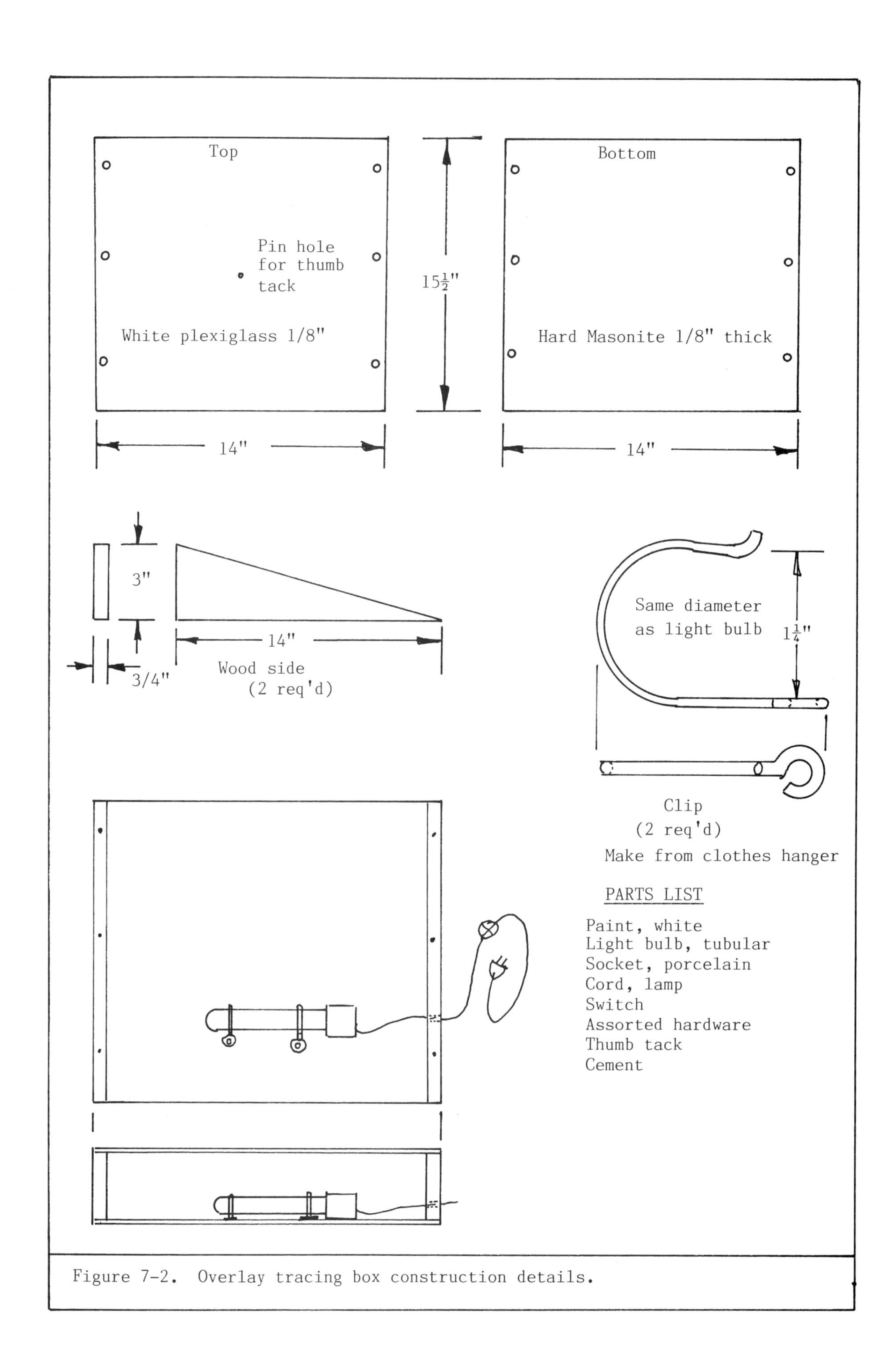

Figure 7-2. Overlay tracing box construction details.

PLAN YOUR SPRING ANTENNA WORK NOW!

THE ARRL ANTENNA BOOK Written by members of the ARRL Technical Department staff and sixteen well-known outside authors, all of whom have done much to contribute to the state-of-the-art in antenna and transmission line theory and practice. The recently published 15th Edition presents the best and most highly regarded information on antenna fundamentals, propagation, transmission lines, Yagis and quads, as well as all of the popular wire antenna designs. You'll find antennas for limited space, portable, mobile, VHF, UHF, microwave and space communications. Contains over 700 pages and 987 figures. **Chapter lineup:** Safety First, Antenna Fundamentals, The Effects of Earth, Selecting Your Antenna System, Loop Antennas, Multielement Arrays, Broadband Antennas, Log Periodic Arrays, Yagi Arrays, Quad Arrays, Long Wire and Traveling Wave Antennas, Direction Finding Antennas, Portable Antennas, Mobile and Maritime Antennas, Repeater Antennas Systems, VHF and UHF Antenna Systems, Antennas for Space Communications, Spacecraft Antennas, Antenna Materials and Accessories, Antenna Supports, Radio Wave Propagation, Transmission Lines, Coupling the Transmitter to the Line, Antenna and Transmission Line Measurements, Smith Chart Calculations, Topical Bibliography on Antennas, Glossary and Abbreviations. Edited by Gerald L. Hall, K1TD, *QST* Associate Technical Editor. Copyright 1988, #2065 $18*.

*For postage and handling add $2.50 ($3.50 for insured parcel post or UPS, please specify)

YAGI ANTENNA DESIGN is based on the series in *Ham Radio* Magazine by the late Dr. James L. Lawson, W2PV. Jim designed and built a highly competitive and successful Amateur Radio contest station. 210 pages cover the following subjects: Performance Calculations, Simple Yagis, Performance Optimization, Loop Antennas, Ground Effects, Stacking, Practical Designs, Designs for 7 through 28 MHz. Hardcover, Copyright 1986. #0410 $15*.

NOVICE ANTENNA NOTEBOOK At last, an antenna book written for the beginner! Don't let the lack of an antenna keep you from getting on the air. With this book you can choose which wire, vertical or beam antenna suits your needs, and you'll be ready for all of the fun of seeing that the antenna you put up really works! Contains pictorial drawings that show dimensions for Novice and Technician band use. Written by W1FB in his usual plain language style that makes him so popular as a *QST* author. Copyright 1988, #2073 $8*

ANTENNA COMPENDIUM We don't have room for all of the good antenna articles that are submitted to *QST;* so we have packed this volume with new material on verticals, quads, loops, Yagis, reduced-size antennas, baluns, Smith Charts, antenna polarization and other interesting subjects. 176 pages, Copyright 1985. #0194 $10*

LOW BAND DXING John Devoldere, ON4UN completely explores the 160, 80, and 40-meter bands. A large portion of this book is devoted to propagation characteristics and design and building of efficient antennas for these bands. 210 pages, Copyright 1987, #047X $10*

HF ANTENNAS FOR ALL LOCATIONS was written by L.A. Moxon, G6XN for the RSGB. Contains 264 pages of practical antenna information. This book is concerned primarily with small wire arrays, but you'll find descriptions of some aluminum antennas as well. Copyright 1982, #R576 $15*.

TRANSMISSION LINE TRANSFORMERS At last there is a source of practical design data covering the use of these devices for both commercial and amateur applications. Written by Dr. Jerry Sevick, W2FMI, this book covers types of windings, core materials, fractional-ratio windings, efficiencies, multiwinding and series transformers, baluns, limitations at high impedance levels and test equipment. Hardcover, 128 pages, Copyright 1987. #0471 $10*.

W1FB'S ANTENNA NOTEBOOK Not everyone has a great deal of real estate to put up a forest of aluminum. Doug DeMaw tells how to get the best performance out of unobtrusive wire antennas and verticals and how to build tuners and SWR bridges. 122 pages, Copyright 1987, #0488 $8* For shipping and handling add $2.50 ($3.50 for insured parcel post or UPS)—please specify.

ARRL, 225 MAIN ST., NEWINGTON, CT 06111

NAME	TITLE	DWG. NO.
SMITH CHART FORM 82-BSPR (9-66)	ANALOG INSTRUMENTS COMPANY, NEW PROVIDENCE, N.J. 07974	DATE

IMPEDANCE OR ADMITTANCE COORDINATES

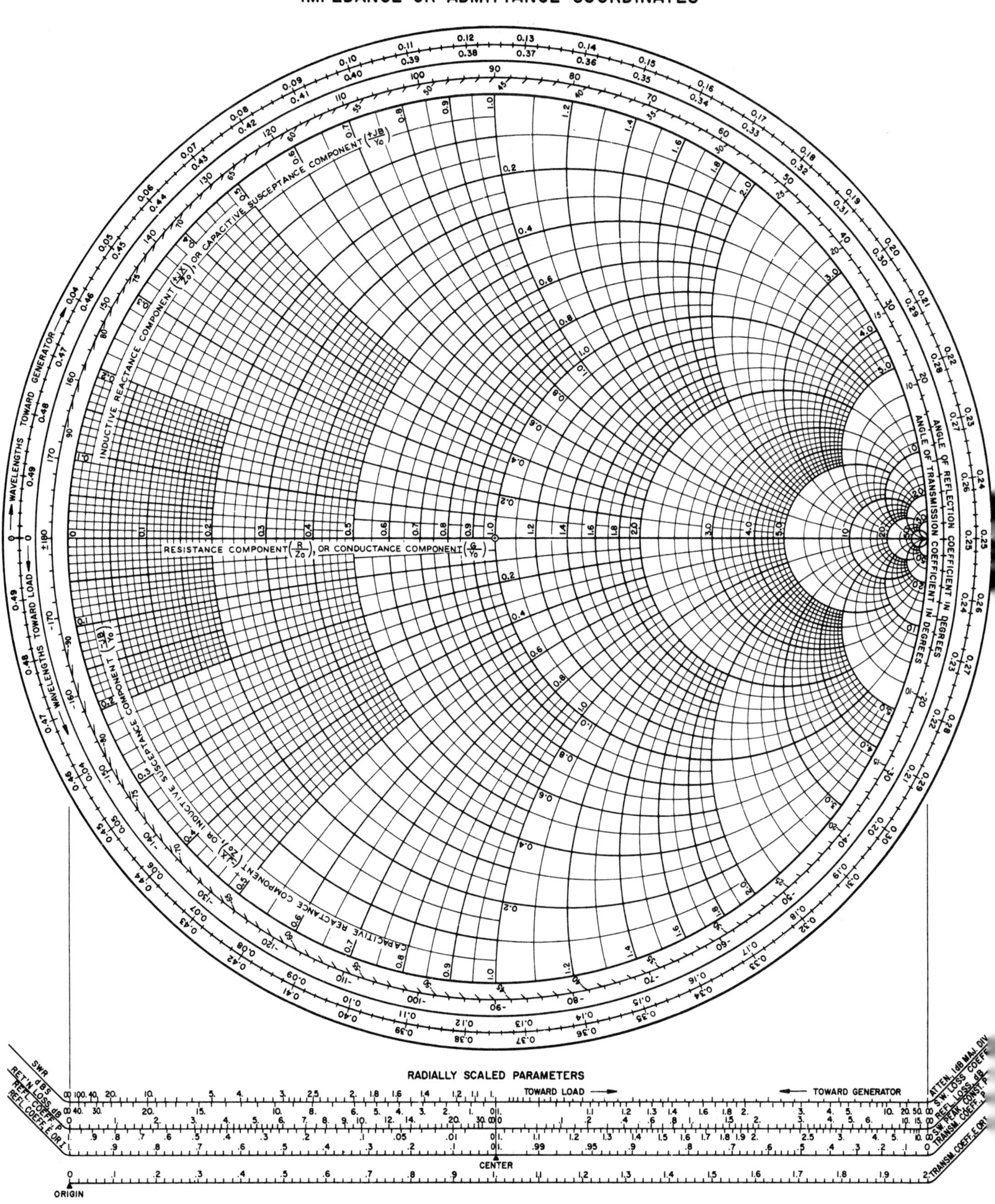

A MEGA-CHART

Notes

NAME	TITLE	DWG. NO.
SMITH CHART FORM 82-BSPR (9-66)	ANALOG INSTRUMENTS COMPANY, NEW PROVIDENCE, N.J. 07974	DATE

IMPEDANCE OR ADMITTANCE COORDINATES

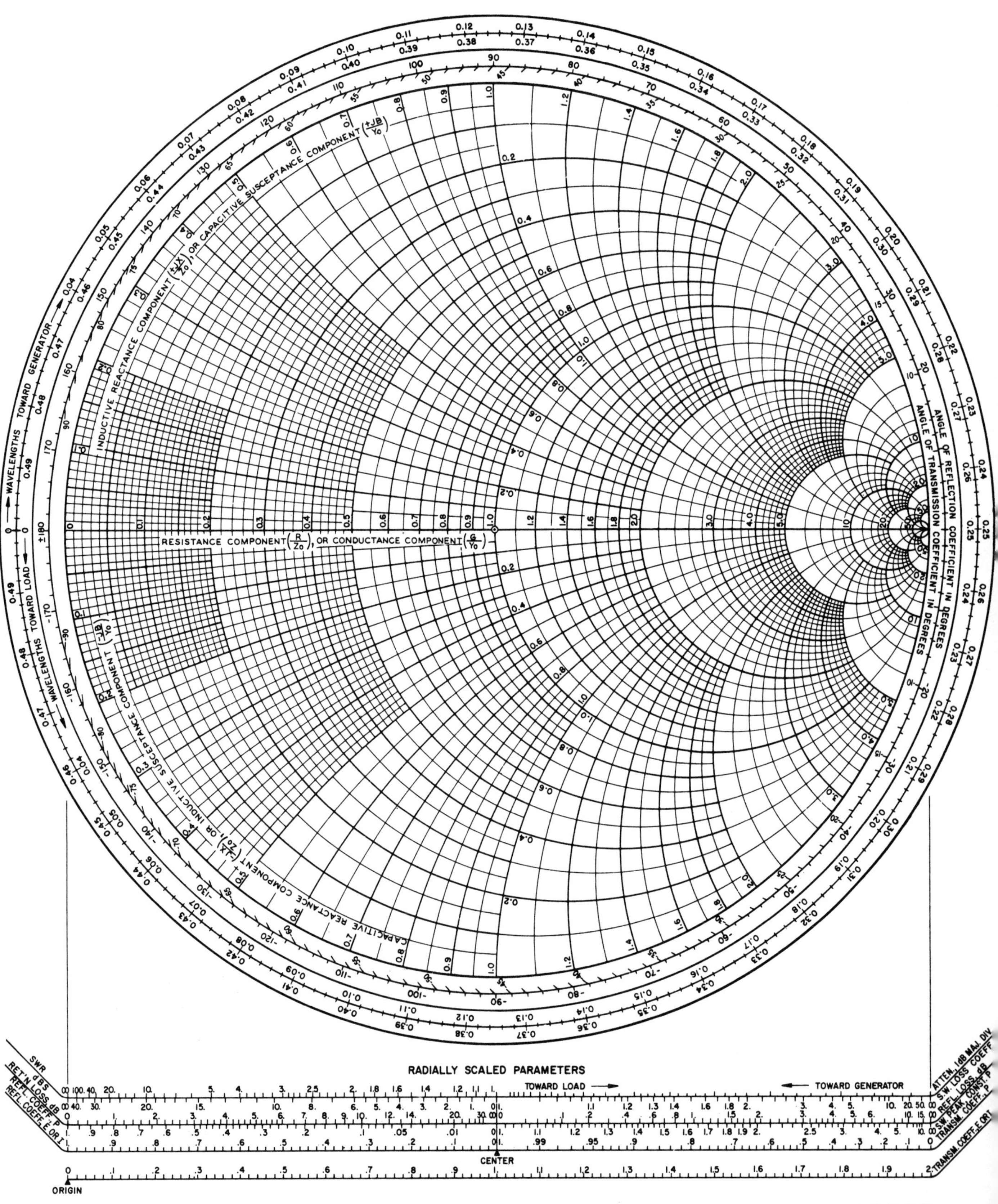

A MEGA-CHART

ANTENNA
IMPEDANCE
MATCHING

PROOF OF
PURCHASE

ARRL MEMBERS

This proof of purchase may be used as a $1.50 credit on your next ARRL purchase or renewal. Validate by entering your membership number—the first 7 digits on your *QST* label—below:

Please use this form to give us your comments on this book. Tell us what you liked best about the book and what improvements you would like to see in future editions

Name ______________________ Call sign ______________

Daytime phone ______________________ Age ______________

Address ______________________

City, State, ZIP ______________________

If licensed, how long? ______________________

Profession (optional) ______________________

From ______________________

____

____

Please affix postage. Post Office will not deliver without sufficient postage.

Editor, Antenna Impedance Matching,
First Edition
American Radio Relay League
225 Main Street
Newington, CT USA 06111

please fold and tape